THE BECKER COLLECTION

THE
BERNARD BECKER
COLLECTION IN OPHTHALMOLOGY

An Annotated Catalog

Third Edition

Compiled by

Lilla Wechsler
Christopher Hoolihan
Mark F. Weimer

THE BERNARD BECKER MEDICAL LIBRARY
Washington University School of Medicine
St. Louis, Missouri

ISBN 0-912260-13-0

Wär' nicht das Auge sonnenhaft,
Wie könnten wir das Licht erblicken?
Läg' nicht in uns des Gottes eigne Kraft,
Nie würd' uns Göttliches entzücken.

Goethe

CONTENTS

PREFACE TO THE THIRD EDITION

It is now twenty years since the Washington University Medical Library began cataloging my collection of books and graphic art related to ophthalmology. This proved to be a major undertaking for Mark Weimer and was continued by Christopher Hoolihan, Susan Alon, and now Lilla Wechsler. Since the second edition of the catalog over one hundred additional items have been added, and still there are many gaps in the collection. These become ever more difficult to fill because of lack of availability and escalating prices.

We hope that the updated catalog will prove useful to other libraries and collectors interested in the history of ophthalmology. Better yet, it may inspire some to visit St. Louis to view the collection first hand. They will have the opportunity to see the other rare book collections in our Library. These include the General Rare Book Collection (1500 volumes, 15th-19th centuries), the Max A. Goldstein Collection in Speech and Hearing (920 volumes, 15th-19th centuries), the Robert E. Schlueter-Paracelsus Collection (500 volumes, 15th-20th centuries), the James Moores Ball Collection (2600 volumes, 15th-19th centuries), the Henry J. McKellops Collection in Dentistry (750 volumes, 16th-19th centuries), and our Monuments of Medicine Collection (5300 volumes, 19th-20th centuries). In addition, visitors are most welcome in the rest of our new Medical Library, completed in 1989. The seventh floor of this impressive structure houses the rare book facility, offering ideal conditions for the care and use of rare books. Visitors will also find an experienced and cooperative staff anxious to help explore our medical heritage.

Taking part in the planning and development of the new Medical Library in collaboration with the Library Committee, the most knowledgeable librarians, and an imaginative architect has been an exciting experience. It has afforded me an additional career to occupy my emeritus years.

Again I want to thank our outstanding librarians Drs. Estelle Brodman, Susan Crawford, and now Mark Frisse and their able assistants for their help and advice, and for making possible the three editions of this catalog.

Bernard Becker, M.D.

PREFACE TO THE FIRST EDITION

My love for reading and delight in browsing through libraries and rare book shops have occupied large segments of my free and travel time. A natural consequence of this hobby was the modest purchase of occasional gems that intrigued and interested me. This permitted further study at home in leisure moments. When the acquired items filled all available corners of my study, and even some extra bookcases, I found it necessary to develop an alphabetical list of authors. It never occurred to me, however, that this was more than just personal fun and an exciting hobby.

As the collection grew, I began to feel rather selfish about the possessions of these rare and sometimes unique books and developed the need to share the experiences they offered with others. It has always been my firm conviction that books, like ideas, do not belong to individuals; they must be available to everyone. The construction of the new Rare Book Annex of the library at Washington University School of Medicine provided the incentive and opportunity to accomplish this goal. In this endeavor I was greatly encouraged by Dr. Estelle Brodman who stimulated me to sort out and list the books. To my surprise I found I have accumulated over 600 volumes! It seemed most appropriate to transfer them to the Medical School Library.

I am very grateful to the Medical School for providing me with the opportunity to share my hobby and its delights with all who are interested. This also permits the collection as such to remain intact and in most elegant surroundings. This is so much more satisfying and meaningful for me. It also affords opportunities for acquiring additional items so as to make this a more complete collection. In addition it may stimulate the contribution and development of collections in other disciplines.

I want to express particular thanks to Mr. Mark Weimer and Dr. Brodman for the enormous efforts they have devoted to cataloging the collection and for their invaluable advice and interest in adding to it. I hope that many will experience the exciting adventures offered by exploring our ophthalmic heritage.

Bernard Becker, M.D.

ACKNOWLEDGMENTS

The third edition of the Becker Catalog is the result of the collaborative efforts and talents of many people. The project was divided into two parts: the bibliographic work needed to create the new entries; and the technical work needed to convert the text from the second edition into a computer text file that was combined with the new entries to provide a digitized catalog. This file was also used to produce a camera-ready copy for the new printed edition, and be a prototype for the publication of future on-line catalogs of the Library's special collections.

We would like to thank everyone who participated in the overall planning of the catalog and who helped to bring it to publication with hard work, expertise, and enthusiasm: Polly Coxe, who assisted with bibliographical research, proofreading and publicity, and was an indispensable advisor all through the compilation of the catalog; Paul G. Anderson, Ph.D., whose comments and advice about the annotations were extremely helpful; Bernard Becker, M.D., who reviewed our text with an "eye expert's eye;" Christopher Hoolihan, the main compiler of the second edition, who provided many helpful suggestions for the third edition; Philip James Skroska, who compiled the appended lists and the indices, and who creatively edited and formatted the new catalog entries, as well as the reference and graphics sections; Cynthia S. Fedders, who worked on the subject headings and proofread all the entries; Samuela Koyfman, who assisted in bibliographic research and in the photographic work; Polly Cummings, who helped with the compilation of the appended lists; James V. Curley, who scanned, edited, and proofread the text of the second edition, and who formatted all the entries for the new edition; Simon Igielnik, Ph.D. and Gary W. Kronk, who were our invaluable computer and software consultants; and Amy Zinsmeyer, our publishing consultant and coordinator, who was responsible for the electronic design and production.

Finally, special thanks to Dr. Becker, whose constant support encouraged us all through the project.

Loretta H. Stucki
Associate Director for Collections

Lilla Wechsler
Rare Book Librarian

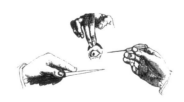

INTRODUCTION

"Books do not merely recount history; they make it."[1]

Robert Darnton

Scientific research, like all other areas of human knowledge, has been transmitted through books for centuries. Alongside new learning technologies, the most essential and fruitful approach to science is still reading, especially, if one intends to explore the history of a discipline. It is one of the greatest rewards of librarianship to help the reader navigate among the myriad of volumes by providing tools, such as bibliographies and catalogs.

The kind of "navigating tool" we present here is closest to the genre of *subject bibliography*, which surveys the contributions made to the literature of a specific cultural discipline,[2] in this case the field of ophthalmology and optics. At the same time, our book is a *catalog* as well, since it describes a particular collection, the Bernard Becker Collection in Ophthalmology. This historical collection of books, manuscripts, and graphics is located at the library of Washington University School of Medicine in St. Louis, Missouri. Since the 10th of May, 1995 not only this collection, but the entire Library bears the name of Dr. Bernard Becker, honoring his exceptional support of the Library, medical scholarship, and the written culture of the biomedical sciences in general. His avid interest in the history of his specialty led him to collect a library of classic works, which before being presented to Washington University was described as "the finest private ophthalmological collection in North America."[3]

This is now the third edition of the Becker Catalog following the first of 1979[4] and the second of 1983.[5] It is divided into sections like the previous editions: Rare Books, Graphics, Post-1900 Imprints, and Indices. The rare book section contains one hundred new entries and almost sixty new cross references in addition to the 426 entries of the second edition. Its temporal scope remains the same, including works published from the end of the fifteenth century to the end of the nineteenth. A subsequent section of the book presents a catalog of eighteen pieces of graphic art relating to the eye, now accompanied by color illustrations of selected items. As appendices we include a revised list of post-1900 imprints representing the twentieth century part of the Becker Collection, followed by a new list of ophthalmological titles selected from other collections of the Library. Finally, the revised subject index and then a combined chronological and geographical index conclude the catalog.

Our third edition follows the bibliographic methods of its predecessors. The new entries were inserted alphabetically, and numbered with decimals. This made it possible to keep the numbering of the second edition, which during the last twelve years has become a highly respected and often cited standard resource in the history of ophthalmology. In order for the new entries to be consistent with the format of the existing entries, some of the lengthy titles are abbreviated, and the imprint statements contain only the accepted English versions

---

[1] Robert Darnton, *The Kiss of Lamourette*. (New York; London: W.W. Norton & Co., 1990), p. 135.

[2] J.D. Cowley, *Bibliographic Description and Cataloguing*. (New York: Burt Franklin, 1970), p. 6.

[3] Christopher Hoolihan and Mark Weimer, comp., *Catalog of the Bernard Becker, M.D. Collection in Ophthalmology*. (St. Louis, Missouri: Washington University School of Medicine Library, 1983), p. 13.

[4] Mark Weimer, comp., *Bernard Becker, M.D. Collection in Ophthalmology*. (St. Louis, Missouri: Washington University School of Medicine Library, 1979).

[5] Christopher Hoolihan and Mark Weimer, comp., *Catalog of the Bernard Becker, M.D. Collection in Ophthalmology*. (St. Louis, Missouri: Washington University School of Medicine Library, 1983).

of place names followed by the last names of publishers with their initials. In accordance with the *Anglo-American Cataloguing Rules* (2nd ed.)[6] and the *Descriptive Cataloging of Rare Books*,[7] publication data retrieved from the colophon or the preliminaries of the book appear without square brackets. We did use brackets when adding supplementary information to the title statements. In the physical description of the books we applied the simplified pagination format introduced by the second edition.

Being akin to a subject bibliography, the *Becker Catalog* identifies particular editions of books, occasionally providing notations specific to the copy owned by the Library. The bibliographic entries are replete with annotations reviewing the content of the books. These annotations include descriptions of medical discoveries, new surgical methods and instruments, treatises on the anatomy and pathology of the eye, therapeutical writings, ophthalmological atlases and textbooks, as well as biographical information about the authors. A book about books, the *Becker Catalog* is designed to offer a comprehensive introduction to the ever growing knowledge about "the keenest of all our senses,"[8] vision.

Lilla Wechsler
Rare Book Librarian

[6] *Anglo-American Cataloguing Rules*. Second edition. (Ottawa, London, Chicago, 1988), p. 62.

[7] *Descriptive Cataloging of Rare Books*. Second edition. (Washington, D.C.: Library of Congress, 1991), p. 27.

[8] Marcus Tullius Cicero, *De oratore*. (Cambridge, Mass.: Harvard University Press, 1976-77), II, LXXXVII, 357.

REFERENCE SOURCES

AmEncOph   *The American encyclopedia and dictionary of ophthalmology.* Edited by Casey A. Wood. Chicago: Cleveland Press, 1913-21.

Austin   Austin, Robert B. *Early American medical imprints 1668-1820.* Washington, D. C.: U. S. Department of Health, Education, and Welfare, Public Health Service, 1961. Reprint. Arlington, Massachusetts: The Printers' Devil, 1977.

Babson   Babson Institute, Library. *A descriptive catalogue of the Grace K. Babson Collection of the works of Sir Isaac Newton and the material relating to him in the Babson Institute Library, Babson Park, Massachusetts.* Compiled by Henry P. Macomber. New York: H. Reichner, 1950.

A supplement to the catalogue of the Grace K. Babson Collection of the works of Sir Isaac Newton and related material in the Babson Institute Library, Babson Park, Massachusetts. Compiled by Henry P. Macomber. Babson Park, Massachusetts: Babson Institute, 1955.

Bayle   Bayle, Antoine Laurent Jessé, and August Jean Thillaye. *Biographie médicale par ordre chronologique d'après Daniel Leclerc, Eloy, etc.* 2 v. Amsterdam: B. M. Israël, 1967.

Beer   Beer, Georg Joseph. *Repertorium aller bis zu Ende des Jahres 1797 erschienenen Schriften über die Augenkrankheiten.* Vienna: C. Schaumburg & Co., 1799.

Benesch   Benesch, Otto. *The drawings of Rembrandt: a critical and chronological catalogue.* 6 v. London: Phaidon Press, 1954-57.

BioMed   Jourdan, Antoine Jacques Louis, ed. *Dictionaire des sciences médicales. Biographie médicale.* 7 v. Paris: C. L. F. Panckoucke, 1820-25.

BioUni   Michaud, Joseph Francois, and Louis Gabriel Michaud. *Biographie universelle (Michaud) ancienne et moderne.* New ed., rev. 45 v. Paris: Desplaces, 1843-65.

Bird   Bird, David T., comp. *A catalogue of sixteenth-century medical books in Edinburgh libraries.* Edinburgh: Royal College of Physicians of Edinburgh, 1982.

Blake   National Library of Medicine (U.S.). *A short title catalogue of eighteenth century printed books in the National Library of Medicine.* Compiled by John Ballard Blake. Bethesda, Maryland: National Library of Medicine, 1979.

BM   British Museum. Department of Printed Books. *General catalogue of printed books, photolithographic* *edition to 1955.* 263 v. London: Trustees of the British Museum, 1959-66.

———— ————. *Ten-year supplement, 1956-1965.* 50 v. 1968.

———— ————. *Five-year supplement, 1966-1970.* 26 v. 1971-72.

BM 15th c. British Museum. Department of Printed Books. *Catalogue of books printed in the XVth century now in the British Museum.* Facsimiles. Lithographic reprint of the 1908 ed. 10 v. London: Trustees of the British Museum, 1962-71.

BM Italian British Museum. Department of Printed Books. *Short-title catalogue of books printed in Italy and of Italian books printed in other countries from 1465 to 1600 now in the British Museum.* London: Trustees of the British Museum, 1958.

BOA British Optical Association, London. *British Optical Association Library and Museum catalogue.* Compiled and edited by John H. Sutcliffe, assisted by Margaret Mitchell and Edith Chittell. 3 v. London: The Council of the British Optical Association, 1932-57.

Brennsohn Brennsohn, Isidorus. *Die Ärzte Estlands vom Beginn der historischen Zeit bis zur Gegenwart: ein biographisches Lexikon. Nebst einer historischen Einleitung über das Medizinalwesen Estlands.* Riga: L. Schumacher, 1922.

Brunet Brunet, Jacques-Charles. *Manuel du libraire et de l'amateur de livres.* 5th ed., rev. 6 v. Paris: Firmin-Didot, 1860-65.

Bynum Bynum, William Frederick, and Roy Porter, eds. *Companion encyclopedia of the history of medicine.* 2 v. London; New York: Routledge, 1993.

Callisen Callisen, Adolph Carl Peter. *Medicinisches Schriftsteller-Lexicon der jetzt lebenden Aerzte, Wundärzte, Geburtshelfer, Apotheker, und Naturforscher aller gebildeten Völker.* 33 v. Copenhagen; Altona: Königl. Taubstummen Institute zu Schleswig, 1830-45.

Chance Chance, Burton. *Ophthalmology.* (Clio medica: a series of primers on the history of medicine.) New York: P. B. Hoeber, 1939.

Choulant Choulant, Johann Ludwig. *Bibliotheca medico-historica: sive, catalogus librorum historicorum de re medica et scientia naturali systematicus.* Leipzig: Engelmann, 1842.

Additamenta ad Lud. Choulanti Bibliothecam medico-historicam. Edited by Julius Rosenbaum. 2 v. Halle: J. F. Lippert, 1842-47.

Copinger Copinger, Walter Arthur. *Supplement to Hain's Repertorium bibliographicum: or, collections toward a new edition of that work.* 2 v. London: H. Sotheran and Co., 1895-1902.

Countway   Francis A. Countway Library of Medicine, Boston. *Author-title catalog of the Francis A. Countway Library of Medicine for imprints through 1959.* 10 v. Boston: G. K. Hall, 1973.

Crook   Crook, Ronald Eric. *A bibliography of Joseph Priestley, 1733-1804.* London: Library Association, 1966.

Cushing   Yale Medical Historical Library. *The Harvey Cushing collection of books and manuscripts.* Compiled by Margaret Brinton and Henrietta Tarlson Perkins. New York: Schuman's, 1943.

Dawson   William Dawson and Sons, London. *Medicine and science: a biblio-graphical catalogue of historical and rare books from the 15th to the 20th century.* William Dawson and Sons, Ltd., catalogue no. 91. London: W. Dawson and Sons, 196-?

Delteil   Delteil, Loys. *Le peintre-graveur illustré: the graphic works of nineteenth and twentieth century artists. An illustrated catalog.* 32 v. Paris: Chez l'auteur, 1906-30. Reprint. New York: Collectors Editions, 1969-70, c1968.

Dezeimeris   Dezeimeris, Jean Eugéne, Charles Prosper Ollivier, and Jacques Raige-Delorme. *Dictionnaire historique de la médecine ancienne et moderne. . . .* 4 v. Paris: Béchet & Labé; Bruxelles: Libraire Médicale Française, 1828-39.

DicAmBio   American Council of Learned Societies. *Dictionary of American biography.* 20 v. and Index; Suppl. 1-8. New York: C. Scribner's Sons, 1928-70.

DicNatBio   Stephan, Sir Leslie, and Sir Sidney Lee, eds. *Dictionary of national biography, founded in 1882 by George Smith . . . from the earliest times to 1900.* Reprint. 22 v. London: Oxford University Press, 1937-38.

————— —————. *Supplement. January 1901-December 1911.* Edited by Sir Sidney Lee. Reprint. London: Oxford University Press, 1920.

————— —————. *1912-1921.* Edited by H. W. C. Davis and J. R. H. Weaver. London: Oxford University Press, 1927.

————— —————. *1922-1930.* Edited by J. R. H. Weaver. London: Oxford University Press, 1937.

Corrections and additions to the Dictionary of national biography, cumulated from the Bulletin of the Institute of Historical Research, University of London, covering the years 1923-1963. Boston: G. K. Hall, 1966.

DicSciBio   American Council of Learned Societies. *Dictionary of scientific biography.* Edited by Charles Coulston Gillispie. 16 v. New York: Scribner, 1970-1980.

Duke-Elder   Duke-Elder, Sir Stewart, ed. *System of ophthalmology.* 15 v. London: Kimpton; St. Louis: C. V. Mosby Company, 1958-76.

Durling   National Library of Medicine (U.S.). *A catalogue of sixteenth century printed books in the National Library of Medicine.* Compiled by Richard Jasper Durling. Bethesda, Maryland: National Library of Medicine, 1967.

A catalogue of incunabula and sixteenth century printed books in the National Library of Medicine: first supplement. Compiled by Peter Krivatsy. Bethesda, Maryland: National Library of Medicine, 1971.

Eloy   Eloy, Nicolas François Joseph. *Dictionnaire historique de la médecine ancienne et moderne: ou mémoires disposés en ordre alphabétique pour servir à l'histoire de cette science, et à celle des médecins, anatomistes, botanistes, chirurgiens et chymistes de toutes nations.* 4 v. Mons: H. Hoyois, 1778.

EncBrit   Yust, Walter, ed. *Encyclopaedia Britannica: a new survey of universal knowledge.* 14th ed. 24 v. Chicago: Encyclopaedia Britannica, c1957.

EncPhil   Edwards, Paul, ed. *The encyclopedia of philosophy.* 8 v. New York: Macmillan Co. & The Free Press; London: Collier-Macmillan, c1967.

Engelmann   Engelmann, Wilhelm. *Bibliotheca medico-chirurgica et anatomico-physiologica. Alphabetisches Verzeichnis der medizinischen, chirurgischen, geburtshülflichen, anatomischen und physiologischen Bücher, welche vom Jahre 1750 bis zu Ende des Jahres 1847 in Deutschland erschienen sind.* Hildesheim: G. Olms, 1965.

Fischer   Fischer, Isidor, ed. *Biographisches Lexikon der hervorragenden Ärzte der letzten fünfzig Jahre. . . . Fortsetzung des Biographischen Lexikons der hervorragenden Ärzte aller Zeiten und Völker.* 2 v. Berlin; Vienna: Urban & Schwarzenberg, 1932-33.

Founders   Haymaker, Webb, and Karl A. Baer, eds. *The founders of neurology: one hundred and thirty-three biographical sketches prepared for the Fourth International Neurological Congress in Paris by eighty-four authors.* Springfield, Illinois: C. C. Thomas, 1953.

Fulton   Fulton, John Farquhar. *A bibliography of the Honourable Robert Boyle, fellow of the Royal Society.* 2nd ed. Oxford: Clarendon Press, 1961.

G–M   Garrison, Fielding Hudson, and Leslie T. Morton. *Morton's medical bibliography: an annotated checklist of texts illustrating the history of medicine (Garrison and Morton).* 5th ed. Edited by Jeremy M. Norman. Aldershot, Hants, England: Scolar Press; Brookfield, Vermont: Gower, c1991.

Garrison   Garrison, Fielding H. *An introduction to the history of medicine, with medical chronology, suggestions for study and bibliographic data.* 4th ed., c1929. Reprint. Philadelphia; London: W. B. Saunders Company, 1960.

Gnudi   Gnudi, Martha Teach and Jerome Pierce Webster. *The life and times of Gaspare Tagliacozzi: surgeon of Bologna, 1545-1599.* New York: H. Reichner, 1950.

Goff   Goff, Frederick Richmond, comp. and ed. *Incunabula in American libraries: a third census of fifteenth century books recorded in North American collections.* New York: Bibliographical Society of America, 1964.

Gorin   Gorin, George. *History of ophthalmology.* Wilmington, Delaware: Publish or Perish, 1982.

Grässe   Grässe, Johann Georg Theodor. *Trésor de livres rares et précieux: ou, Nouveau dictionnaire bibliographique.* 7 v. Dresden: R. Kuntze, 1859-69.

Gray   Gray, George John. *A bibliography of the works of Sir Isaac Newton, together with a list of books illustrating his works.* 2nd ed., rev. Cambridge, England: Bowes and Bowes, 1907. Facsimile reprint. London: Dawsons, 1966.

GW   Kommission für den Gesamtkatalog der Wiegendrucke. *Gesamtkatalog der Wiegendrucke.* 2nd ed., rev. reprinting of 1st ed. 8 v. Stuttgart:

A. Hiersemann; New York: H. P. Kraus, 1968-78.

Haeser   Haeser, Heinrich. *Lehrbuch der Geschichte der Medicin und der epidemischen Krankheiten.* 2nd ed., rev. 2 v. Jena: F. Mauke, 1853-1865.

Hain   Hain, Ludwig Friedrich Theodor. *Repertorium bibliographicum: in quo libri omnes ab arte typographica inventa usque ad annum MD. typis expressi ordine alphabetico vel simpliciter enumerantur vel adcuratius recensentur.* 2 v. Stuttgart: J. G. Cotta; Paris: J. Renouard, 1826-38.

Haller Chir   Haller, Albrecht von. *Bibliotheca chirurgica: qua scripta ad artem chirurgicam facientia a rerum initiis recensentur.* 2 v. Bern: E. Haller; Basel: J. Schweighauser, 1774-1775.

Haller Med   Haller, Albrecht von. *Bibliotheca medicinae practicae: qua scripta ad partem medicinae practicam facientia a rerum initiis ad a. MDCCLXXV recensentur.* Edited by F. L. Tribolet (v. 3) and Joachim Dietrich Brandis (v. 4). 4 v. Basel: J. Schweighauser; Bern: E. Haller, 1776-88.

Harvard   Harvard College Library, Department of Printing and Graphic Arts. *Catalogue of books and manuscripts. Part I. French 16th century books.* 2 v.; *Part II. Italian 16th century books.* 2 v. Compiled by Ruth Mortimer under the supervision of Philip Hofer and William A. Jackson. Cambridge, Massachusetts: Belknap Press of Harvard University Press, 1964-74.

Heirs University of Iowa, Hardin Library for the Health Sciences. *Heirs of Hippocrates: the development of medicine in a catalogue of historic books in the Hardin Library for the Health Sciences, the University of Iowa.* Compiled and edited by Richard Eimas. 3rd ed. Iowa City, Iowa: University of Iowa Press, 1990.

Hirsch Hirsch, August, ed. *Biographisches Lexikon der hervorragenden Ärzte aller Zeiten und Völker.* 2nd ed. 6 v. Berlin; Vienna: Urban & Schwarzenberg, 1929-1935.

Hirschberg Hirschberg, Julius. "Geschichte der Augenheilkunde." v. 12-15 in *Handbuch der gesammten Augenheilkunde.* Edited by A. Graefe and Th. Saemisch. 2nd ed. 16 v. Leipzig: Wilhelm Engelmann; Berlin: Springer, 1899-1930.

Hirschberg, Julius. *The history of ophthalmology.* Translated by Frederick C. Blodi. 11 v. Bonn: J. P. Wayenborgh, 1982-   .

Huard Huard, Pierre Alphonse, Zensetsou Ohya, and Ming Wong. *La médicine japonaise des origines à nos jours.* Paris: R. Dacosta, 1974.

Hubbell Hubbell, Alvin Allace. *The development of ophthalmology in America 1800 to 1870: a contribution to ophthalmologic history and biography.* Chicago: W. T. Keener & Co., 1908.

James James, Robert Rutson. *Studies in the history of ophthalmology in England prior to the year 1800.* Cambridge, England: University Press for the British Journal of Ophthalmology, 1933.

Kaufman Kaufman, Martin, Stuart Galishoff, and Todd L. Savitt, eds. *Dictionary of American medical biography.* 2 v. Westport, Connecticut; London: Greenwood Press, 1984.

Kelly (1912) Kelly, Howard Atwood. *A cyclopedia of American medical biography: comprising the lives of eminent deceased physicians and surgeons from 1610 to 1910.* 2 v. Philadelphia: Saunders, 1912.

Kelly (1920) Kelly, Howard Atwood, and Walter Lincoln Burrage. *American medical biographies.* Published in 1912 under the title *A cyclopedia of American medical biography.* Baltimore: Norman, Remington Co., 1920.

Kelly (1928) Kelly, Howard Atwood, and Walter Lincoln Burrage. *Dictionary of American medical biography: lives of eminent physicians of the United States and Canada, from the earliest times.* First published in 1912 under the title *A cyclopedia of American medical biography.* 2 v., and then in 1920 under the title *American medical biographies.* New York: D. Appleton and Co., 1928.

Keynes Keynes, Geoffrey, Sir. *A bibliography of George Berkeley, Bishop of Cloyne: his works and his critics in*

Klebs

the eighteenth century. Oxford: Clarendon Press, 1976.

Klebs, Arnold Carl. *Incunabula scientifica et medica.* Hildesheim: G. Olms, 1963.

Krivatsy

National Library of Medicine (U.S.). *A catalogue of seventeenth century printed books in the National Library of Medicine.* Compiled by Peter Krivatsy. Bethesda, Maryland: National Library of Medicine, 1989.

Lorenz

Lorenz, Otto Henri. *Catalogue général de la librairie française.* Edited by Daniel Jordell (v. 12-27) and Henri Stein (v. 28-32). 34 v. Paris: various publishers, 1867-1945.

Madan

Madan, Falconer. *Oxford books: a bibliography of printed works relating to the university and city of Oxford, or printed or published there.* 3 v. Oxford: Clarendon Press, 1895-1931.

Manchester

University of Manchester, Library. *Catalogue of medical books in Manchester University Library 1480-1700.* Compiled by Ethel M. Parkinson, assisted by Audrey E. Lumb. Manchester: Manchester University Press, 1972.

Michaelis

Michaelis, Eduard. *Albrecht von Graefe, sein Leben und Wirken.* Berlin: G. Reimer, 1877.

Mondor

Mondor, Henri. *Doctors & medicine in the works of Daumier.* Notes and catalogue by Jean Adhémar. Translated by C. de Chabanne. Boston: Boston Book and Art Shop, 1960.

More

More, Louis Trenchard. *Isaac Newton: a biography.* New York: Charles Scribner's Sons, 1934. Reprint. New York: Dover Publications, 1962.

Niklaus

Diderot, Denis. *Lettre sur les aveugles.* Edition critique. Edited by Robert Niklaus. Geneva: E. Droz, 1951.

NLM

Army Medical Library (U. S.). *Index-catalogue of the Library of the Surgeon General's Office, United States Army: authors and subjects. 1st Series.* 16 v. Washington : Government Printing Office, 1880-95.

———— ————. *2nd Series.* 21 v. 1896-1916.

———— ————. *3rd Series.* 10 v. 1918-1932.

———— ————. *4th Series.* 11 v. 1936-1955.

National Library of Medicine (U. S.). Index-catalogue of the Library of the Surgeon General's Office, National Library of Medicine. 5th Series. *3 v. 1959-61.*

Norman

Hook, Diana H., and Jeremy M. Norman, comps. *The Haskell F. Norman library of science and medicine.* 2 v. San Francisco: J. Norman, 1991.

NUC Library of Congress (U. S.). *The national union catalog, pre-1956 imprints; a cumulative author list representing Library of Congress printed cards and titles reported by other American libraries.* Compiled and edited with the cooperation of the Library of Congress and the National Union Catalog Subcommittee of the Resources Committee of the Resources and Technical Services Division, American Library Association. 754 v. London; Chicago: Mansell, 1968-81.

NYAM New York Academy of Medicine, Library. *Author catalog of the library.* 43 v. Boston: G. K. Hall, 1969.

Olivier Olivier, Eugène, Georges Hermal, and R. de Roton. *Manuel de l'amateur de reliures armoriées françaises.* 30 v. Paris: Ch. Bosse, 1924-38.

Orr American College of Surgeons, Library. *A catalogue of the H. Winnett Orr historical collections and other rare books in the library of the American College of Surgeons.* Chicago: American College of Surgeons, 1960.

Osler Osler, Sir William. *Bibliotheca Osleriana: a catalogue of books illustrating the history of medicine and science. Collected, arranged and annotated by Sir William Osler, and bequeathed to McGill University.* Oxford: Clarendon Press, 1929.

Ovio Ovio, Giuseppe. *Storia dell'oculistica.* 2 v. Cuneo: Ghibaudo, 1950-52.

Packard Packard, Francis Randolph. *History of medicine in the United States.* 2 v. New York: P. B. Hoeber, 1931.

Pagel Pagel, Julius Leopold, ed. *Biographisches Lexikon hervorragender Ärzte des neunzehnten Jahrhunderts: mit einer historischen Einleitung.* Berlin; Vienna: Urban & Schwarzenberg, 1901.

Pastore Pastore, Nicholas. *Selective history of theories of visual perception: 1650-1950.* New York: Oxford University Press, 1971.

Pauly Pauly, Alphonse. *Bibliographie des sciences médicales: bibliographie—biographie—histoire—épidémies—topographies—endémies.* Paris: Tross, 1874.

Ploucquet Ploucquet, Wilhelm Gottfried. *Initia bibliothecae medico-practicae et chirurgicae realis sive repertorii medicinae practicae et chirurgicae.* 8 v. Tübingen: J. G. Cotta, 1793-97.

Poggendorff Poggendorff, Johann Christian. *(J. C. Poggendorff's) biographisch-literarisches Handwörterbuch zur Geschichte der exakten Wissenschaften. . . .* (v. 1-4). Hrsg. von B. W. Feddersen und A. J. von Oettinger (v. 3); A. J. von Oettinger (v. 4) Leipzig: J. A. Barth, 1863-1904.

J. C. Poggendorff's biographisch-literarisches Handwörterbuch für Mathematik, Astronomie, Physik, Chemie und verwandte Wissenschaftsgebiete. *(v. 5-6). Hrsg. von der Sächsischen Akademie der Wissenschaften zu Leipzig. Leipzig: Verlag Chemie, 1925-40.*

Biographisch-Literarisches Handwörterbuch der exakten Naturwissenschaften. . . . (v. 7a-7b[1-4]). Hrsg. von der Sächsischen Akademie der Wissenschaften zu Leipzig. Red. von Rudolph Zaunick und Hans Salié. Berlin: Akademie-Verlag, 1955-73.

Polyak   Polyak, Stephan Lucian. *The vertebrate visual system: its origin, structure, and function and its manifestations in disease with an analysis of its role in the life of animals and in the origin of man; preceded by a historical review of investigations of the eye, and of the visual pathways and centers of the brain.* Chicago: University of Chicago Press, 1957.

Pybus   University of Newcastle upon Tyne, Library. *Catalogue of the Pybus Collection of medical books, letters and engravings, 15th–20th centuries, held in the University Library, Newcastle upon Tyne.* Compiled by Joan S. Emmerson. Manchester: Manchester University Press, 1981.

Reichling   Reichling, Dietrich, Ludwig Hain, and Walter Arthur Copinger. *Appendices ad Hainii-Copingeri Repertorium bibliographicum:*

additiones et emendationes. 7 v. Munich: I. Rosenthal, 1905-11. Reprint. 2 v. Milan: Görlich, 1953.

Reynolds   University of Alabama Medical Center, Reynolds Historical Library. *Rare book and collections of the Reynolds Historical Library: a bibliography.* Compiled by Martha Lou Thomas. University, Alabama: University of Alabama Press, 1968.

RoyMedSoc   Royal Medical and Chirurgical Society, Library. *Catalogue of the library of the Royal Medical and Chirurgical Society of London.* Compiled by Benjamin Robert Wheatley. 3 v. London: Royal Medical and Chirurgical Society, 1879.

Sarton   Sarton, George. *Introduction to the history of science.* (Carnegie Institution of Washington, publication no. 376.) 3 v. Baltimore: Williams & Wilkins Co., c1927-1948. Reprint,1962.

Schmitz   Schmitz, Emil Heinz. *Handbuch zur Geschichte der Optik.* Bonn: J. P. Wayenborgh, 1981-   .

Schullian   Schullian, Dorothy May, and Francis Erich Sommer. *A catalogue of incunabula and manuscripts in the Army Medical Library.* New York: H. Schuman for the Army Medical Library, 1948?

Shaw   Shaw, Ralph Robert, and Richard H. Shoemaker, comps. *American bibliography: a preliminary check-*

list for 1801–1819. 19 v. New York: Scarecrow Press, 1958-1963.

Sherman Sherman, Paul D. *Colour vision in the nineteenth century: the Young-Helmholtz-Maxwell theory.* Bristol: A. Hilger, 1981.

Snyder Snyder, Charles. *Our ophthalmic heritage.* Boston: Little, Brown & Co., c1967.

STC Pollard, Alfred William, and Gilbert Richard Redgrave, comps. *A short-title catalogue of books printed in England, Scotland & Ireland, and of English books printed abroad, 1475-1640.* London: Bibliographical Society, 1926. Reprint. Oxford: University Press, 1946.

STC (2nd ed.) Pollard, Alfred William, Gilbert Richard Redgrave, William Alexander Jackson, Frederic Sutherland Ferguson, and Katharine F. Pantzer, comps. *A short-title catalogue of books printed in England, Scotland & Ireland, and of English books printed abroad, 1475-1640.* 2nd ed., rev. 3 v. London : Bibliographical Society, 1976-1991.

Thacher Thacher, James. *American medical biography : or, memoirs of eminent physicians who have flourished in America. To which is prefixed a succinct history of medical science in the United States, from the first settlement of the country.* 2 v. Boston: Richardson & Lord; Cotton & Barnard, 1828. Reprint. New York: Da Capo Press, 1967.

Thorndike Thorndike, Lynn. *A history of magic and experimental science.* 8 v. New York: Columbia University Press, 1923-58.

Vapereau Vapereau, Gustave. *Dictionnaire universel des contemporains contenant toutes les personnes notables de la France et des pays étrangers.* . . . 5th ed., rev. Paris: Hachette & Co., 1880.

Waller Uppsala Universitet, Bibliotek. *Bibliotheca Walleriana. The books illustrating the history of medicine and science collected by Dr. Erik Waller and bequeathed to the Library of the Royal University of Uppsala. A catalogue.* . . . Compiled by Hans Sallander. 2 v. Stockholm: Almqvist & Wiksell, 1955.

Wallis Wallis, Peter John, and Ruth Wallis. *Newton and Newtoniana, 1672-1975, a bibliography.* Folkestone, England: Dawson & Sons, 1977.

Wellcome Wellcome Historical Medical Library. *A catalogue of printed books in the Wellcome Historical Medical Library. I: books printed before 1641; II: books printed from 1641 to 1850, A-E; III: books printed from 1641 to 1850, F-L.* 3 v. London: Wellcome Historical Medical Library, 1962-66.

WellcomeSubj Wellcome Institute for the History of Medicine. *Subject catalogue of the history of medicine and related sciences.* 18 v. Munich: Kraus International Publications, 1980.

Who's Who Stephenson, H. H., ed. *Who's who in science (international) 1912.* London: Churchill, 1912.

Willius–Dry Willius, Fredrick Arthur, and Thomas Jan Dry. *A history of the heart and the circulation.* Philadelphia: W. B. Saunders Co., 1948.

Wing Wing, Donald Goddard, comp. *Short-title catalogue of books printed in England, Scotland, Ireland, Wales and British America, and of English books printed in* *other countries, 1641-1700.* 2nd ed., rev. 3 v. New York: Modern Language Association of America, 1972-1988.

Wood Wood, Anthony à. *Athenae Oxonienses. An exact history of all the writers and bishops who have had their education in the University of Oxford. To which are added the Fasti, or Annals of the said University.* New ed., with additions, and a continuation by Philip Bliss. 4 v. London: F. C. & J. Rivington, 1813-20.

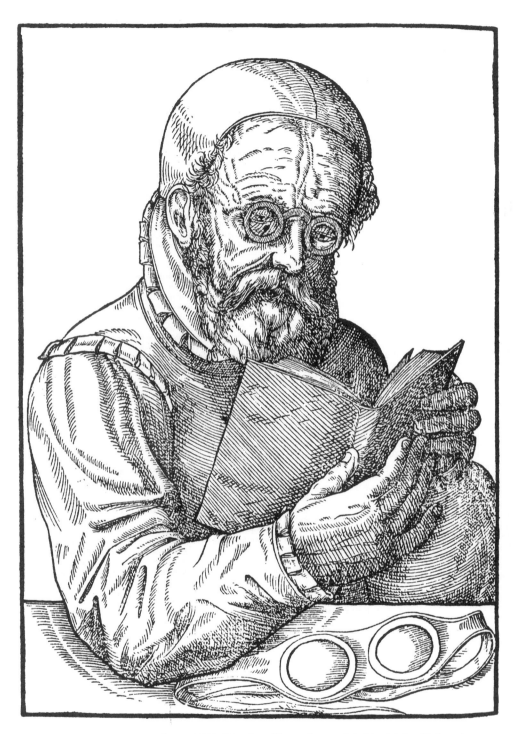

(35) Bartisch, Georg. *Augendienst*, 1583. Woodcut illustration on fol. 31. (14.5 x 20.5 cm.)

RARE BOOKS

1   Abū Bakr al-Ḥasan ibn al-Khaṣīb, 9th cent.

Liber genethliacus, sive De nativitatibus, non solum ingenti rerum scitu dignarum copia, verum etiam iucundissimo illarum ordine conspicuus. Nuremberg: J. Petrejus, 1540.

74 leaves; 20 cm. (4to)

An early sixteenth century astrological work on the art of calculating nativities and predicting the health of newborns, first published under the title *De nativitatibus* (Venice: Alovisius de Sancta Lucia, 1 June 1492). According to the text of the first edition, this work was translated from the Arabic in 1218. Seven chapters treat the ocular affections which could be expected with particular planetary alignments at the time of birth.

Sarton I:603.

2   Académie Royale de Chirurgie (Paris).

Mémoires de l'Académie Royale de Chirurgie. Paris: Charles Osmont, 1743-74.

5 v. (viii, [2], [ix]-x1, 778, [2] p., 21 plates; [4], xcviii, [6], 613 p., 23 plates; [6], 139, [5], 680 p., 20 plates; [4], 123, [1], 699 p., 11 plates; [4], xvi, 928 p., 19 plates); 28 cm. (4to)

Established by royal edict of Louis XV, the Académie Royale de Chirurgie held its first meeting in December of 1731, and issued the first volume of its proceedings in 1743. The five volumes of the *Mémoires* contain twelve articles on the surgery of the eye, the most important of which is Jacques Daviel's original description of his operation for the treatment of cataract by extraction of the lens. The articles on ophthalmic surgery are:

—Bordenhave, Toussaint, 1728-1782. "Examen des réflexions critiques de M. Molinelli, inserées dans les Mémoires de l'Institut de Bologne, contre le mémoire de M. Petit, sur la fistule lacrymale inseré parmi ceux de l'Académie Royale des Sciences de Paris, année 1734." II:161-174.

—Idem. "Mémoire dans lequel on propose un nouveau procédé pour traiter le renversement des paupières." V:97-109.

—Daviel, Jacques, 1693-1762. "Sur une nouvelle méthode de guérir la cataracte par l'extraction du cristalin." II:337-352; *followed by* "Rémarques sur la mémoire de M. Daviel." II:352-354.

—Hoin, Jean Jacques Louis, 1722-1772. "Sur une espèce de cataracte nouvellement observée." II:425-430.

—La Faye, Georges de, 1699-1781. "Pour servir à perfectionner la nouvelle méthode de faire l'opération de la cataracte." II:563-577.

—La Forest (de). "Nouvelle méthode de traiter les maladies du sac lacrymal, nommées communement, fistules lacrymales." II:175-190.

—Le Dran, Henri François, 1685-1770. "Sur un oeil éraillé." I:440-443.

—Louis, Antoine, 1723-1792. "Réflexions sur l'opération de la fistule lacrymale." II:193-213.

—Idem. "Précis historique de la doctrine des auteurs sur l'opération qu'ils ont proposée pour remédier au renversement des paupières." V:110-128.

—Idem. "Mémoire sur plusieurs maladies du globe de l'oeil; ou l'on examine particulièrement les cas qui exigent l'extirpation de cet organe, & la méthode d'y procéder." V:161-224.

—Morand, Sauveur François, 1697-1773, & Verdier, César, 1685-1759. "Rapport des opérations de la cataracte par l'extraction du cristallin, faites devant les Commissaires de l'Académie, par M. Poyet . . . ." II:578-583.

Imprint varies throughout the five volumes: t. II, Delaguette, 1753; t. III, idem, 1757; t. IV., P. Alex. Le Prieur, 1768; and t. V, P. Fr. Didot, 1774.

3   Adams, George, 1750-1795.

An essay on vision, briefly explaining the fabric of the eye, and the nature of vision: intended for the service of those whose eyes are weak or impaired: enabling them to form an accurate idea of the true state of their sight, the means of preserving it, together with proper rules for ascertaining when spectacles are necessary, and how to choose them without injuring the sight. London: R. Hindmarsh, 1789.

vi, [2], 153, [1], 14 p., [1] plate; 22 cm. (8vo)

Adams, a famous London and court optician, earned a worldwide reputation as a maker of spectacles and microscope lenses. In this work he endeavored "to do away a general prejudice in favour of spectacles [and] to diffuse more generally a knowledge of the subject among the venders of this article, particularly those who live in the country" (Preface, p.[iii]-iv). The final section gives an account of squinting, methods of ascertaining its nature, and the best remedies for its cure. A priced catalogue of mathematical and scientific instruments made and sold by the author follows the text.

BOA I:2; Hirschberg §470.

4   Adams, Sir William, 1783-1827.

Practical observations on ectropium, or eversion of the eye-lids, with the description of a new operation for the cure of that disease; on the modes of forming an artificial pupil, and on cataract. London: J. Brettell for J. Callow, 1812.

xvi, 252, [2] p., 3 plates; 23 cm. (8vo)

Publisher's advertisements (16 p.) bound-in.

William Adams, a pupil of John Cunningham Saunders and founder of Exeter's West of England Eye Infirmary, was a rather pretentious though highly regarded ophthalmic surgeon and one of the central figures in the controversy which raged between 1806 and 1820 over the treatment of Egyptian ophthalmia [cf. Edmondston (122) and Vetch (389)]. In this book, his first published work, Adams described a method of treating eversion of the eyelids by the removal of an angular part of the lid. Adam's new operation for forming an artificial pupil, however, was simply a revival of the procedures employed by Cheselden and Sharpe. Originally the operation of iridectomy was undertaken for the purely optical purpose of forming an artificial pupil rather than as the curative measure it was to become in the hands of Beer (37-40) and von Graefe. Adams assumed his wife's family name and was known as Sir William Rawson after 1825.

AmEncOph I:92; BOA I:2; Hirschberg §630; Wellcome II:14.

4.1   Adams, Sir William, 1783-1827.

A treatise on artificial pupil, in which is described, a series of improved operations for its formation; with an account of the morbid states of the eye to which such operations are applicable. London: Baldwin, Cradock, & Joy, et al., 1819.

vii, [1], 134, [50], xi, [1] p., [1] plate: tables; 22 cm.

Provenance: Inscribed by the author to Viscount Castlereagh.

Partial contents: "The first annual report, detailing the cases of all the pensioners, who, during the last year, have been treated and discharged from the institution founded by government, for the cure of the blind pensioners afflicted with various diseases of the eye . . ." (p. [1-50] following the treatise).

This treaties contains "a description of all operations for the formation of artificial pupil which the author considered worthy of notice" (BOA II:1). The text is a significantly revised version of Adams's *Practical observations* (4). Modifying Cheselden's operation, Adams introduced a new method to form an artificial pupil by using a small iris scalpel of his own design. He describes this instrument on page 32 of the present treatise.

The decorative volume contains a hand-colored plate and is covered with a fine contemporary red morocco binding with gold- and blind-tooling; the edges of the text block are gilt all around.

AmEncOph I:93; BOA II:1; Dawson 75; Gorin, p. 74; NUC 482:618.

5   Aetius, of Amida, 502-575.

Libri sexdecim nunc primum latinitate donati, in quibus cuncta quae ad artem curandi pertinent sunt congesta . . . in tres divisum est tomos. Quorum primus, septem libros continet a Joanne Baptista Montano . . . latinitate donatos. Secundus autem, libros sex Jano Cornario . . . interprete. At tertius, libros tres habet ab eodem Joanne Baptista Montano felicissime latinos factos. Venice: L. Giunta, March, January, June, 1534.

[12], 303 [1], [8], 300, 303-304, [2], 157 (i.e. 155), [2], [48] p.; 32 cm. (fol.)

The first complete Latin edition of Aetius's famous *Tetrabiblion*, published before the incomplete Greek *editio princeps* of the same year. Aetius, chamberlain and physician to the Emperor Justinian, "collected together works of other men which might have been forgotten but for him. Among them may be mentioned Rufus of Ephesus, Antyllus, Leonides, Soranus, Philumenus" (G-M 33). The seventh book, "De oculorum morbis," contains the most exhaustive account of eye diseases in the literature of antiquity.

Durling Suppl. 2; Hirschberg §248.

6   Aguilon, François d', 1566-1617.

Opticorum libri sex philosophis iuxtà ac mathematicis utiles. Antwerp: Officina Plantiniana, by the widow and sons of J. Moretus, 1613.

[48], 684, [44] p.: ill.; 36 cm. (fol.)

An elaborately illustrated and printed book whose six vignettes and frontispiece, engraved by Theodore Galle, are from drawings by Peter Paul Rubens. A landmark of baroque book illustration, this is one of only seven works known to have been illustrated by Rubens.

(6) Aguilon, François d'. *Opticorum libri sex philosophis iuxtà ac mathematicis utiles*, 1613. Copperplate illustration on p. 1. (14.3 x 10 cm.)

A classic in the science of optics, the *Opticorum* is a skillful synthesis of the works of Euclid, Alhazen (Ibn al-Haitham), Witelo, Bacon, Risner, and Kepler, and includes important and original observations on the properties of light, the nature of vision, the optic ray and horopter, and projections by mathematical theorems. Stereographic projections, known from the time of Hipparchus, were first named and fully discussed by Aguilon in this work. "The subject of binocular vision was successfully studied by Aguilon. . . . His theory is more correct than that of Dr. Whewell or Mr. Wheatstone. . . . Optical writers who lived after the time of Aguilon seem to have considered the subject of binocular vision as exhausted in this admirable work" (Sir David Brewster). Aguilon was rector of the Jesuit college in Antwerp.

BOA I:2; Hirschberg §313.

Alberti, Michael, 1682-1757, praeses.

See Arnoldi (26.1).

Alcoatin, 12th cent.

Congregatio sive Liber de oculis, quem compilavit Alcoatin, Christianus Toletanus anno dominicae incarnationis MCLIX. Publié d'aprés les manuscrits des bibliothèques de Metz et d'Erfurt, avec introduction sur l'histoire des oculistes arabes.

In Collectio ophthalmologica veterum auctorum (82), fasc. 2.

7 Algarotti, Francesco, conte, 1712-1764.

Il Newtonianismo per le dame ovvero dialoghi sopra la luce e i colori. Naples: s.n., 1737.

xi, [1], 300, [4] p.: engr. front.; 23 cm. (4to)

The first edition of the first successful popularization of Newtonian optics. Algarotti's considerable literary ability and genuine interest in the sciences combined to produce this elegant presentation of Newtonian ideas, arranged in the form of six imaginary dialogues with the Marchesa di E. . . . Its influence is attested by the publication of ten Italian, five English, four French, three Dutch, and individual German and Swedish editions between 1738 and 1832.

The young Venetian's immediate acceptance into the best circles of the capitals of Europe assured him the acquaintance of the most brilliant men of the day and the most advanced ideas. Algarotti was already planning a popularization of Newton in a series of dialogues similar to Fontenelle's *Entretiens sur la pluralité des mondes*, when he was invited to Cirey by Voltaire, who was himself planning a like work (394). He returned to Venice in 1736 after nearly two years in Paris and London, where the general approbation of his dialogues induced him to ready the manuscript for publication.

Wallis 194; Wellcome II:30.

8 Alhazen (Ibn al-Haitham), 965-1039.

Opticae thesaurus . . . libri septem, nunc primùm editi. Ejusdem Liber de crepusculis & nubium ascensionibus. Item Vitellonis Thuringopoloni libri X. Omnes instaurati . . . adjectis etiam in Alhazenum commentariis, à Federico Risnero. Basel: E. Episcopius & heirs of N. Episcopius for Officina Episcopiana, 1572.

[6], 288, [8], 474, [2] p.: ill.; 34 cm. (fol.)

First printed edition of a fundamental work on optics, it was translated from the Arabic in the twelfth century and became the foundation of Western optical science through Witelo, Roger Bacon, Peckham and Kepler. The *Book of optics* is followed by the *Treatise on twilight*, in which height of the atmospheric moisture responsible for the refraction of the sun's rays is calculated. This work, generally ascribed to Alhazen, is probably the work of Abū ʿAbd Allāh Muhammad ibn Muʿādh al-Jayyani who lived in the latter part of the eleventh century. Cf. A. I. Sabra. "The authorship of the *Liber de crepusculis*," *Isis*, 58:77-85 (1967).

The *Perspective* of Witelo (422.1), a commentary on Alhazen's *Optics* first published in 1535, is included in this work edited by Friedrich Risner. The reprint edition of this work (New York: Johnson Reprint Corp., 1972) contains a full introduction by David Lindberg.

BOA I:3; Wellcome I:3044 (Haitham, Ibn al).

ʿAlī ibn ʿĪsā, al-Kahhal, 10th cent.

Epistola Jhesu filii Haly de cognitione infirmitatum oculorum sive memoriale oculariorum quod compilavit Ali ben Issa. Avec les deux textes juxtaposés de la traduction arabo-latine et de la traduction hébraïco-latine publiés d'après les manuscrits de la Bibliothèque Nationale et les incunables.

In Collectio ophthalmologica veterum auctorum (82), fasc. 3.

9 ʿAlī ibn ʿĪsā, al-Kahhal, 10th cent.

Memorandum book of a tenth-century oculist for the use of modern ophthalmologists. A translation of the Tadhkirat of Ali ibn Isa of Baghdad (cir. 940-1010 A.D.), the most complete, practical and original of all the early textbooks on the eye and its diseases. 1st ed. in English by Casey A. Wood. Chicago: Lakeside Press for Northwestern University, 1936.

xxxix, [1], 232 p., [16] plates; 27 cm.

"The *Tadhkirat al-Kahhalin* was one of the oldest and best of the medieval Arabic works on ophthalmology. It carefully described 130 diseases of the eye and became the standard work on the subject in the Middle East" (G-M 5815).

Hirschberg §268.

10 Allbutt, Sir Thomas Clifford, 1836-1925.

On the use of the ophthalmoscope in diseases of the nervous system and of the kidneys; also in certain other general disorders. London and New York: Macmillan and Co., 1871.

xii, [4], 405 p., [2] plates; 23 cm.

"The number of physicians who are working with the ophthalmoscope in England may, I believe, be counted upon the fingers of one hand" (Pref., p. 9). Allbutt was one of the first to employ the ophthalmoscope in Britain, and to extend its use beyond the diagnosis of ocular diseases. In this work Allbutt strove to explain to his contemporaries the numerous and important indications of intracranial disease provided by ophthalmoscopic examination. The author never entered into ophthalmic practice per se, but used his ophthalmological knowledge as an aid to his general clinical practice.

BOA I:4; Chance, p. 169-70; Hirsch I:92.

Allbutt, Sir Thomas Clifford, 1836-1925.

See Walton (399.1).

11 Alphonse, (Doctor), de Grand Boulogne.

Mémoire sur deux instruments nouveaux destinés à l'extraction et à l'abaissement de la cataracte. Marseilles: M. Olive, 1843.

35 p., [l] plate; 21 cm.

Modifications of the keratotome and the couching needle and their application in the extraction and depression operations for cataract are described.

12 Ammon, Friedrich August von, 1799-1861.

Ophthalmo paracenteseos historia. Specimen medico-historicum quo commentatur in varias huius operationis ad cataractam sanandam methodos hucusque institutas, et in instrumenta hunc in usum inventa. Göttingen: H. Dieterich, 1821.

xii, 88 p., [l] plate; 21 cm.

The first booktrade edition of Ammon's doctoral thesis, an historical survey of cataract operations, which he defended at the University of Göttingen on August 25, 1821. Hirsch (I:118) described this work as "an extremely learned compilation of all the operations pertaining to the subject, with descriptions and illustrations of all the instruments used."

Hirschberg §516-517; Waller 12514.

13 Ammon, Friedrich August von, 1799-1861.

De genesi et usu maculae luteae in retina oculi humani obviae. Quaestio anatomico-physiologica. Weimar: Landes-Industrie-Comtoir, 1830.

[6], 24 p., [l] plate; 26 cm.

An anatomical and physiological study of the macula lutea or yellow spot of Soemmerring, which was presented as the author's inaugural dissertation as professor of general pathology, materia medica, and clinical medicine and surgery in the Medico-Chirurgical Academy at Dresden.

Hirschberg §516-517.

14 Ammon, Friedrich August von, 1799-1861.

De iritide. Leipzig: B. G. Teubner (Dresden) for Weidmann, 1838.

vi, 48 p., [2] plates; 32 cm.

One of the most significant works of the celebrated ophthalmologist on the subject of iritis, this treatise, written in 1835, was first presented in Paris where it was awarded a medal by the Société Medico-Pratique. Ammon's work on iritis was so thorough and carefully founded on pathological and anatomical observations that it made other works on the subject appear elementary.

Hirschberg §516-517.

14.1 Ammon, Friedrich August von, 1799-1861.

Klinische Darstellungen der Krankheiten und Bildungsfehler des menschlichen Auges, der Augenlider und der Thränenwerkzeuge nach eigenen

Beobachtungen und Untersuchungen. Berlin: G. Reimer, 1838-1847.

4 pts. in 1 v. (viii, [2], 69, [1] p., 23 plates; viii, 31 p., 12 plates; viii, 90 p., 20 plates; [2], xxxvi p.); 41 cm.

A systematic summary and pictorial exposition of eye diseases including outward appearance, pathological anatomy and histopathology. This magnificent atlas containing 965 colored illustrations etched on 55 folio plates was published in four parts: parts 1 and 2 in 1838, part 3 in 1841, and part 4 in 1847. Part 2 specifically deals with the diseases of the eyelids, the lacrimal apparatus and the orbit. Part 3 describes congenital diseases of the visual system, and part 4 contains a preface to the entire work and a cumulative index. The work is described as "probably the best summary of the knowledge of diseases of the eye prior to the introduction of the ophthalmoscope" (G-M 5852). A French translation by V. F. Szokalski was published in Berlin and Paris in 1847.

BOA I:5; G-M 5852; Hirsch I:119-120; Hirschberg §517.

15 Ammon, Friedrich August von, 1799-1861.

Die plastische Chirurgie nach ihren bisherigen Leistungen kritisch dargestellt. Berlin: F. Nies (Leipzig) for G. Reimer, 1842.

xxvi, 310 p.; 23 cm.

This study was awarded the medal of the medical society of Ghent in 1840 and was subsequently translated into French and Italian. Blepharoplasty and canthoplasty are treated fully in this work, one of the most comprehensive on plastic surgery up to that time.

Hirschberg §516-517; Waller 340; Wellcome II:40.

Andersen, S. Ry, 1915- , ed.
See Soemmerring, D. W. (347).

15.1 Andreae, August Wilhelm, 1794-1867.

Zur ältesten Geschichte der Augenheilkunde. Programm der K. Medicinische-Chirurgischen Lehr-Anstalt zu Magdeburg. Magdeburg: Königl. Medicinische-Chirurgische Lehr-Anstalt, 1841.

113, [1] p.; 22 cm.

Provenance: Signed by the author for Dr. I. N. Schan(?).

August Andreae was accepted by the University of Berlin at the age of 17. He graduated in just three years, and then studied under Georg Joseph Beer and Eduard Jaeger in Vienna. He started his medical practice in Magdeburg in 1817, and lec-

tured at the Royal Medical and Surgical College of Magdeburg in pathology, therapy and–with particular success–in ophthalmology. He was a prolific medical author, and earned a distinguished place among medical historians with his two essays on ancient medicine. This volume contains Andreae's earlier essay about Egyptian, Indian, Hebrew and ancient Greek ophthalmiatrics, together with a speech delivered at the college in October, 1840. This essay was republished with Andreae's later historical writing, *Die Augenheilkunde des Hippokrates*, in 1843.

Engelmann, p. 17; Hirsch I:135.

16 Anel, Dominique, 1679-1730.

Lettres diverses, ou les critiques de la critique del signor Francesco Signorotti en faveur de la nouvelle methode de guerir la fistule lacrimale nouvellement inventée. Turin: J. F. Mairesse & J. Radix, 1713.

158, [2] p.; 19 cm. (4to)

Bound with Anel (17, 18, 341).

Hirschberg §360-361.

17 Anel, Dominique, 1679-1730.

Nouvelle methode de guerir les fistules lacrimales, ou recüeil de differentes pieces pour & contre, & en faveur de la même methode nouvellement inventée par Dominique Anel. Turin: P. J. Zappatte, 1713.

[16], 34 p.; 19 cm. (4 to)

Bound with Anel (16, 18, 341).

"Lachrymal duct catheterized for the first time" (G-M 5826). A collection of works on Anel's new method of treatment which includes the first edition of his *Observation singuliere sur la fistule lacrimale*, together with pieces which illustrate both contemporary support and opposition to his method. Anel "will always be remembered for his transformation of the classical treatment of lacrimal disease by such crude methods as the use of chemical caustics, the actual cautery and even the use of molten lead into the more civilized technique of probing and syringing" (Duke-Elder 13:675).

Bound with this collection of separate works is Anel's *Suite de la nouvelle methode de guerir les fistules lacrimales* (1714) which also includes letters in support of his method from such influential men as Woolhouse, Lancisi, Mery and Fontenelle.

Hirschberg §360-361; Waller 426.

NOUVELLE METHODE
DE GUERIR LES FISTULES LACRIMALES,
Ou Recüeil de differentes Pieces pour &
contre, & en faveur de la même Methode

nouvellement inventée

PAR DOMINIQUE ANEL

Docteur en Chirurgie , cy-devant Chirurgien
Major dans les Armées de S. M. T. C.,
& enfuite dans celles de S. M. I.

ex Dono authoris

A TURIN. M.DCCXIII.

Chez Pierre Jofeph Zappatte Jmpr. de la Ville.
Avec permiffion des Superieurs.

(17) Anel, Dominique. *Nouvelle methode...*, 1713. Title
page. (14 x 19 cm.)

18   Anel, Dominique, 1679-1730.

Suite de la nouvelle methode de guerir les
fistules lacrimales, ou discours apologetique, dans
lequel on a inseré differentes pieces en faveur de la
même methode inventée l'an 1713. Turin: J. F.
Mairesse & J. Radix, 1714.

[24], 316, [4] p.; 19 cm. (4to)
Bound with Anel (16, 17, 341).

Hirschberg §360-361.

19   Ango, Pierre, 1640-1694.

L'optique divisée en trois livres ou l'on
démontre d'une maniere aisée tout ce qui regarde
1° la propagation & les proprietez de la lumiere.
2° La vision. 3° La figure & la disposition des
verres qui servent à la perfefectionner [*sic*].

Paris: E. Michallet, 1682.

[8], 120, 125-367, [1] p., [1] plate: ill.; 15 cm. (12mo)

Ango's treatise is of significance to the history of optics because it established the outline of a wave theory of light nearly
eight years in advance of Huygen's *Traité de la lumière* (198).
Both Ango and Huygens acknowledged making use of an unpublished manuscript by the Jesuit scientist Ignace Gaston
Pardies (1636-1673) which may have suggested a wave theory
based on optical experiments with reflected and refracted rays.

BOA I:6.

Anonymi tractatus de egritudinibus oculorum.

See Tractatus.

Antyllus, 3rd/4th cent.

See Aetius, of Amida (5).

Apian, Peter, 1495-1552, ed.

See Witelo (422.1).

Arago, Dominique François Jean, 1786-1853.

See Young (423.2).

20   Arlt, Ferdinand, Ritter von, 1812-1887.

Die Krankheiten des Auges für praktische Ärzte
. . . . Dritter unveränderter Abdruck. Prague: F. A.
Credner & Kleinbub, 1855-56.

3 v. (xvi, 288 p., [1] plate; [4], 354 p.; [4], 441, [3] p.): ill.; 23
cm.

"Epoch-making" has been the term used to describe the first
appearance of this title in 1851. It is one of the most important
works of the greatest figure in the history of the Viennese school
of ophthalmology in the nineteenth century. The first volume
describes the diseases of the conjunctiva and cornea; the second the diseases of the sclera, iris, choroid and lens; and the
third the diseases of the vitreous body, retina, eye muscles,
palpebrae, lacrimal apparatus and orbit. The first edition was
published between 1851 and 1856. A third edition of the first
and second volumes was already called for by 1855. The first
edition of the third volume was published in 1856, the same
year that Arlt arrived at the University of Vienna.

Hirschberg §1231.

21 Arlt, Ferdinand, Ritter von, 1812-1887.

Über die Verletzungen des Auges mit besonderer Rücksicht auf deren Gerichtsärztliche Würdigung. Vienna: W. Braumüller, 1875.

[2], 128 p.; 23 cm.

"An important work dealing with the medico-legal aspects of eye injuries. English translation by C. S. Turnbull, 1878" (G-M 5912).

G-M 5912; Hirsch I:198; Hirschberg §1233; Waller 467.

22 Arlt, Ferdinand, Ritter von, 1812-1887.

Klinische Darstellung der Krankheiten des Auges zunächst der Binde-, Horn- und Lederhaut dann der Iris und des Ciliarkörpers. Vienna: W. Braumüller, 1881.

vii, [1], 316 p., [1] plate; 23 cm.

Published thirty years after the first appearance of his text-book, Arlt's *Klinische Darstellung* limits itself to a discussion of the diseases of the conjunctiva, cornea, sclera, iris and ciliary body. Published when Arlt was already sixty-nine years old, he wrote in the foreword, "Meine Gesundheit und die Beurtheilung des Gebotenen seitens der Fachgenossen werden für die Fortsetzung dieses Unternehmens entscheidend sein."

Hirsch I:198; Hirschberg §1233.

23 Arlt, Ferdinand, Ritter von, 1812-1887.

Zur Lehre vom Glaucom. Vienna: W. Braumüller, 1884.

[4], 142 p., VI plates: ill.; 24 cm.

Hirsch I:199; Hirschberg §1233.

24 Arlt, Ferdinand, Ritter von, 1812-1887.

Clinical studies on diseases of the eye including those of the conjunctiva, cornea, sclerotic, iris and ciliary body. . . . Translated by Lyman Ware. Philadelphia: P. Blakiston, Son, & Co., 1885.

viii, [9]-325 p., [1] plate; 24 cm.

The authorized translation by Lyman Ware (1841-1916) of Arlt's *Klinische Darstellung der Krankheiten der Binde-, Horn- und Lederhaut, dann der Iris und des Ciliarkörpers* (22). An Edinburgh edition of the Ware translation was published the same year.

Arnaldus de Villanova, d. 1313?

Libellus regiminis de confortatione visus. Editus circa annum 1308. Publié pour la première fois d'après le manuscrit de la Bibliothèque de Metz.

In Collectio ophthalmologica veterum auctorum (82), fasc. 1.

25 Arnemann, Justus, 1763-1806?

Uebersicht der berühmtesten und gebräuchlichsten chirurgischen Instrumente älterer und neuerer Zeiten. Göttingen: Vandenhoek-Ruprechtische Verlage, 1796.

236, [2] p.; 17 cm (8vo)

"Ouvrage utile et savant, qui offre une histoire assez complète des instrumens dont l'arsenal chirurgical s'est composé aux differentes époques de l'art" (BiogMed I:365). Arnemann lists hundreds of surgical instruments and their inventors, as well as providing references to the publications where they are described and illustrated. Ophthalmological instruments are described in "Von den Augeninstrumenten" (p. 42-78).

BioMed I:365; Blake, p. 20; Hirsch I:207; Waller 481; Wellcome II:59.

26 Arnold, Friedrich, 1803-1890.

Anatomische und physiologische Untersuchungen über das Auge des Menschen. Heidelberg & Leipzig: K. Groos, 1832.

vii, [1], 168 p., 3 plates; 28 cm.

Publisher's advertisements (4 p.) bound in.

Arnold, a pupil of Tiedemann, was professor of anatomy successively at Zurich, Freiburg, Tübingen, and Heidelberg and was among the pioneers in the scientific study of the anatomy of the eye. Among other observations, Arnold noted the lymphatic channels of the cornea and the location of nerves on the iris. The engraved plates illustrate microscopical enlargements of different parts of the eye.

Hirschberg §1004; Waller 483.

Arnold, Julius, 1835-1915.

See Wecker (408.1).

26.1 Arnoldi, Johann Friedrich, respondent.

Dissertatio inauguralis medica, de visus obscuratione a partu, quam . . . praeside Dn. D.

Michaele Alberti pro gradu doctoris subjiciet respondens Johannes Fridericus Arnoldi, Biesenroda-Mansfeldensis. Halle: J. Ch. Hendel, 1732.

28 p.; 21 cm. (4vo)

A doctoral dissertation by Johann Friedrich Arnoldi about vitiation of sight at birth. Most bibliographies credit the work to Michael Alberti, who was the praeses (faculty moderator) of this thesis submitted at the University of Halle in August, 1732. As a follower and successor of Georg Ernst Stahl, Alberti was professor of theoretical medicine, physiology, dietetics, pharmacology, and botany in Halle. His tenure on the faculty lasted for forty-two years, and over three hundred dissertations and disputations are attributed to him (Haeser I:671).

Beer II:22; Haller Med IV:398; Hirschberg §428; Wellcome II:23, 59.

26.2 Aubert, Hermann Rudolf, 1826-1892.

Physiologie der Netzhaut. Breslau: E. Morgenstern, 1865.

[2], xii, 394 p.: ill.; 24 cm.

Provenance: Leland Stanford Junior University Library (bookplate).

Hermann Aubert was born in Frankfurt on the Oder, studied in Berlin, and received his doctorate in 1850. He taught medicine at the University of Breslau, and later was professor of physiology and rector at the University of Rostock. His richly illustrated *Physiology of the retina* describes physiological elements of vision, including the senses of light, color, and space, as well as binocular and stereoscopic vision.

BM 8:215; Hirsch I:238; NUC 25:381; Poggendorff III:49.

27 Bacon, Roger, 1214?-1294.

Perspectiva. In qua, quae ab aliis fuse traduntur, succincte, nervose & ita pertractantur, ut omnium intellectui facile pateant. Nunc primum in lucem edita opera & studio Johannis Combachii. Frankfurt am Main: W. Richter for A. Humm, 1614.

[8], 189 (i.e. 207) p., [4] plates: ill.; 19 cm. (4to)

Bound with Bacon (28).

This is the first edition of Part V of Bacon's *Opus majus* (written 1266-1267) which did not appear in its entirety until 1733. Bacon's contribution to ophthalmology was chiefly in the field of optics and his *Treatise of mirrors* indicates that he understood well the properties of lenses and spherical mirrors. It has been generally held [see Smith's *Compleat system of op-*

tics (345); remarks 81-88 and 111-121] that Bacon was the first to write about the practical utility of lenses and the relevant and frequently quoted passages (especially p. 159-160) are quite explicit about his use of a plano-convex glass to magnify writing. More recently G. Ten Doesschate ["Some Historical Notes on Spectacles and on Beryllus," *British Journal of Ophthalmology* 30:660-664 (1946)] has argued that credit and perhaps even priority should be accorded to Robert Grosseteste and John Peckham for their work with lenses earlier in the thirteenth century.

BOA I:10; Hirschberg §300.

28 Bacon, Roger, 1214?-1294.

Specula mathematica: in qua, de specierum multiplicatione, earundemque in inferioribus virtute agitur. Liber omnium scientiarum studiosis apprime utilis, editus opera & studio Johannis Combachii. Frankfurt am Main: W. Richter for A. Humm, 1614.

[8], 83 p.: ill.; 19 cm. (4to)

Bound with Bacon (27).

Part IV of the author's *Opus majus* which was written at the request of Pope Clement IV. Bacon believed deeply in the practical utility of mathematics in almost every field of study.

29 Bader, Charles, 1825-1899.

Plates illustrating the natural and morbid changes of the human eye. London: N. Trübner & Co., 1868.

32 p., X plates; 23 cm.

This small atlas was originally intended to accompany Bader's *The natural and morbid changes of the human eye, and their treatment* (London, 1868). The plates were published somewhat later than the book because of difficulties the author encountered with lithographers. Lithographed by F. Schlotterbach after the original watercolors of R. Schweizer, the plates were published by the noted lithographic firm of Day & Son. They were considered of such quality that the atlas was often sought independent of the text.

Bader was a German ophthalmologist who settled in London after the political disturbances of 1848. Hirschberg credits him with having made the ophthalmoscope known in England. He was an original, even brilliant surgeon, who somehow escaped the serious attention of his British colleagues.

BOA I:10; Hirschberg §668.

Bager, Philipp Thomas, respondent.

"De synechia, sive praeternaturali adhaesione corneae cum iride."

In Dissertationes medicae selectae Tubingenses (112) 1:110-143.

30   Bailey, Walter, 1529-1593.

A briefe treatise touching the preseruation of the eie-sight, consisting partly in good order of diet, and partly in vse of medicines. London: R. Waldegrave, 1586.

[6], 23 p.; 14 cm. (8vo)

This original edition of Bailey's first and most important book is also the first separate work in the English language devoted to ophthalmology. The author's observations on the preservation of sight are complemented by the opinions of a variety of Arabic and medieval authorities, especially those of Rhazes, Avicenna and Arnaldus de Villanova.

According to D'Arcy Power ["Dr. Walter Bayley and his works," *Med.-Chir. Trans.* 90: 415-454 (1907)], each of Bailey's works were first printed for private circulation, and then reprinted for general distribution. The two issues of this title are supposed to differ in the signing of the first gathering and in the presence of a printer's ornament on the last page of the preface. The first page of the preface in our copy is signed Aiii as in Power's second printing, but is lacking the ornament which is supposed to appear in the re-issue.

A briefe treatise was often republished in the 17th century: first at Oxford in 1602, again at Oxford in 1616 (30.1) under the title *Two treatises concerning the preservation of eie-sight* (with a compendium on the diseases of the eye from the works of Fernel and Riolan); without acknowledgement in Banister's 1622 *Treatise* (32); twice more at London in 1626 and 1633; and finally at Oxford again in 1654 and 1673.

Durling 506; Hirsch I:302; James, p. 48; STC 1193.

30.1   Bailey, Walter, 1529-1592.

Two treatises concerning the preseruation of eie-sight. The first written by Doctor Baily sometimes of Oxford, the other collected out of those two famous phisicions Fernelivs and Riolanvs. Oxford: Joseph Barnes for John Barnes, 1616.

[8], 64 p. (first and last leaves blank); 15 cm. (8vo)

This edition of Bailey's *A briefe treatise* (30) with the exception of its title page, is thought to have been printed in London

by G. Eld (STC [2nd ed.] 1196) rather than in Oxford by Joseph Barnes, since its woodcut initials and head-piece were quite unknown in Oxford at the time (Madan I:105). "The preface is no doubt by John Barnes and alludes to the worth and undeserved obscurity of Bailey's work" (Ibid.). The second work, *A treatise of the pricipall diseases of the eyes*, is here printed in English for the first time, and "is apparently extracted in part from the *Ars bene medendi* of Jean Riolan, the elder. The compiler is unknown, although A. à Wood, in his *Athenae oxonienses*, v. 1 (1813), p. 586, states that both [treatises] now go under the name of Bailey" (NUC 30:653).

BM 10:37; BOA II:10 (1602 ed.); James, p. 49; Krivatsy 978; Madan I:105; NUC 30:653; STC (2nd ed.) 1196; Wellcome I:629; Wood I:586.

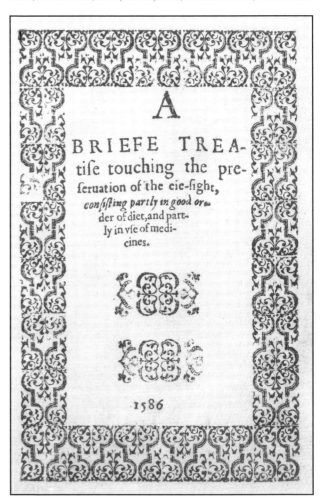

(30) Bailey, Walter. *A briefe treatise...*, 1586. Title page. (9 x 14 cm.)

31   Banières, Jean, b. 1700.

Examen et réfutation des Elémens de la philosophie de Neuton de M. Voltaire, avec une dissertation sur la réflexion & la réfraction de la lumière. Paris: Lambert, Durand, 1739.

[4], xcviii, [10], 308, [4] p., 5 plates; 20 cm. (8vo)

A critical examination and refutation of Voltaire's *Elémens de la philosophie de Neuton* (394), published the year following the first appearance of Voltaire's immensely popular book. The author divides his work into as many chapters as appear in Voltaire's, giving them identical titles, as he sets about refuting Voltaire's Newtonian concepts of light, reflection, refraction, etc. Banières was a confirmed Cartesian, and took heated exception to Voltaire's dismemberment of his mentor's scientific ideas.

Wallis 44.

32   Banister, Richard, 1570?-1626.

A treatise of one hundred and thirteene diseases of the eyes, and eye-liddes. The second time published, with some profitable additions and certaine principles and experiments. London: F. Kyngston for T. Man, 1622.

[240] leaves; 15 cm. (12mo)

"Although much of this is a translation of Guillemeau, the first 112 pages are Banister's own work, *Banister's Breviary*. He was an itinerant but honest oculist; he noted the hardness of the eye ball in glaucoma" (G-M 5820).

The book has been thoroughly analyzed by Arnold Sorsby in an article in the *British Journal of Ophthalmology* 16:345-355 (1932). Sorsby believed that Banister has been unjustly accused of plagiarism and as a consequence his *Breviary* has been ignored by historians of the eye. See also Arnold Sorsby's "Richard Banister and the beginnings of English ophthalmology" in *Science, medicine and history*, edited by E. Ashworth Underwood, (London, 1953), 2:42-55.

G-M 5820; Hirschberg §352; STC 1362; Wellcome I:2998.

Bartholin, Caspar, 1585-1629.

See Bartholin, Thomas (33).

33   Bartholin, Thomas, 1616-1680.

Anatomia, ex Caspari Bartholini parentis Institutionibus, omniumque recentiorum & propriis observationibus tertiùm ad sanguinis circulationem reformata. Leyden: F. Hack, 1651.

[16], 576, [14] p., [7] plates: ill.; 20 cm. (8vo)

Third edition of Bartholin's *Anatomia*, a much-used seventeenth century anatomical textbook. The author, professor of anatomy at Copenhagen, was particularly interested in pathological anatomy and the discovery of the lymphatics. The book is essentially a revision of his father's *Institutiones anatomicae* (Wittenberg, 1611) with illustrations after Vesalius, Ruysch, Casserius and others. A chapter (p. 341-352) and two plates are devoted to the eye.

Hirschberg §369; Wellcome II:107.

Bartholin, Thomas, 1616-1680.

"De cerebri substantia pingui" and "De oculorum suffusione."

In Borri, G. F. *Epistolae duae* (55).

34   Bartisch, Georg, 1535-1607?

Οφθαλμοδουλεια. Das ist, Augendienst. Newer und wolgegründter Bericht von Ursachen und Erkentnüs aller Gebrechen, Schäden und Mängel der Augen und des Gesichtes. . . . Dresden: M. Stöckel, 1583.

[28], 274, [8] leaves: ill.; 31 cm. (fol.)

"Bartisch, the founder of modern ophthalmology, was a skilful operator and the first to practise the extirpation of the bulbus in cancer of the eye. The illustrations in his book form a comprehensive picture-book of Renaissance eye-surgery; some of the woodcuts show the parts of the eye lying successively one under the other, by means of pictures superimposed on each other like the pages of a book" (G-M 5817).

The *Augendienst* is the first modern work on eye surgery and one of the earliest surgical works printed in the vernacular. The ninety-one remarkable woodcuts which illustrate this book were probably executed by Hans Hewamaul after Bartisch's own drawings.

BOA I:14; G-M 5817; Hirschberg §320; Waller 756; Wellcome I:697.

35   Bartisch, Georg, 1535-1607?

Οφθαλμοδουλεια. Das ist, Augendienst. Newer und wolgegründter Bericht von Ursachen und Erkentnüs aller Gebrechen, Schäden und Mängel der Augen und des Gesichtes. . . . New York: Editions

Medicina Rara, 1977? (Dresden: M. Stöckel 1583).

[28], 274, [8] leaves: ill.; 31 cm.

"... printed for the members of the Editions Medicina Rara at the presses of The Scolar Press.... The plates for this printing were made from a copy of the original 1583 edition, belonging to the Herzog August Bibliothek, Wolfenbüttel, West Germany. Five hundred copies have been bound in full leather and are numbered in Roman numerals I-D.... This copy is number LII" (colophon).

Bartisch, Georg, 1535-1607?
See Print 15.

35.1 Bate, Robert Brettell, fl. 1824-1837.

To all who value their sight. A few practical suggestions and illustrations, intended briefly to awaken the attention of every individual to the condition of his sight; and enable him to promote the improvement and preservation of that invaluable faculty. London: R. Taylor for the author, 1825.

20 p.; 22 cm.

A short essay promoting the use of spectacles, which according to the author are "not capable of restoring, but will almost entirely preserve" good eyesight (p. 6). The work includes medical explanations of near and far-sightedness, and describes the disadvantages of using magnifying glasses and monocles. It emphasizes the proper use of spectacles and the importance of "equality and uniformity of light" for reading (p. 18-19). The title page indicates that the pamphlet was "sold by ... all opticians and booksellers" for a sixpence in London, but however popular, it became an extremely rare item due to its ephemeral nature. A fourth edition is known to have been published in 1830 (OCLC).

BM 12:652.

35.2 Baudet-Dulary, Alexandre François, 1790-1878.
Thése sur l'oeil et la vision. Paris: Didot, Jr., 1814.

[2], 19, [1] p.; 25 cm.
Bound with Fournier (140.1).

Baudet-Dulary was a follower of F. M. C. Fourier (1772-1837), social critic and utopian socialist (EncPhil III:215). Building on Fourier's theory that humanity should be organized into "phalanxes," Baudet-Dulary established a socialistic colony on his own estate in the Paris area. His better known writings

are devoted to fields such as sociology, philosophy, hygiene, and physiognomy. This work, his doctoral dissertation about the anatomy of the eye and about vision, is his only known ophthalmological writing.

Hirsch I:381.

Baumgarten, Friedrich Moritz Oswald, 1813-1849.
See Ammon (15).

Bayley, Walter, 1529-1593.
See Bailey (30, 30.1).

Becker, Johann Hermann, 1700-1759, respondens.
See Becker, Peter (36.1).

36 Becker, Otto Heinrich Enoch, 1828-1890.

Atlas der pathologischen Topographie des Auges ... Gezeichnet von Carl und Julius Heitzmann, Robert Sattler und Friedrich Veith. Lithographirt von Julius Heitzmann. I [-III] Lieferung. Vienna: W. Braumüller, 1874-78.

3 pts., XXX plates; 36 cm.

A colleague of Eduard Jaeger and Arlt in Vienna in the early 1860s, and Knapp's successor at Heidelberg after his departure for New York in 1868, Becker made several important contributions to ophthalmic literature, including the present atlas. This set, which once belonged to the noted Philadelphia ophthalmologist Charles A. Oliver, is lacking the first Lieferung (1874).

Hirschberg §1188, 1189, 1190.

36.1 Becker, Peter, 1672-1753, praeses.

Novam hypothesin, de duplici visionis et organo et modo dioptrico altero, altero catoptrico, quorum hoc insectis, illud vero animantibus reliquis concessisse natura videtur ... D. 12 Sept. anno MDCCXX ... submittunt praeses M. Petrus Becker ... & respondens Johannes Hermannus Becker.... Rostock: N. Schwiegerov, 1720.

[24] p.; 20 cm. (4to)

An academic disputation purporting to offer a new hypothesis about mechanisms of refraction and reflection in the eyes of insects and other animals, as well as humans. Johann Hermann Becker wrote this work under the direction of his uncle, Peter Becker, a professor of mathematics in Rostock and author of a number of works on mathematics, astronomy, and physics. Johann Becker later became a professor of theology at the University of Greifswald, but nevertheless continued to publish on optics and astronomy.

BM 13:836; NUC 42:422; Poggendorff I:126.

36.2   Beer, August, 1825-1863.

Einleitung in die höhere Optik. Braunschweig: F. Vieweg and Son, 1853.

xiii, [3], 430 p., [2] plates: 262 ill.; 22 cm.

August Beer, a lecturer at the University of Bonn, was author of works in a variety of fields related to the study of physics and mathematics including photometry, electrostatics, magnetism, elasticity, and gravity. This work is "an introduction to higher optics, including a detailed description of the properties of light, the oscillation theory of light, the propagation,

(38.1) Beer, Georg Joseph. *Das Auge...*, 1813. Plate [2]: "Leidensgeschichte des blinden Mannes." (8 x 10 cm.)

polarization and transference of light" (BOA I:18). A French translation by M. C. Forthomme, and a second German edition revised by Victor von Lang were published in 1858 and 1882.

BM 13:1096; BOA I:19; NUC 43:141.

37   Beer, Georg Joseph, 1763-1821.

Praktische Beobachtungen über den grauen Staar und die Krankheiten der Hornhaut. Vienna: C. F. Wappler, 1791.

275, [1] p., 3 plates; 20 cm. (8vo)

The first work by this "prolific and prominent author, one of the most brilliant ophthalmologists, who must be reckoned amongst the most important contributors to the promotion of modern ophthalmology" (Hirsch I:422). In addition to providing what Hirschberg describes as an extraordinarily accurate description of gray or senile cataract and its operations, the author discusses corneal affections including the ocular complications of measles, staphyloma, and pterygium. Of particular interest are the first two plates comprising fifteen illustrations hand-colored by the author.

Hirschberg §469; Wellcome II:130.

38   Beer, Georg Joseph, 1763-1821.

Moyens infaillibles de conserver sa vue en bon état jusqu'a une extrême vieillesse et de la rétablir et la fortifier lorsqu'elle s'est affaiblie; avec la manière de s'aider soi même, dans des cas accidentels qui n'exigent pas la présence des gens de l'art, et celle de traiter les yeux pendant et après la petite-vérole; traduit de l'allemand . . . auxquels on a ajouté quelques observations sur les inconvéniens et dangers des lunettes communes. 5. éd., revue et corrigée. Paris: Paquet, Blaise, Monnot, Antoine, 1812.

x, [11]-160 p., [1] plate; 20 cm. (8vo)
Bound with Williams (419-421).

Hirschberg §469.

38.1   Beer, Georg Joseph, 1763-1821.

Das Auge, oder Versuch das edelste Geschenk der Schöpfung vor dem höchst verderblichen Einfluss unseres Zeitalters zu sichern. Vienna: Camesina, 1813.

[iii]-viii, 158, [2] p., [6] plates; 19 cm.

A collection of treatises discussing various subjects including the physiological and psychological aspects of blindness, the types of eye deficiencies, the care of the eyes, the use of spectacles, and the "raging spectacle mania" in Vienna. The last chapter is the 1806 report of Beer's private eye clinic for the poor, which received royal patronage that year. The title page of the book is not typeset, but is an etched plate. Like the third plate, it also bears the engraved phrase "Beer del[ineabat]" suggesting that these plates were etched after Beer's drawings.

BM 13:1100; Dawson, p. 49; Hirsch I:423; NUC 43:146; Waller 828.

39 Beer, Georg Joseph, 1763-1821.

Lehre von den Augenkrankheiten, als Leitfaden zu seinen öffentlichen Vorlesungen entworfen. Vienna: A. Strauss for Camesina, 1813 (Vol. 2: Heubner & Volke, 1817).

2 v. (xx, 636 p., 4 plates; xvi, li, [1], 680 p., 5 plates); 23 cm. (8vo)

First published in 1792, this influential textbook dictated the techniques of ophthalmological practice for several generations. "He described the symptoms of glaucoma and noted the luminosity of the fundus in aniridia. He was a distinguished iridectomist. Many of his pupils became famous ophthalmic surgeons" (G-M 5842). Seven of the plates were drawn and hand-colored by the author and include forty-four carefully executed illustrations of abnormal eye conditions. Cf. Huldrych M. Koelbing, "Georg Joseph Beer's Lehre von den Augenkrankheiten (Wien 1813-1817) im Zusammenhang mit der Medizin seiner Zeit," *Clio Medica* 5:225-248 (1970).

G-M 5842; Hirschberg §469; Wellcome II:130.

40 Beer, Georg Joseph, 1763-1821.

Art of preserving the sight unimpaired to extreme old age: and of re-establishing and strengthening it when it becomes weak. To which are added observations on the inconveniences and dangers arising from the use of common spectacles. By an experienced oculist. 5th ed., considerably augmented and improved. London: B. Clarke for H. Colburn, 1828.

xi, [1], 259 p., [1], plate; 20 cm.

Beer opposed the injudicious use of common spectacles and in explanation published *Pflege gesunder und geschwachter Augen* (1800). This work was translated into English in 1813 and quickly went through many editions. The book described above seems to be a re-issue of the fifth London edition published in 1822. It appears that the author's name is not found on the title pages of any of the many editions of the English translation.

Hirschberg §469; Wellcome II:130.

Beer, Georg Joseph, 1763-1821.

See also Weiss (410.2).

Beger, Christoph Paul, respondent.

"De hydrophthalmia, & hydrope oculi."

In Dissertationes medicae selectae Tubingenses (112) 2:[1]-18.

Beger, Philipp Thomas, respondent.

"De synechia, sive praeternaturali adhaesione corneae cum iride."

In Dissertationes medicae selectae Tubingenses (112) 1:110-143.

41 Benedict, Traugott Wilhelm Gustav, 1785-1862.

De pupillae artificialis conformatione libellus. Leipzig: F. C. G. Vogel, 1810.

viii, 47 p., [1], plate; 23 cm. (4to)

The various methods of creating an artificial pupil surgically for purely optical purposes are described including the operations of coretotomy (iridotomy), corectomy (iridectomy) and coredialysis (iridodialysis). The procedures of Cheselden, Janin, Wenzel, and Daviel are reviewed but the author focuses on Beer's operation which became the prototype of all forms of iridectomy.

Hirschberg §501.

42 Benedict, Traugott Wilhelm Gustav, 1785-1862.

Monographie des grauen Staares. Breslau: C. F. Barth, 1814.

vii, [1], 180 p.; 23 cm. (4to)

A treatise on the diagnosis, etiology, and treatment of cataracts based on careful observations and conscientious judgement. The author's greatest contribution to ophthalmology was his discovery of the etiologic relationship between cataract and diabetes. Benedict personally suffered the ridicule of his contemporaries for his habit of praying before each operation.

Hirschberg §501.

43 Benevoli, Antonio, 1685-1756.

Nuova proposizione intorno alla caruncola dell'uretra detta carnosità . . . Aggiuntavi in fine una lettera . . . sopra la cateratta glaucomatosa. Florence: G. Manni, 1724.

[10], 197, [1] p.; 19 cm. (8vo)

Benevoli acquired a great reputation in the two branches of surgery treated in this work: lithotomy and cataract extraction. The letter to Valsalva reprinted here was originally published in 1722 and contains Benevoli's observation that cataract was caused by the loss of transparency of the lens rather than by the formation of a membrane in the vitreous body. As a result of the publication of this letter Benevoli was accused by Pierre Paoli, a surgeon of Lucca, of plagiarizing Heister's opinions on cataract and there followed a spirited exchange of charges, counter-charges and justifications.

Hirschberg §402; Wellcome II:143.

44 Benevoli, Antonio, 1685-1756.

Dissertazioni I. Sovra l'origine dell'ernia intestinale finora non stata avvertita. II. Intorno alla piu frequente cagione dell'iscuria, o sia ritenzione dell'orina nella vescica. III. Sopra il leucoma, detto volgarmente maglia dell'occhio. Aggiuntevi quaranta osservazioni tre delle quali sulla rachitide, e le altre in diversi casi di chirurgia. Florence: G. Albizzini, 1747.

xii, 252 p.; 24 cm. (4to)

At the time this work was published Benevoli was professor of surgery at Florence and oculist (and later chief surgeon) at the hospital of Santa Maria Nuova. The third *dissertazione* in this collection (p. 55-78) deals with the treatment of leukoma. Three of the forty *osservazioni* discuss ophthalmological topics: XXI, "Rilassamento della cornea ridotta poi all'esser suo naturale" (p. 161-63); XXIII, "Estrazione di un occhio cancheroso" (p. 167-70); and XXIV, "Estirpazione infelice di un sarcoma dall'orbita destra" (p. 170-75).

Blake, p. 41; Hirsch I:458; Hirschberg §402; Wellcome II:143.

45 Berkeley, George, Bishop of Cloyne, 1685-1753.

An essay towards a new theory of vision. Dublin: A.

Rhames for J. Pepyat, 1709.

xiv, [10], 187 p.; 20 cm. (8vo)

Berkeley's most important work in psychology, containing his "empiristic theory of visual perception which came to dominate all discussions of the subject at least through the end of the nineteenth century" (Pastore, p. 71). Smith (345, 346) and Porterfield (302) criticized Berkeley's optical theories and sought to refute them through scientific experiments. The printer, Aaron Rhames, was one of Dublin's leading printers, and is remembered for having printed the first complete English Bible in Ireland. Cf. Burton Chance, "George Berkeley and 'An essay towards a new theory of vision,'" *Transactions of the American Ophthalmological Society* 40:43-53 (1942).

Hirschberg §455; Keynes 1; Wellcome II:149.

46 Bernard, Claude, 1813-1878.

Précis iconographique de médecine opératoire et d'anatomie chirurgicale. Paris: Crapelet & H. Lahure for Méquignon-Marvis, 1848.

[4], xxiii, [1], 488 p., 114 plates; 18 cm.

Bernard, considered the greatest French physiologist of the nineteenth century, collaborated with Huette on this illustrated textbook of surgery which was reprinted as late as 1873 and translated into English, German, Dutch, Italian, and Spanish. The importance of the work is suggested by the fact that it was given to each surgeon in the United States Army during the Civil War. Nearly fifty pages (p. 110-159) and seven colored plates are devoted to ophthalmic surgery.

Hirschberg §502.

Bernia, Girolamo, fl. 1642-1665, ed.
See Grimaldi (163).

47 Bernstein, Johann Gottlob, 1747-1835.

Neues chirurgisches Lexicon oder Wörterbuch der Wundarzenkunst neuerer Zeiten. Neue vermehrte Auflage. Gotha: C. W. Ettinger, 1787-88.

2 v. (xii, 768; [2], 788, [2] p.); 21 cm. (8vo)

The second edition of a surgical dictionary that became a standard reference work among German-speaking surgeons, being augmented and reprinted many times under various titles through the first quarter of the 19th century. The *Lexicon* contains numerous articles on ocular surgery.

Blake, p. 44: Hirschberg §426.

48   Berry, George Andreas, 1853-1940.

Diseases of the eye. A practical treatise for students of ophthalmology. Philadelphia: Lea Brothers & Co., 1889.

xvii, [3], 670 p.: ill.; 23 cm.

"Detailed discussion of the symptoms and treatment of diseases of the eye. Special emphasis is laid on the subject of foreign bodies in the eye, and on sympathetic ophthalmia" (BOA I:21, Edin. ed.). One of the interesting features of this work from the point of view of book illustration is the provision of fifty-six chromolithographs in the text, rather than on separate plates. An Edinburgh edition was issued the same year.

49   Bidloo, Govard, 1649-1713.

Exercitationum anatomico-chirurgicarum decas. Leyden: J. Luchtmans, 1704.

[6], 62, 61*-62*, 63-108 p., 7 plates; 18 cm. (8vo)

Bound with the 1656 The Hague edition of Scultetus's *Armamentarium chirurgicum* (337).

A collection of ten anatomical and surgical essays by the celebrated Leyden anatomist. In the two essays on the nerves Bidloo maintains that the nerves do not contain fluid but are rather a mass of fibers. In the seventh essay, "De oculo purulento" (p. 73-82), the treatment for hypopyon is described.

Hirsch I:527; Waller 1037; Wellcome II:165.

Bilger, Carl Ferdinand, respondent.

"De ungue oculi, s[eu] pure inter corneae lamellos collecto."

In Dissertationes medicae selectae Tubingenses (112) 2:114-140.

50   Billi, Domenico, fl. 1750.

Breve trattato delle malatie degli occhi. Ancona: Bellelli, 1749.

xx, 224, [2] p., 1 plate; 19 cm. (8vo)

Very little is known of Domenico Billi and this book seems to be his only published work. In the preface he explained that he undertook the compilation in an effort to expose Italian surgeons to the trans-Alpine advances in ophthalmology and to remove treatment of eye diseases from itinerant quacks. Hirschberg, who provides the only information about Billi, found this work of value in tracing the development of Italian ophthalmology. Burton Chance (p. 58) describes this as "the earliest treatise in Italian."

Hirschberg §406.

Biot, Jean-Baptiste, 1774-1862.

See Farrar (133.1).

50.1   Bischoff, Johann, 1716-1779.

Neue optische Beyträge hauptsächlich zu Vergrösserungsgläsern und einigen merkwürdigen Vortheilen bey Fernröhren. Ulm; Frankfurt am Main; Leipzig: Ch. U. Wagner for Gaum, 1760.

3 leaves, 69, [1] p., 2 folded plates; 18 cm. (8vo)

Provenance: M. G. Roesler, Prof., 1772 (inscription); Tabi Kasinó, 1878 (stamp); Ernst Lajos gyüjteménye (stamp).

Bound with Bischoff (50.2).

A treatise offering new contributions to the development of optical instruments, especially of magnifying glasses and telescopes. The author, Johann Bischoff, was a clergyman in Bernhausen, near Stuttgart, for whom optics was an avocation. Most of his writings pertain to this field, but he also published in the fields of mathematics and physics.

NUC 58:617; Poggendorff I:204.

50.2   Bischoff, Johann, 1716-1779.

Beyträge zur Optic, hauptsächlich zu solchen Vergrösserungsgläsern und Fernröhren, bey denen die Collectiv- oder Sammelgläser angebracht werden. Ulm; Frankfurt am Main; Leipzig: Ch. U. Wagner for Gaum, 1764.

52 p.; 18 cm. (8vo)

Bound with Bischoff (50.1).

Bischoff's second treatise on improvements in optical instruments (cf. 50.1). Despite a four year separation of the imprints, all extant copies feature the two treatises bound together as single volumes. They are fine examples of 18th century typographic art with clearly set Gothic type, handsome woodcut title vignettes, and head- and tail-pieces.

NUC 58:617; Poggendorff I:204.

51   Blacklock, Thomas, 1721-1791.

Poems . . . together with an essay on the education of the blind. To which is prefixed a new account of the life and writings of the author. Edinburgh: A. Chapman & Co. for W. Creech and T. Cadell (London), 1793.

viii, xxv, [1], 262 p.; 27 cm. (4to)

The second part of this volume contains the first English edition of Haüy's incunabulum on the education of the blind, translated by the blind Scottish poet Blacklock. Blacklock, who lost his sight at the age of six months as a result of smallpox, became the protege of the Edinburgh philosopher David Hume who encouraged his literary efforts. The notice on Blacklock in the *Dictionary of national biography* reports incorrectly that this translation was never published.

52 Blankaart, Steven, 1650-1702.

Anatomia reformata, sive concinna corporis humani dissectio, ad neotericorum mentem adornata. Editio novissima plurimis recens inventis, tabulisque novis emendatior ac locupletior. Accedit ejusdem authoris De balsamatione nova methodus, à nemine antehac similiter descripta. Leyden: J. Luchtmans & C. Boutestein, 1695.

[14], 759, 750-51, 762-63, 754-55, 766-67, 758-59, [14] p., [84] plates; 20 cm. (8vo)

Illustrated with eighty-four plates, this popular anatomical text, present here in the third Leyden edition, was reprinted a number of times in the seventeenth century. The proper placement of such a large number of plates required instructions to the binder which are given in five languages—Latin, German, Dutch, Spanish, and French. Despite these detailed polyglot instructions, evidence of the wide distribution expected for this work, sixteen plates are incorrectly placed in this copy.

A chapter on the eye (p. 297-319) treats primarily the lachrymal system drawing heavily on the anatomical work of Steno (359) and Nuck (276).

Hirschberg §345. Wellcome II:177.

52.1 Blumenbach, Johann Friedrich, 1752-1840.

De ocvlis levcaethiopvm et iridis motv commentatio. Göttingen: Ch. Dieterich, 1786.

38 p., 1 color plate; 23 cm. (4to)

Physician, natural philosopher, historian, and bibliographer, Johann Friedrich Blumenbach is often referred to as the "founder of scientific anthropology." He studied human beings as objects of natural history, classifying subdivisions of the species on the basis of facial features and skin color. As professor of medicine, Blumenbach taught at the University of Göttingen for more than sixty years. He was a pioneer lecturer of comparative anatomy, and emphasized its importance

in anthropological research (cf. Heirs 1113, 1116; Hirsch I:576-577). This fairly early work of Blumenbach is a study on albinism, mutations of eye color, and movements of the iris.

Blake, p. 51; Callisen II:352; Dawson, p. 68.

Bock, Emil, 1857-1916.

See Stellwag von Carion (357).

53 Boerhaave, Hermann, 1668-1738.

Praelectiones publicae de morbis oculorum.... Editio altera Gottingensi multo emendatior. Accesserunt huic editioni ejusdem autoris Introductio in praxim clinicam, praelectiones de calculo, aliquot morborum historiae, & consilia. Paris: G. Cavelier, 1748.

[8], 376 p., 4 plates; 17 cm. (12mo)

Boerhaave, considered the father of the modern method of clinical instruction, had a world-wide reputation as a physician and teacher and his lectures and writings exerted an enormous influence on the practice of medicine in the eighteenth century. He was the first to describe accurately the muscular fibers in the ciliary body, but his greatest contribution to ophthalmology was in the broad dissemination which he gave to the revolutionary doctrine of Maître-Jan (243-44) and Brisseau (63) on the true nature of cataract.

Hirschberg §332; Waller 1223; Wellcome II:191.

53.1 Boissonneau, Auguste, fl. 1840-1867.

Rapport adressé a S. M. Guillaume II . . . sur les suites déplorables de l'ophthalmie militaire observées depuis son invasion et traitées gratuitement par l'application des yeux artificiels pendant le cours des années 1842, 1843 & 1844. Paris: s.n., 1844.

xii, [2], 58 p.; 24 cm.

Auguste Boissonneau, a professor of ocular prostheses in Paris, published several writings about movable artificial eyes. This booklet contains a report and some documentation about his activities between 1842 and 1844. The report is addressed to William II of the Netherlands and concerns the debilitating effects of ophthalmia in the royal military forces. The volume also includes a collection of letters and other documents about Boissonneau's achievements in applications of the artificial eye.

NUC 64:316.

(6) Aguilon, François d'. *Opticorum libri sex philosophis iuxtà ac mathematicis utiles*, 1613. Copperplate illustration on p. 105. (14.3 x 10 cm.)

54   Bonnet, Amédée, 1802-1858.

Traité des sections tendineuses et musculaires dans le strabisme, la myopie, la disposition à la fatigue des yeux, le bégaiement, les pieds bots, les difformités du genou, les torticolis, les resserrements des machoires, les fractures . . . suivi d'un mémoire sur la névrotomie sous-cutanée. Paris & Lyons: Dumoulin, Ronet & Sibuet (Lyons) for J. B. Baillière, Germer-Baillière & C. Savy (Lyons), 1841.

[4], lxiv, 664 p., 16 plates; 21 cm. (8vo)

A detailed study of the relationship of the ocular muscles to the fibrous capsule of the eye and its implications for the operation for strabismus. The author re-discovered and more fully described the ocular capsule first observed by Tenon (373) and now eponymously known by both names. Bonnet is credited with reviving the operation for enucleation: "Since his classical description all operations for the ablation of the globe have been based upon the details elucidated by him, for it was Bonnet who first sought to conserve the capsule of Tenon, thereby protecting the soft parts of the orbit from injury" (Chance, p. 141).

Hirschberg §495; Wellcome II:200.

Bordenave, Toussaint, 1728-1782.

"Examen des réflexions critiques de M. Molinelli, insérées dans les Mémoires de l'Institut de Bologne, contre le mémoire de M. Petit, sur la fistule lacrymale, inseré parmi ceux de l'Académie Royale des Sciences de Paris, année 1734."

In Académie Royale de Chirurgie, *Mémoires* (2).

Bordenave, Toussaint, 1728-1782.

"Mémoire dans lequel on propose un nouveau procédé pour traiter le renversement des paupières."

In Académie Royale de Chirurgie, *Mémoires* (2).

Bordenave, Toussaint, 1728-1782.

See Pellier de Quengsy (292).

55   Borri, Giuseppe Francesco, 1627-1695.

Epistolae duae. I. De cerebri ortu & usu medico. II. De artificio oculorum humores restituendi. Ad Th. Bartholinum. Copenhagen: D. Paulli, 1669.

[4], 68 p.; 19 cm. (4to)

This work contains an exchange of letters between Borri and the famous Danish physician Thomas Bartholin. Borri explains his method of the restitution of the eye fluid by infusion of celandine juice, a secret which he claims to have obtained from the English chemist Sir Robert Southwell. Although Borri's method was proved ineffective, it led to important discoveries in the field of ophthalmological research.

Hirschberg §319; Wellcome II:206.

56   Bose, Adolph Julian, 1742-1770.

De morbis corneae ex fabrica ejus declaratis. Leipzig: Widow of Langenhemius, 1767.

36 p.; 22 cm. (4to)

A doctoral degree in medicine was conferred on Bose by the University of Leipzig in 1767 and the following year he was appointed extraordinary professor of medicine at Wittenberg. He held this chair for only two years before his early death at the age of twenty-eight. His doctoral dissertation deals with the diseases of the cornea and includes numerous references to the earlier literature on the subject.

57   Botti, Giuseppe, 17th cent.

Cecità illuminata, cioè breve compendio della formazione, e struttura dell'occhio, e delle sue parti constituenti; d'onde si mostra come si formi la visione, con l'assegnazione de mali dell' occhio, e le loro cause, col modo di guarirle per mezzo del salutifero estratto di varie essenze. Parma: G. Rossetti, 1698.

63, [1] p.; 15cm. (8vo)

An uncommon tract on the anatomy and physiology of the eye, written by a member of the Duchess of Parma's household. The author also discusses various diseases of the eye and recommends treatment with an extract from various essences.

58   Bouchut, Eugène, 1818-1891.

Du diagnostic des maladies du système nerveux par l'ophthalmoscopie. Paris: G. Baillière, 1866.

xx, 503 p. + atlas ([28] p., XII plates): ill.; 22 cm.

"Si la découverte de cet instrument a été l'origine de progrès importants pour l'étude des maladies de l'oeil, sachons qu'il peut être la source de progrès non moins précieux dans le diagnostic des maladies cérébro-spinales en nous donnant le moyen de découvrir au travers de l'oeil les altérations qui se produissent dans les différentes parties de la moelle et du cerveau" (Introduction, p. xix-xx).

Published six years before Allbutt's classic work on the use of the ophthalmoscope in the diagnosis of the diseases of the nervous system (10). Unlike Allbutt, who never returned to the subject, Bouchut was the author of two subsequent works on the subject, his *Atlas d'ophthalmoscopie médicale* (Paris, 1876), and the *Cérébroscopie* (Paris, 1877). Hirschberg (XV:553) quotes Bouchut as stating about his work in ophthalmoscopy, "I have done for the brain what Auenbrugger and Laennec with the help of auscultation and percussion have done for the diagnosis of lung and heart diseases."

Hirsch I:648; Hirschberg §1287; Osler 2092.

Boudt, Cornelis de, engr.
See Prints 5, 6.

Bourgeois, Jacques.
Advis aux curieux de la conservation de leur veue. Sur les lunettes dyoptiques, nouvellement mises en usage, pour l'utilité publique. (Facsimile) Paris, 1645. *In* Heymann (190).

Boury, Johann Wilhelm, respondent.
"De maculis corneae earumque operatione chirurgica, apotripsi."
In Dissertationes medicae selectae Tubingenses (112) 2:261-328.

59   Bowen, John.
Practical observations on the removal of every species and variety of cataract, by hyalonyxis, or vitreous operation, illustrated by cases; with critical and general remarks on the other methods employed. London (Paris?): Callow & Wilson, 1824 (1823?).

x, [4], 120 p., [1] plate; 22 cm.

The author's purpose in writing this book was to point out "some general method of removing the diseased lens, by which we can indiscriminately act in all cases, whether the cataract be *fluid, soft, hard, lenticular,* or *capsular*" (p. 5). Bowen advocated "hyalonyxis" or the surgical puncture of the vitreous humor as in keratonyxis in all cases of cataract. Scarpa and Saunders, in confining their use of this procedure to soft cataracts and particularly juvenile cataracts, were the first to dis-

criminate in undertaking the discission or needling operation. Little is known of the author beyond what he reveals in this work. Bowen had practiced as an ophthalmic surgeon for fifteen years before writing this book and had spent the previous seven years in Europe, chiefly in Italy. Bowen speculates on the geographic incidence of eye disease and suggests a correlation with the presence of "sulphureous matter" as evidenced by the high proportion of eye disease and blindness in volcanic areas such as Naples, Sicily, and especially the towns near Mount Vesuvius. Guthrie (*Lectures on operative surgery*, p. 300) noted that Bowen's book was actually printed and published in Paris in October 1823.

BOA I:27; Hirschberg §638.

60   Bowman, Sir William, 1816-1892.
Lectures on the parts concerned in the operations on the globe, and on the structure of the retina, delivered at the Royal London Ophthalmic Hospital, Moorfields, June 1847. From the *London Medical Gazette*. London: Wilson & Ogilvy, 1848.

45 p.: ill.; 21 cm.

"Bowman did more than any other man to advance ophthalmic surgery in England. The above work is the first to include a sound description of the microscopical anatomy of the eye and the ciliary ('Bowman's') muscle. The book consists of several lectures given at the London Ophthalmic Hospital and published in the *Lond. Med. Gaz.* in 1847. Part of it is reprinted in *Med. classics*, 1940, 5:292-336" (G-M 1505). The copy described is an offprint of the original journal article.

Hirschberg §647-649.

60.1   Boyer, Lucien A. H., 1808-1890.
Recherches sur l'opération du strabisme. Mémoire présenté a l'Académie Royale des Sciences. Paris: Lancette, G. Baillière . . . , 1842-44.

2 v. in 1 ([4], iii, [1], 320 p., X plates; [4], 114, [6] p., 2 plates): diagrs., 24 cm.

Born of French parents in Turin, Lucien Boyer studied in Paris, where he received his medical degree in 1836. From 1852 to 1870 he was physician to the Senate of the Second Empire. Boyer published on uterine tumors, hernia and diathesis, but his name is best known for his study of treatments for strabismus. In this work, which he presented to the Académie Royale des Sciences, he argues for the importance of the strabismus operation. He discusses the anatomical and physiological aspects of strabismus in addition to describing methods, tools, and possible results of the surgery.

AmEncOph II:1266; BM 25:250; Hirsch I:667; Hirschberg §495; NUC 71:55.

60.2 Boyle, Robert, 1627-1691.

A disquisition about the final causes of natural things: wherein it is inquir'd, whether, and (if at all) with what cautions, a naturalist should admit them? . . . To which are subjoyn'd, by way of appendix, Some uncommon observations about vitiated sight. London: H. C. for J. Taylor, 1688.

[16], 274, [6] p.; 18 cm. (8vo)

Provenance: William Wilshere, Hitchin (bookplate).

"Physicist, physiologist, chemist, and philosopher, Boyle was one of the great scientists and intellects of the seventeenth century. This work contains Boyle's discussion of many physiological matters, especially those concerning the eye and defective vision. Boyle recognized that the site of the cataract is in the optic lens, and he included a number of case histories to substantiate his findings. . . . [Page 157] contains the famous passage in which Boyle relates his conversation with William Harvey on how he discovered the circulation of the blood" (Heirs, p. 203-204). The appended *Some uncommon observations about vitiated sight* (p. [239]-274) has a separate title page.

Cushing B556; Fulton 186A; Heirs 567; Krivatsy 1726; Reynolds 614; Waller 10766; Wellcome II:224; Wing B3946(var.).

Brecht, Carl David, respondent.

"Tobiae leucomata."

In Dissertationes medicae selectae Tubingenses (112) 1:312-340.

60.3 Brenta, Luigi.

Fenomeni della visione. Milan: O. Manini, 1838.

39, [1] p., 3 plates; 24 cm.

The volume consists of a letter by Luigi Brenta, an optician in Milan, to an unnamed physicist, followed by the description of Brenta's optical experiments and observations. His investigations concern electromagnetic force in the eye, divergency of light-beams, and images on the retina. This copy of the book is bound in its original printed wrapper and was signed by the author on the bottom of the third plate.

NUC 702:181.

Bresler, J., trans.

See Ramón y Cajal (309.1).

61 Brewster, Sir David, 1781-1868.

Memoirs of the life, writings and discoveries of Sir Isaac Newton. Edinburgh: T. Constable and Co., 1855.

2 v. (xxii, [2], 478 p., [1] plate; xi, [1], 564 p., [1] plate): ill., port.; 23 cm.

Originally published in one volume in 1831, Brewster entirely rewrote and expanded his life of Newton after having the opportunity to examine papers in the possession of the Earl of Portsmouth to which he'd not had access before. Trained as a clergyman in the Established Church of Scotland, Brewster abandoned the pulpit for a life of scientific inquiry. He was the author of numerous articles on optics, and is particularly noted for his work in the understanding of the polarization of light.

Wallis 370.

Breyer, Julius Friedericus, respondent.

"De ophthalmia venerea et peculiari in illa operatione."

In Dissertationes medicae selectae Tubingenses (112) 3:94-134.

Briggs, James, d. 1848, trans.

See Scarpa (328).

62 Briggs, William, 1642-1704.

Ophthalmo-graphia, sive oculi ejusque partium descriptio anatomica, nec non, ejusdem nova visionis theoria. Leyden: P. van der Aa, 1686.

312, [12] p., [3] plates; 13 cm. (12mo)

Briggs, who studied at Montpellier under Vieussens, was one of the few seventeenth century physicians who specialized in the treatment of the eye. He was the first to describe and depict the papilla of the optic disk. "In dealing with the retina, Briggs specially notes and figures the papilla . . . we no longer find the lens filling the whole of the inside eye as in most earlier diagrams; and the retina is postulated as the percipient layer and not the choroid, while the function of the lens in transmitting and refracting the light is recognized" (James, p. 78). Newton derived much of his knowledge of the anatomy of the eye from this work and contributed an appreciation to Briggs's other work, *Nova visionis theoria*.

Hirschberg §305; Waller 1456; Wellcome II:238.

63 Brisseau, Michel, 1676-1743.

Traité de la cataracte et du glaucoma. Paris: L. d'Houry, 1709.

[16], 260, [12] p., 4 plates; 17 cm. (12mo)

"Brisseau was the first to demonstrate the true nature and location of cataract" (G-M 5825).

Often overlooked but of equal significance to the history of ophthalmology are Brisseau's observations on glaucoma. In this work he clearly distinguishes between cataract and glaucoma, and for the first time glaucoma is described as a disease of the vitreous humor and not of the lens. The treatise on cataract was written in 1705 and originally communicated to the Académie Royale des Sciences by a colleague because the author was 'merely a physician.' The book concludes with the author's response to the objections raised by De La Hire, Mery, Littre and St. Yves.

Hirschberg §325-326; Waller 1464; Wellcome II:240.

Bronner, Edward, trans.

See Selected monographs (338.1).

63.1 Brücke, Ernst Wilhelm, Ritter von, 1819-1892.

Anatomische Beschreibung des menschlichen Augapfels. Berlin: G. Reimer, 1847.

[4], 70 p., [1] color plate: ill.; 28 cm.

"A remarkable all-round physiologist and anatomist, Brücke's investigations covered all branches of the subject, including the luminosity of the eye in animals (1845), phonetics (1856-62), the semilunar valves (1855), and artistic anatomy (1892) . . ." (Orr 478). His optical works constituted the basis for the invention of the ophthalmoscope (cf. Gorin, p. 127; Hirsch I:729). This treatise, a descriptive anatomy of the human eye, was published shortly before Brücke was appointed professor of physiology at the University of Königsberg, where he taught ophthalmology during the winter semester of 1848/49.

Hirsch I:730; NUC 80:244; NYAM 6:544.

Brunn, Walter Albert Ferdinand von, 1876-1952.

See Stromayr (366).

63.2 Budge, Julius Ludwig, 1811-1888.

Über die Bewegung der Iris. Für Physiologen und Ärzte. Braunschweig: F. Vieweg & Son, 1855.

x, [2], 206 p., [3] folding plates: ill.; 23 cm.

"An important book marking a progress in the investigation of pupillary movements. Budge emphasized that contraction and dilatation were active processes, a view later confirmed by [Karl] Voelckers and [Victor] Hensen" (Dawson 1081). For the discoveries described in it, this work was awarded the *Prix Monthyon* by the Academy of Sciences in Paris and another prize by the Academy of Medicine in Brussels. Julius Budge was professor of anatomy and physiology in Bonn and later in Greifswald, and in addition to this classic of ophthalmology he published treatises on the central nervous system and the blood circulation in the liver.

Dawson 1081; G-M 1510; Hirsch I:755.

Bull, Charles Stedman, 1844-1912, ed.

See Stellwag von Carion (355) and Wells (413).

64 Burnett, Swan Moses, 1847-1906.

A theoretical and practical treatise on astigmatism. St. Louis: J. H. Chambers & Co., 1887.

viii, 245, [1] p.: ill.; 23 cm.

The most important work of a distinguished American ophthalmologist. Of this work Hirschberg wrote, "Nach Donders Schrift *Astigmatus und cylindr. Gläser*, Berlin 1862, ist die Arbeit von Burnett die erste ausführliche Sonderschrift über Astigmatismus in der Welt-Literatur, klar, vollständig eingehend, auch mit genauer Literatur-Angabe" (§767).

Professor of ophthalmology and otology at Georgetown University, Burnett was also a noted collector of art and books. His first wife, Frances E. Hodgson, was the author of *Little Lord Fauntleroy*.

BOA I:35; Hirschberg §767.

65 Büsch, Johann Georg, 1728-1800.

Tractatus duo optici argumenti. Hamburg: C. E. Bohn, 1783.

[12], 132 p., [l], plate; 17 cm. (8vo)

Two optical essays by the professor of mathematics at Hamburg. In dealing with myopia the author is particularly scornful of Boerhaave's work on the diseases of the eye (53) noting that it was hardly worthy of mention. Boerhaave attributed myopia to either an overly convex cornea or to an enlarged

(6) Aguilon, François d'. *Opticorum libri sex philosophis iuxtà ac mathematicis utiles*, 1613. Copperplate illustration on p. 151. (14.3 x 10 cm.)

eyeball. Haller, who edited and published Boerhaave's lectures from the manuscript notes of different students, also rated the mathematical portion of Boerhaave's work as particularly deficient.

Hirschberg §432.

Caille, Claude-Antoine, praeses.

See Michel (259.1).

Camerer, Alexander, praeses.

"De ophthalmia venerea et peculiari in illa operatione."

In Dissertationes medicae selectae Tubingenses (112) 3:94-134.

Camerer, Johann Gottfried, respondent.

"De conjunctivae et corneae, oculi tunicarum, vesiculis ac pustulis."

In Dissertationes medicae selectae Tubingenses (112) 1:143-168.

66   Camper, Petrus, 1722-1789.

Dissertatio physiologica de quibusdam oculi partibus. Leyden: E. Luzac, Jun., 1746.

[6], 28, [2] p., 1 plate; 22 cm. (4to)

A remarkable figure in eighteenth century science and medicine, Camper entered the University of Leyden at age twelve and graduated twelve years later, taking two degrees simultaneously. Both this entry and number 67 are Camper's dissertations for these degrees. The present thesis was written for his medical degree. The *quidam partes* referred to in the title are the lens and the orbit only, described prior to a brief examination of the physiology of vision. Camper was the author of a remarkable treatise on the eye (*De oculorum fabrica et morbis*) which he never published. It did not appear in print until 1913 as part of the *Opuscula selecta Neerlandicorum de arte medica* (fasc. II).

Hirsch I:813; Hirschberg §433.

67   Camper, Petrus, 1722-1789.

Dissertatio optica de visu. Leyden: E. Luzac, 1746.

[6], 25, [1] p., [1] plate; 21 cm. (4to)

The dissertation of the Dutch anatomist who discovered the fibrous structure of the lens. This was the first of his numerous anatomical memoirs.

Hirschberg §433.

68   Camper, Petrus, 1722-1789.

Optical dissertation on vision, 1746. Facsimile of the original Latin text, with a complete translation and an introduction by G. ten Doesschate. Nieuwkoop: B. de Graaf, 1962.

29, [3], [6], 25, [1], [2], 31, [3] p., [2] plates; 26 cm.

Series: Dutch classics on the history of science, 3.

" . . . made after the copy in the Bibliotheca Medica Neerlandica, Amsterdam . . . present edition limited to five hundred copies . . ." (colophon).

Cangiano, Emmanuele, trans.

See Florio (138).

68.1   Canton, Edwin, d. 1885.

On the arcus senilis, or, fatty degeneration of the cornea. London: R. Hardwicke, 1863.

[8], 228 p., 3 plates: ill.; 23 cm.

Provenance: Signed by the author for H. Skelton.

Edwin Canton studied and worked as an assistant surgeon at the Royal Westminster Ophthalmic Hospital, and later as a surgeon at Charing Cross Hospital in London. He was named Fellow of the Royal College of Surgeons in 1845. A well-known lecturer and successful operative surgeon, Canton also was a prolific medical author in ophthalmology, surgery, and pathology (cf. Hirsch I:820). This work, which originally was published in *The Lancet* (1850, 1853, and 1863), discusses the arcus senilis, its pathology, formation, occurrences, and treatment.

BOA I:37; Dawson 1173; NUC 94:218.

69   Cappuri, Antonio.

De peculiari cataracta in anteriorem oculi cameram prolapsa commentarius. Bologna: Laelius a Vulpe, 1794.

19, [3] p.; 24 cm. (4to)

Observations on a particularly difficult operation during which the cataract had slipped into the anterior chamber of the eye. The author was a surgeon at Lucca.

Blake, p. 77.

69.1 Carcano Leone, Giovanni Battista, 1536-1606.

Anatomici libri II. In quorvm altero de cordis vasorum in foetu vnione pertractatur, ostenditurq[ue] hac in re explicanda solum Galenumueritatis scopum attigisse, reliquos omnes anatomicos lapsos fuisse. . . . In altero de musculis, palpebrarum atq[ue] oculorum motibus deseruientibus, accuratè differitur. . . . Pavia: G. Bartolo, 1574.

2 v. in 1 (44 leaves; 44 leaves); 15 cm. (8vo)

Provenance: D. Luigi Zangrandi (stamp); —Withdrawn by the Wellcome Library (stamp).

"The first volume of Carcano's treatise deals with the source of the vessels in the fetus, and contains the first clear description of the foramen ovale and ductus arteriosus since that of Galen. The second volume includes the first exact description of the lacrimal duct . . . and the route taken by the tears" (Norman 398; cf. Hirsch I:828). Carcano was born in Milan, studied in Pavia, then became a military surgeon, and at the age of 25 he was appointed director of the military hospital in Milan. Later in Padua he studied under Fallopio, and in 1573 was named professor of anatomy in Pavia, where he taught for 25 years.

G-M 1479; Norman 398; Wellcome I:1276; Willius-Dry, p. 45.

70 Carron du Villards, Charles Joseph Frédéric, 1801-1860.

Recherches pratiques sur les causes qui font échouer l'opération de la cataracte selon les divers procédés. Paris: Bacquenois for J. Rouvier & E. Le Bouvier, 1835.

[6], xii, 384 p., 2 plates; 21 cm.

An analysis of the causes of accidents and failures in the operations for cataract which draws heavily on the experience of the author's teachers, Scarpa and Maunoir. Some years later, Maunoir (251) published a short memoir on this same subject to document his disagreement with Carron du Villards on some points he considered of extreme importance. This copy, in a special extra-binding with an elaborate coat-of-arms in gilt on both covers, is probably from the library of Ferdinand II of the House of Bourbon, King of the Two Sicilies.

Hirschberg §568.

71 Carron du Villards, Charles Joseph Frédéric, 1801-1860.

Guide pratique pour l'étude et le traitement des maladies des yeux. Paris: Cosson for Société Encyclographique des Sciences Médicales, 1838.

2 v. ([8], xii, 556 p., [2] plates; [4], 644 p., [2] plates); 22 cm.

"Carron du Villards taught ophthalmology in Paris; his book is one of the best of the period" (G-M 5853). The extensive bibliography, with entries arranged chronologically under a number of specific subjects, was derived from Beer's *Bibliotheca ophthalmica* (Vienna, 1799) though it does not include the critical annotations found in Beer's work.

The author spent some time in North Africa, Mexico, Central and South America and his books are interesting for the information he gathered there about ophthalmological subjects.

Hirschberg §568; Wellcome II:305.

71.1 Carter, Robert Brudenell, 1828-1918.

On defects of vision which are remediable by optical appliances. A course of lectures delivered at the Royal College of Surgeons of England. . . . London: Macmillan & Co., 1877.

[8], 145, [1] p.: ill.; 23 cm.

A series of lectures describing defects of refraction, accommodation, and convergence in the eye. The author offers treatments for presbyopia, hyperopia, myopia, astigmatism, and asthenopia with the aid of contemporary modern appliances. Robert Carter was the founder of the eye clinic in Nottingham and author of several works on ophthalmic surgery. He considered himself "a conspicuously unsuccessful general practitioner in the country" until the age of forty. Coming to London in his forty-first year, he became surgeon to the Royal South London Ophthalmic Hospital within the year, thus beginning a second, longer, and eminently successful career as one of the most distinguished British ophthalmic surgeons of the late nineteenth century.

BOA I:38; Hirsch I:844-845; NUC 97:210.

72 Carter, Robert Brudenell, 1828-1918.

The modern operations for cataract; being the Lettsomian lectures for 1884. London: Macmillan and Co., 1884.

83 p.; 23 cm.

"Three Lettsomian lectures on the operations for cataract in use by 1884. The author advises preliminary iridectomy and discusses the advantages of early operation" (BOA I:38).

BOA I:38; Hirschberg §671.

Carter, Robert Brudenell, 1828-1918, trans.

See Scheffler (330).

73   Cavalieri, Bonaventura, 1598-1647.

Lo specchio ustorio overo trattato delle settioni coniche, et alcuni loro mirabili effetti intorno al lume, caldo, freddo, suono, e moto ancora. Bologna: C. Ferroni, 1632.

[16], 224 p., [1], 10 leaves: ill.; 21 cm. (4to)

The first edition of this important work on conic sections and their application to different branches of physics. Cavalieri demonstrated for the first time that a projectile follows a parabolic trajectory; and also introduced here the conception of the inertia of bodies, later elaborated by Newton.

74   Chandler, George, d. 1822.

A treatise on the diseases of the eye, and their remedies; to which is prefixed, the anatomy of the eye; the theory of vision; and the several species of imperfect sight. London: T. Cadell, 1780.

v, [3], 191 p., 4 plates; 23 cm. (8vo)

This book was an early attempt at compiling a state-of-the-art textbook of ophthalmology. Sprengel, a contemporary medical historian, severely criticized Chandler's work as a worthless compilation and a poor copy of the works of Heister, St. Yves, and others.

Hirschberg §395; Wellcome II:325.

75   Chandler, George, d. 1822.

Abhandlung über die Krankheiten des Auges und die dagegen anzuwendenden Heilmittel nebst vorausgeschickter Betrachtung über die Zergliederung des Auges, Theorie des Sehens und die verschiedenen Arten des unvollkommenen Gesichts. Leipzig: Weygand, 1782.

[8], 200 p., [2] plates; 18 cm. (8vo)

A German translation of Chandler's treatise on eye diseases (74). Chandler had a reputation as an extremely rapid operator in England.

Hirschberg §395.

75.1   Chérubin d'Orléans, Father, 1613-1697.

La vision parfaite: ou le concours des deux axes de la vision en un seul point de l'objet. Paris: S. Mabre-Cramoisy, 1677-81.

2 v. in 1 ([26], 168, [20] p., 17 plates; [28], 84, 87-217, 216-224, [16] p., 13 plates): ill.; 33 cm. (fol.)

"First edition of an important work on optics which is rarer

(75.1) Chérubin d'Orléans. *La vision parfaite*, 1677-81. Copperplate illustration on p. [3]. (17.5 x 8.5 cm.)

than the author's *Dioptrique oculaire*. Chérubin, whose real name was François Lasseré, discussed the invention of a binocular telescope and also an opera glass. He hoped that a clearer image would be formed by the use of both eyes. There are many fine illustrations of different types of telescopes, and the book is an excellent specimen of 17th century printing" (BOA II:20).

BOA II:20; Krivatsy 2429; NUC 105:503.

76   Chevalier, Arthur, 1830-1872.

Hygiène de la vue ouvrage utile a tout le monde. Troisième édition. Paris: Ch. Albessard, 1864.

164 p.: ill.; 16 cm.

A popular work on the preservation of sight and the proper use of spectacles. The author was a member of the celebrated family of Paris opticians, and the son of Charles Louis Chevalier, a pioneer in photographic optics in Daguerre's time. Arthur Chevalier was himself an early worker in the field of microphotography, while continuing the family business to the third generation.

77   Chevalier, Arthur, 1830-1872.

L'art de conserver la vue ouvrage utile à tous. Troisième édition entièrement refondue. Paris: P. Brunet, 1870.

[4], viii, 175, [3] p.: ill.; 18 cm.

Though parts of the text and many of the illustrations are identical, this work differs considerably from Chevalier's *Hygiène de la vue* (76).

78   Chevallier, Jean Gabriel Auguste, 1778-1848.

Le conservateur de la vue, suivi du catalogue général et prix courant des instrumens d'optique, de mathématiques et de physique, de la fabrique et du magasin de l'auteur. Paris: Prudhomme for the author, 1810.

[6], viii, 163, [5], xlvii, [1] p., 8 plates; 22 cm. (8vo)

Chevallier, Ingénieur-Opticien de le Prince de Condé, was celebrated for his many inventions and perfections of a great variety of instruments. This is the first of many editions of this popular and practical work on optics. It contains the catalogue of instruments (called for on the title page), omitted from some later editions, and it seems to be the only edition with every

copy signed (half-title, verso) by the author.

Hirschberg §470.

79   Classen, August, 1835-1889.

Ueber das Schlussverfahren des Sehactes. Rostock: G. B. Leopold's Universitäts-Buchhandlung (Ernst Kuhn), 1863.

vi, 76 p.: ill.; 23 cm.

Hirschberg §1136.

80   Classen, August, 1835-1889.

Physiologie des Gesichtssinnes zum ersten Mal begründet auf Kant's Theorie der Erfahrung. Braunschweig: F. Vieweg & Son, 1876.

xviii, [2], 202 p.; 23 cm.

Kantian idealism had a profound influence on scientists such as Helmholtz, Du Bois-Reymond, Virchow and others of their generation, separating their thinking from the romantic *Naturphilosophie* that colored German thought throughout the first half of the nineteenth century.

The present work is a perfect example of Kantian influences on the scientific thought of the period. A German ophthalmologist whose works centered principally in physiological optics, Classen here examines contemporary theories in the physiology of vision in light of Kantian epistemology.

81   Cleoburey, William, 1793-1853.

A review of the different operations performed on the eyes, for the restoration of lost and the improvement of imperfect vision; in which the most judicious and successful methods of operating on these organs are described, and the general causes of failure faithfully delineated. Also a full account of the various structures and diseases of the eyes and their appendages; together with the necessary mode of treatment: the whole being the result of several years of extensive practice in this important department of surgery. London: W. Clowes for T. & G. Underwood, 1826.

viii, 288, [2] p.; 23 cm.

The cataract operations of depression, extraction, and discission and methods for forming an artificial pupil are reviewed and illustrated with case histories from the author's practice in Oxford. The chaotic arrangement of this work prompted one contemporary reviewer [*London Medical Repository* 26:126-135 (1826)] to suggest "Desultory Remarks" as an alternate title.

Waller 2010; Wellcome II:358.

82 Collectio ophthalmologica veterum auctorum.

Par P. Pansier. Paris: J. B. Baillière and Son, 1903-1933.

7 fascicles; 26 cm.

Contents: fasc. 1. Arnaldus de Villanova, Libellus regiminis de confortatione visus — Johannes de Casso, Tractatus de conservatione visus (1903); fasc. 2. Alcoatin, Congregatio sive liber de oculis (1903); fasc. 3. ʿAlī ibn ʿĪsā, Memoriale oculariorum (1903); fasc. 4. David Armenicus, De oculorum curationibus (1904); fasc. 5. Zacharias, Tractatus de passionibus oculorum (1907); fasc. 6. Anonymi tractatus de egritudinibus oculorum (1908); fasc. 7. Constantinus Africanus, Liber de oculis — Galenus, Littere ad Corisium (1909, 1933).

In these seven fascicles, which appeared between 1903 and 1933, Pansier published for the first time selected manuscripts of the great ancient and medieval physicians and philosophers on vision and the eye. Drawing on his extensive knowledge of early ophthalmology and the manuscript resources of many European libraries, he has made available the little known or previously unknown ophthalmological writings of Arnaldus de Villanova, Johannis de Casso, Alcoatin, ʿAlī ibn ʿĪsā, David Armenicus, Zacharias, Constantinus Africanus, and Galen. The editor's introductory comments and bibliographical notes and his translation of the Arabic passages add to the usefulness of this work. The final fascicle, scheduled for publication in 1909 and finally issued in 1933, carries both imprint dates and includes Pansier's description of the difficulties he encountered in obtaining support to complete this series.

Waller 2066.

Collimitius, Georgius, 1482-1535, ed.
See Witelo (422.1).

83 Colombat, Marc, 1797-1851.

Traité des maladies et de l'hygiène des organes de la voix. 2. éd. Paris: Moquet for Mansut, 1838.

400 p., 2 plates; 23 cm.

An important work in the field of laryngology by one of the early specialists in this field.

84 Colombier, Jean, 1736-1789.

Dissertatio nova de suffusione seu cataracta; oculi anatome & mecanismo locupletata. Amsterdam: P. F. Didot (Paris), 1765.

viii, 194, [2] p.; 16 cm. (12mo)

The only ophthalmological work of Colombier, a French military surgeon, this treatise deals with the nature of cataract, its causes, diagnosis, and prognosis and presents a survey of the operative methods of several different practitioners. The author, a well-known cataract extractor, was one of the first to prefer extraction to couching or the operation of depression.

Hirschberg §335.

Combach, Johann, 1585-1651, ed.
See Bacon (27 & 28).

Conring, Hermann, 1606-1681, ed.
See Feyens (135).

Constantinus Africanus, 1018-1087?

Liber de oculis.

In Collectio ophthalmologica veterum auctorum (82), fasc. 7.

Cooper, Sir Astley Paston, bart., 1768-1841.
See Neue Bibliothek (272.1).

85 Cooper, William White, 1816-1886.

Practical remarks on near sight, aged sight, and impaired vision; with observations upon the use of glasses and on artificial light. London: G. J. Palmer for J. Churchill, 1847.

ix, [3], 216 p., [1] plate: ill.; 20 cm.

"Investigations of theories of light and principles of reflection and refraction. Chapters on the structure of the eye, the causes, symptoms, and treatment of myopia and presbyopia, the effect of artificial light on the eye" (BOA I:45).

BOA I:45; Hirschberg §672; Wellcome II:389.

86 Cooper, William White, 1816-1886.

On wounds and injuries of the eye. London: J. Churchill, 1859.

xii, 330 p., III plates: ill.; 23 cm.

According to Hirschberg, English ophthalmic textbooks of the nineteenth century gave especial attention to injuries of the eye. This work however is the first to be entirely devoted to the subject. Praised by Hirschberg for its completeness and clarity, the book is illustrated with wood engravings and lithographs after drawings by the author.

BOA I:45; Hirsch II:100; Hirschberg §672.

87 Coper, Johann, praeses.

De oculo. Bremen: H. Brauer, 1671.

36 p.: ill.; 19 cm. (4to)

An early thesis on the anatomy of the eye illustrated with a full page engraving of the human eye and a schematic representation of its constituent parts. The thesis was presented at Bremen by Henricus Schweling, a pupil of Johann Coper.

Cornarius, Janus, 1500-1558, trans.

See Aetius, of Amida (5).

87.1 Courtivron, Gaspard le Compasseur de Créqui-Montfort, marquis de, 1715-1785.

Traité d'optique, où, l'on donne la théorie de la lumiere dans le système newtonien, avec de nouvelles solutions des principaux problêmes de dioptrique & de catoptrique. Paris: Durand & Pissot, 1752.

v, [1], 192 p., 7 plates: ill.; 24 cm. (4to)

"An 18th century optical treatise in which Newton's theory of light is discussed, and the author suggests solutions for various problems of dioptrics" (BOA I:46). A physician in the French cavalry and a member of the Académie des Sciences, Courtivron was the author of several works in optics, geometry, and physics.

BOA I:46; NUC 125:210; Poggendorff I:490.

Culver, Charles Mortimer, trans.

See Landolt (228).

88 Cunier, Florent, 1812-1853.

Mémoire sur l'ophthalmie contagieuse qui regne dans la classe pauvre et ouvrière. Brussels and Leipzig: C. Muquardt, . . . et al., 1849.

52 p.; 23 cm.

Ophthalmia was rampant in the working class districts of Brussels in the 1840s, posing so serious a health problem as to attract the attention of the government. This pamphlet, addressed to the mayor of the city, examines the causes and treatment of ophthalmia, and the necessity of alleviating the misery of Brussels's afflicted population. The most important Belgian ophthalmologist of the first half of the nineteenth century, Cunier was a highly original ophthalmic surgeon, a prolific author, and the founder of the Annales d'Oculistique.

Cureau de la Chambre, Marin, 1594-1669.

See La Chambre, Marin Cureau de, 1594-1669.

89 Curtis, John Harrison, b. 1778.

A treatise on the physiology and diseases of the eye: containing a new mode of curing cataract without an operation; experiments and observations on vision, also on the inflection, reflection, and colours of light; together with remarks on the preservation of sight, and on spectacles, reading-glasses, etc. London: J. Moyes for Longmans, 1833.

[8], 222, [2] p., [1] plate; 23 cm.

A colored frontispiece captioned "The connexion of the organs of sight & hearing illustrated" suggests the author's motivation for writing this layman's work. Curtis, a noted aurist and founder of the Royal Dispensary for Diseases of the Ear, writes in the introduction that he had repeatedly observed that in cases of deafness accompanied by visual defects "the healthy action of the nerves of the ear has extended its influence to the eye." The book is an admixture of curious and nonsensical theory with sound scientific observation. Curtis believed that affections of the eye were "all nearly the same disease, varying only in situation and degree, and . . . are derived from similar sources." He further stated that the most common source of these affections is a "derangement of the digestive organs, acting on the abdominal ganglia and great sympathetic nerve." On the other hand, the section on comparative ophthalmic anatomy and physiology (p. 49-64) was, according to Shastid, "the best by far since those of Aristotle and As-Sadili." This section is given in toto by Shastid in American encyclopedia of ophthalmology, 5:3594-3600.

AmEncOph 5:3593-3600; BOA I:48; Hirschberg §470; Wellcome II:421.

90 Dalrymple, John, 1803-1852.

The anatomy of the human eye. London: F. Warr for Longmans, 1834.

[2], vii, [3], 294, [10] p., 5 plates; 23 cm.

"First English work on ocular anatomy" (G-M 1497). That the systematic study of the anatomy of the eye was still very much in its infancy is indicated by the fact that the author took as his model Zinn's *Descriptio anatomica oculi humani* (426) a work nearly eighty years old. Despite his admiration of Zinn's great work, Dalrymple was rather careless in quoting his writings, and the Latin excerpts are full of errata and citation errors.

BOA I:49; G-M 1497; Hirschberg §640; Wellcome II:428.

91 Dalrymple, John, 1803-1852.

Pathology of the human eye. London: J. Churchill, 1852.

[81] p., XXXVI plates; 38 cm.

Dalrymple only just lived to complete this work, his *magnum opus*. The excellent plates were lithographed by W. Baggs after the watercolors of Messrs. W. H. Kerney and Leonard, which they prepared under the supervision of Dalrymple and his colleague John Scott.

The preparation of the atlas was begun before the publication of Helmholtz's description of the ophthalmoscope (1851), and issued the year after. It is interesting to speculate how successive editions might have differed had Dalrymple lived to make use of the new instrument.

Hirsch II:173; Hirschberg §640.

Danti, Ignazio, 1537-1586, trans.
See Euclid (125).

Daumier, Honoré Victorin, 1808-1879.
See Prints 10, 11.

David Armenicus, 12th cent.
Compilatio in libros de oculorum curationibus Accanamosali et diversorum philosophorum de Baldach.

In Collectio ophthalmologica veterum auctorum (82), fasc. 4.

92 David, Jean Pierre, 1737-1784.

Recherches sur la maniere d'agir de la saignée, et sur les effets qu'elle produit relativement à la partie où on la fait. 2. éd. rev. et corr. Paris: Vallat-La-Chapelle, 1763.

xxiv, 333, [3] p.; 17 cm. (12mo)

Bloodletting, the subject of this treatise, though often much abused, was an important and potentially effective therapy employed by physicians and ophthalmologists for centuries. The author, a Rouen surgeon, married the daughter of Le Cat (234), chief surgeon at Rouen's Hotel Dieu. David was later chosen by his father-in-law to succeed him in that office. Here he deals primarily with general bloodletting or venesection and only the procedures employed rather than their application to specific diseases. While the old practice of venesection had little application in the treatment of eye diseases, temporal phlebotomy was advocated in acute infections of the eye as late as 1910 and in 1918 Elliot suggested the use of leeches in the non-operative treatment of congestive glaucoma.

Daviel, Jacques, 1696-1762.
"Sur une nouvelle méthode de guérir la cataracte par l'extraction du cristalin."

In Académie Royale de Chirurgie, *Mémoires* (2).

Daviel, Jacques, 1696-1762.
See Pellier de Quengsy (292).

93 Daviel, Jacques Henri.

Utrum, cataractae tutior extractio forsicum ope? Theses anatomicae et chirurgicae. Paris: Widow of Delaguette, 1757.

[2], 17 p.; 25 cm. (4to)

A dissertation on cataract extraction by the son of Jacques Daviel. In this work the younger Daviel takes up the theme of his father's earliest critics at the Académie Royale de Chirurgie, regarding the instruments used by the elder Daviel in the operation of extraction. Curiously, his father is mentioned by name only once, in a footnote on page nine having nothing to do with the operation for which his father was noted.

Hirschberg §350, 355.

94 Delacroix, Henri 1842-1890.

Jacques Daviel à Reims. Reims: F. Michaud; Paris: G. Masson, 1890.

90 p., IV plates: port.; 25 cm.

Jacques Daviel stayed briefly at Reims in 1751, an account of which is given here along with letters exchanged between Daviel and the Reims surgeon J.-B. Caqué. The correspondence relates principally to Daviel's operation for the extrac-

(6) Aguilon, François d'. *Opticorum libri sex philosophis iuxtà ac mathematicis utiles*, 1613. Copperplate illustration on p. 195. (14.3 x 10 cm.)

tion of cataract. Delacroix was an ophthalmologist at Reims who died shortly before this work was ready for publication.

Hirschberg §346.

95 Delingette, E. P.

Dissertation sur l'ophtalmie aiguë. Strasbourg: Levrault, 1815.

[4], 19 p.; 23 cm. (4to)

As a military surgeon in the Napoleonic army in Egypt, the author treated many cases of Egyptian ophthalmia. This dissertation on trachoma is based on the experience acquired in the treatment of these cases.

96 Demours, Antoine Pierre, 1762-1836.

Traité des maladies des yeux, avec des planches coloriées représentant ces maladies d'après nature, suivi de la description de l'oeil humain, traduite du Latin de S. T. Soemmerring. Paris: F. Didot for the author & Crochard, 1818.

3 v. + atlas (xxxvi, 551 p.; [6], 518 p.; [6], 517, [2] p.; 126 p., 80 plates); 21 cm. (8vo), atlas 27 cm. (4to)

This four volume work, one of the most important and elaborate books on the diseases of the eye published to that time, includes the first full description of glaucoma in which heightened intraocular pressure is recognized (1:468-472; 3:203-276). The work is a compilation of hundreds of carefully annotated case histories obtained in the course of the author's twenty years of experience and from his father's nearly fifty years of practice. Credit for the observations on glaucoma belongs principally to the father, Pierre Demours (97), who was the superior clinical investigator, though it is quite properly shared with the son who excelled as a surgeon. The final volume contains a French translation of the Latin edition of S. T. Soemmerring's *Abbildungen des menschlichen Auges* (348). The sixty-five plates include remarkable specimens of early color illustration.

Hirschberg §374.

97 Demours, Pierre, 1702-1795, trans.

Essais et observations de medecine de la Société d'Edinbourg, ouvrage traduit de l'Anglois, & augmenté par le traducteur d'observations concernant l'histoire naturelle, & les maladies des yeux. Paris: H. L. Guerin (Vol. 2-7: H. L. & J. Guerin), 1740-1747.

7 v. (l, 432, 429-31, [13], 129, [2] p., 5 plates; xxiv, 543 p., 4 plates; [8], 543 p., 5 plates; vii, [1], 674, [6] p., 4 plates; xii, 604 p., 6 plates; [8], 573 p.; [6], 523, [1] p.); 17 cm. (12mo)

To his translation of the Philosophical Society of Edinburgh's *Medical essays and observations* Demours has added (1:1-129, 2nd sequence) observations on the natural history of salamanders and case histories involving mydriasis and staphyloma. Demours, father of Antoine Pierre Demours, published many essays on ocular anatomy and is often credited with the first description of the posterior membrane of the cornea now known as 'Descemet's membrane'. The Philosophical Society of Edinburgh was the immediate precursor of the Royal Medical Society of Edinburgh. A biographical notice of Demours is included in his son's *Traite des maladies des yeux* (96)1: [xxvii]-xxxiii.

Hirschberg §371.

98 Denonvilliers, Charles Pierre, 1808-1872.

Traité théorique et pratique des maladies des yeux, par C. Denonvilliers . . . et L. Gosselin. Paris: Labé, 1855.

vii, [1], 955 p.; 19 cm.

A separate printing of those sections of the *Compendium de chirurgie pratique* (3 v., Paris, 1840-61) dealing strictly with the diseases of the eye. These sections on ocular pathology were prepared by Denonvilliers and Leon Gosselin (1815-1887), who collaborated with Auguste Bérard (1802-1846) on the *Compendium* itself.

BOA I:51; Hirsch II:227; Waller 2365.

Derby, Hasket, 1835-1914, trans.

See Graefe (160).

99 Descartes, René, 1596-1650.

L'homme . . . et la formation du foetus, avec les remarques de Louis de La Forge. A quoy l'on a ajouté Le monde ou traité de la lumière. . . . Seconde édition, revue & corrigée. Paris: C. Angot, 1677.

[64], 511, [9] p.: ill.; 25 cm. (4to)

Second French edition of Descartes' principal statement of his mechanistic physiology. The editor, Claude Clerselier (1614-84) added Descartes' *Le monde, ou traité de la lumière* to this printing of *L'homme*. Like the latter, *Le monde* had originally been published in 1664, but in a text hastily prepared and printed with many errors.

In the preface the editor states that *Le monde* might well be read first, as it contains Descartes' notion of matter as motion, and matter in motion as the ultimate law of the universe. All Descartes' scientific explanations were hence mechanistic, including his physiology.

The greater part of *L'homme* is given to a detailed examination of sensation, and of the physiology of vision in particular. According to Stephen Polyak (Polyak, p. 100-101) Descartes "produced a remarkable hypothesis of the intrinsic organization of the visual system which was far ahead of his time," and more specifically, stated "for the first time, a clearly conceived and expressed idea of a topographical projection or representation of the retina on the brain" (ibid, p. 103).

Neither *L'homme* nor *Le monde* were published during Descartes's lifetime. He thought it wiser to withhold their publication following Galileo's condemnation in 1633. The physiological basis of the *Dioptrique*, however, was founded on the system described in the unpublished *L'homme*.

The illustrations in the text are from woodblocks cut from designs found in Descartes's own manuscript, and from drawings by Gérard de Gutschoven and Louis de La Forge (1632-1666?), whose "Remarques . . . sur la Traité de l'homme" makes up a considerable part of the volume. On many of the cuts the designer is indicated by a D, G or F.

Osler 933 (imprint of T. Girard. See 3rd note to 944).

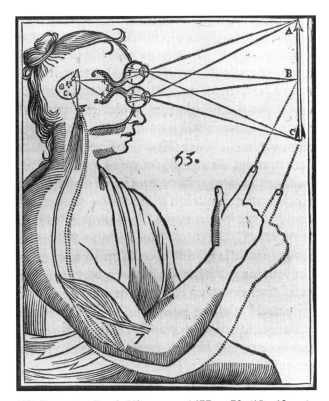

(99) Descartes, René. *L'homme...*, 1677, p. 72. (10 x 12 cm.)

100   Descartes, René, 1596-1650.

Opera philosophica. Editio ultima, nunc demum hac editione diligenter recognita, & mendis expurgata. Amsterdam: D. Elsevir, 1677-78.

[38], 222; [16], 248; [24], 92, [4]; [12], 191, [1]; 164, 88 p.: ill., port.; 20 cm. (4to)

Contents: Principia philosophiae (1677);—Specimina philosophiae: seu, Dissertatio de methodo . . . . Dioptrice, et meteora (1677);—Passiones animae (1677);—Meditationes de prima philosophia (1678);—Appendix, continens objectiones quintas & septimas in . . . Meditationes de prima philosophia . . . & duabus epistolis, una ad Patrem Dinet . . . altera ad . . . Gisbertum Voetium (1678).

Collected philosophic works of one of the most original and influential scientific minds of the seventeenth century, who also laid the foundations of modern critical philosophy. The *Specimina philosophiae* is a collection of three essays originally published together in 1637. The second of these, the *Dioptrice*, was Descartes's principal work on optics; while in the third, the *Meteora*, he continues the discussion of the laws of reflection and refraction. Each title in the volume has a separate title-page. The engraved portrait is lacking.

Wellcome II:452.

100.1   De Schweinitz, George Edmund, 1858-1938.

Diseases of the eye. A hand-book of ophthalmic practice, for students and practitioners. Philadelphia: W. B. Saunders, 1893.

xii, 17-641 p., 2 plates: ill.; 23 cm.

A comprehensive handbook of ophthalmology that was published in ten editions and five reprints over 32 years, and was at the time the most respected work in its field. Garrison calls it a "sterling text-book" (Garrison, p. 613), and remarks that De Schweinitz did "much valuable work on the toxic amblyopia" (ibid.). The career of George de Schweinitz included practices at the University of Pennsylvania, the Philadelphia General Hospital, the Philadelphia Polyclinic, and the Jefferson Medical College. He was president of the College of Physicians of Philadelphia between 1910 and 1913, and was founder and director of the U.S. Army's ophthalmological school at Camp Greenleaf, Fort Oglethorpe, Georgia.

BOA I:188-189 (1906 and 1924 eds.); Fischer II:1428 (1892 and 1924 eds.); Kaufman I:196-197 (1892 ed.; reprints); Osler 3948 (1892 ed.).

101 Deshais-Gendron, Louis Florent, fl. 1770.

Traité des maladies des yeux, & des moyens & opérations propres à leur guérison. Paris: C. J. B. Herissant, 1770.

2 v. (xii, 389, [7] p.; [4], iv, 438, [2] p.); 17 cm. (12mo)

In 1762 Deshais-Gendron became the first professor of ophthalmology when he was named demonstrator of ophthalmology at the Ecole de Chirurgie in Paris by Lamartinière, chief surgeon to the King and director of all colleges of surgery in France. The book is dedicated to Lamartinière and, to prevent unauthorized reprintings, the dedicatory epistle is initialed by the author as required in the *Avis* (p. xii). While German contemporaries such as Richter and Haller held a rather low opinion of the book, it served as a standard authority for nearly thirty years and later historians have viewed it as a more than adequate work for its period.

BOA I:75; Hirschberg §376; Waller 3469.

102 Desmarres, Louis Auguste, 1810-1882.

Traité théorique et pratique des maladies des yeux. Paris: L. Martinet for G. Baillière, 1847.

viii, 904 p.: ill.; 22 cm.

The principal work by the author and, after Carron du Villards's treatise (71), the second systematic textbook in French on diseases of the eye. Desmarres was one of the leading French ophthalmologists of his time who made important contributions to ophthalmic surgery.

Hirschberg §591-594; Wellcome II:457.

103 Desmarres, Louis-Auguste, 1810-1882.

Traité théorique et pratique des maladies des yeux. . . . Deuxième édition revue, corrigée et augmentée. Paris: G. Baillière, 1854-58.

3 v. ([4], 636; [4], 598; xi, [1], 816 p.): ill.; 23 cm.

Originally published in one volume in 1847 (102), the three volume second edition was almost completely rewritten with numerous additions made to the text. In this latter edition Desmarres was able to include descriptions of pathological states made possible only by the use of the ophthalmoscope, the description of which had just been published by Helmholtz in 1851. The first volume is introduced by an anatomical description of the eye translated from the German of Ernst Wilhelm Brücke (1819-1892).

Hirsch II:241; Hirschberg §593-594.

104 Desmonceaux, (Abbé), 1734-1806.

Traité des maladies des yeux et des oreilles, considérées sous le rapport des quatre parties ou quatre ages de la vie de l'homme; avec les remédes curatifs, & les moyens propres à les préserver des accidens. Paris: Lottin, 1786.

2 v. (xxvi, 382, 381-480 p., [2] plates; vi, 316, 316 bis-317 bis, 317-494, [2] p., [2] plates); 20 cm. (8vo)

A priest, physician, and ophthalmologist, the author has often been improperly accorded the honor of being the first to propose the removal of the transparent lens in high-grade myopia. In actuality it was Joseph Higgs of Birmingham who first proposed this procedure in 1745. Haller mentioned extraction of the lens for this purpose but made no claim to have actually performed the operation. It seems likely that Baron Wenzel performed the first reclination and extraction of the lens as a means of relief of high-grade myopia sometime prior to 1775 at the suggestion of Father Desmonceaux.

BOA I:52; Hirschberg §384.

Deutsche Ophthalmologische Gesellschaft (Heidelberg).

See Festschrift (134.1).

105 Deval, Charles, 1806-1862.

Chirurgie oculaire ou traité des opérations chirurgicales qui se pratiquent sur l'oeil et ses annexes, avec un exposé succinct des différentes altérations qui les réclament, ouvrage contenant la pratique opératoire de F. Jaeger et de A. Rosas, professeurs d'ophthalmologie a Vienne; d'après des documens recueillis par l'auteur aux cliniques de ces professeurs, et accompagné de planches représentant un grand nombre d'instrumens et les principaux procédés opératoires. Paris: P. Renouard for G. Baillière, 1844.

viii, 739 p., 6 plates; 22 cm.

The second French work devoted exclusively to ocular surgery, the first being Pellier de Quengsy's *Précis ou cours d'operations sur la chirurgie des yeux* (293). The surgical instruments of Beer, Jaeger, Rosas and others are illustrated and fully described.

Hirschberg §589.

106 Deval, Charles, 1806-1862.

Traité de l'amaurose ou de la goutte-sereine. Ouvrage contenant des faits nombreux de guérison de cette maladie. Dans des cas cécité complète. Paris: V. Masson, 1851.

[4], iv, 441 p.; 21 cm.

Hirsch II:251; Hirschberg §589.

107 Deval, Charles, 1806-1862.

Traité théorique et pratique des maladies des yeux. Paris: Ch. Albessard et Bérard, 1862.

xvi, 1056 p., XII plates: ill.; 25 cm.

This final work may be said to represent the culmination of Deval's life's work. It is the product of twenty years' practice and observation during which time the author examined more than 20,000 cases. The present work and the two preceding titles are Deval's three most important contributions to ophthalmic literature.

BOA I:52; Hirsch II:251; Hirschberg §589.

108 Devaux, Jean, 1649-1729.

L'art de faire les raports en chirurgie; où l'on enseigne la pratique, les formules, & le stile le plus en usage parmi les chirurgiens commis aux raports. Nouvelle éd., rev., corr., & augm. Paris: Widow of L. d'Houry, 1743.

xii, 576, 577/8-671/2, 673-689 p.; 17 cm. (12mo)

A series of royal decrees established in seventeenth century France a system of medical jurists, surgeons and physicians appointed for each town to examine and report on all wounded or murdered persons. Devaux's work served as a style manual for the preparation of such surgical reports. A section (p. 102-110) treats reports on the diagnosis and prognosis of wounds of the eye. This edition includes the additions and corrections of Sauveur François Morand (1697-1773).

109 Diderot, Denis, 1713-1784.

Lettre sur les aveugles, a l'usage de ceux qui voyent. London: s.n., 1749.

220, [2] p., 6 plates; 16 cm. (8vo)

The *Lettre* was based on the story of an Englishman named Saunderson (consistently spelled Saounderson throughout), born blind, who on his death-bed denied the existence of a creator because he had never seen the things in nature which

he had been told about. Diderot claimed that the moral and intellectual views of the blind are completely different from those of sighted people. The heterodox views expressed in this essay aroused much opposition and led to the author's imprisonment for several months. This copy closely corresponds with Niklaus's description of "l'edition princeps"; however, it contains unrecorded title-page and textual variants.

Hirschberg §344; Niklaus, p. [103]; Wellcome II:466.

110 Dieffenbach, Johann Friedrich, 1792-1847.

Ueber das Schielen und die Heilung desselben durch die Operation. Berlin: A. W. Hayn for A. Förstner, 1842.

viii, 220 p., 3 plates; 22 cm.

"The first successful attempt at treating strabismus by myotomy. The operation was later abandoned owing to the frequently disastrous final effects. A preliminary paper appeared in *Med. Ztg.* [*Medicinische Zeitung*] 1839, 8, 227" (G-M 5856). The present work is a full account of the author's method for correcting strabismus by severing the tendons of the eye muscles. The results of 1,200 operations are summarized. Dieffenbach and Stromeyer shared the Monthyon prize of the Institut de France for their pioneering studies of this procedure.

G-M 5856; Hirschberg §491; Waller 2447; Wellcome II:466.

111 Dionis, Pierre, 1643-1718.

Cours d'operations de chirurgie, démontrées au Jardin royal. Brussels: t'Serstevens & A. Claudinot, 1708.

[22], 615, [25] p., [10] plates: ill.; 19 cm. (8vo)

"Dionis taught operative surgery at the Jardin-du-Roi, Paris, a famous training ground for surgeons" (G-M 5575). First published in Paris in 1707 and reprinted the following year in Brussels, this famous compendium of surgery passed through many editions and was translated into Latin, English, and even Chinese. The sixth demonstration includes descriptions of the operations and illustrations of the instruments required for surgery of the eye and eyelids.

Hirschberg §330; Waller 2474; Wellcome II:471.

112 Dissertationes medicae selectae Tubingenses.

Oculi humani affectus medico-chirurgice

consideratos. Denuo in lucem editae cura et studio Christian Friedr. Reuss. Tübingen: J. G. Cotta, 1783-1785.

3 v. ([10], 370 p.; [4], 392 p.; [4], 415 p.); 18 cm. (8vo)

Contents: *see* Mauchart, praeses (preceding 248).

A collected edition of ophthalmological writings, most of which were theses by the pupils of Burchard David Mauchart. Mauchart was professor of anatomy and surgery at the University of Tübingen and one of the outstanding ophthalmologists of his time. Included in this collection of twenty-seven works is an oration by Mauchart on the English ophthalmologist John Taylor (370, 371, 372), to which the editor, Christian Friedrich Reuss (1745-1813), has added a list of Taylor's works.

Hirschberg §412.

113 Divoux, Johannes Petrus.

De praecipuis oculorum affectibus. Strasbourg: J. H. Heitz, 1734.

[4], 130, [2] p.; 19 cm. (4to)

The principal diseases of the eye are reviewed in this thesis submitted to the University of Strasbourg by a student from the town of Colmar. Extensive bibliographic footnotes are included.

114 Dixon, James, 1813-1896.

A guide to the practical study of diseases of the eye: with an outline of their medical and operative treatment. London: J. Churchill, 1855.

xxiv, 391 p.: ill.; 20 cm.

The first edition of Dixon's most important work, written while consulting surgeon to the Royal London Ophthalmic Hospital. A contemporary of Bowen and White Cooper, Dixon held a distinguished place among London ophthalmic surgeons. Heavily grieved by his wife's death in 1870, he retired from practice to his country home in Dorking, where he devoted the remaining twenty-five years of his life to the study of history and English literature.

BOA I:54; Hirsch II:279; Hirschberg §641.

114.1 Do you want a friend?

Printed for the blind. London: J. Gall (Edinburgh) for the Religious Tract Society, ca. 1830.

10 leaves; 24 cm.

Series: Tracts for the blind.

A religious tract printed by the philanthropist James Gall, who developed a style of embossed type to be read by the sense of touch. His alphabet was an attempt to improve Valentine Haüy's (181) relief type used for the education of the blind in late eighteenth century France. Haüy's style was more like cursive writing, whereas Gall's style featured angular imitations of the Roman antiqua font. With his new method, Gall published several works, mostly for use at the Asylum for the Blind in Glasgow. Later his alphabet was criticized as ineffective and was replaced by letters developed by John Alston (cf. AmEncOph I:253-255, VII:5339-5340).

Doesschate, Gezienus ten, trans.

See Camper (68).

115 Donders, Franciscus Cornelis, 1818-1889.

On the anomalies of accommodation and refraction of the eye. With a preliminary essay on physiological dioptrics. . . . Translated from the author's manuscript by William Daniel Moore. London: The New Sydenham Society, 1864.

xvii, [3], 635 p.: ill.; 22 cm.

The author of more than 340 works on physiology and ophthalmology, this book stands as Donders's greatest achievement. It was the basis of all succeeding studies on refraction, accommodation, and their anomalies; and ranks with the labors of Helmholtz in the field of physiological optics. Written originally in Dutch, the manuscript was translated into English by William Daniel Moore (1813-1871) and published for the first time in this New Sydenham Society edition.

BOA I:55; Chance, p. 70; Cushing D221; DicSciBio IV:163; G-M 5893; Heirs 997; Hirsch II:293; Hirschberg §1040.

116 Donders, Franciscus Cornelis, 1818-1889.

An essay on the nature and the consequences of anomalies of refraction. . . . Translated under the supervision of the Kirschbaum School of Languages and Bureau of Translation of Philadelphia. Revised and edited by Charles A. Oliver. Philadelphia: P. Blakiston's Son & Co., 1899.

x, [9]-80, [2] p., 1 plate: ill.; 23 cm.

BOA I:55; Hirschberg §767.

Duane, Alexander, 1858-1926.

See Fuchs (144).

117   Dufau, Pierre Armand, 1795-1877.

Des aveugles: considérations sur leur état physique, moral et intellectuel, avec un exposé complet des moyens propres à améliorer leur sort à l'aide de l'instruction et du travail. 2. éd., rev., augm., et accompagnée de quatre planches en relief. Paris: W. Remquet for J. Renouard, 1850.

[6], xxx, [2], 348 p., 4 plates; 22 cm.

Written by the director of the Institution Nationale des Aveugles in the tradition established by the author's predecessors, Haüy (181) and Guillié (169), this work stands as an important contribution to the theory and practice of educating the blind to read and learn useful manual skills. Originally published in 1837, Dufau's book was awarded the coveted prize of the Académie Française which the year before had been given to de Tocqueville's classic study of democracy in America. Braille's system of writing and musical notation, introduced first in 1829 but not officially adopted by the Institution until 1854, the cursive script developed by Haüy, and an embossed map are illustrated by the plates. This copy, in a signed binding by Hanimann, carries a presentation inscription to Demarze, a member of the consultative commission for the Institution, signed by the author's widow.

118   Duffin, Edward Wilson, 1800-1874.

Practical remarks on the new operation for the cure of strabismus or squinting. London: Wilson & Ogilvy for J. Churchill, 1840.

xiv, [2], 147 p., 10 plates; 22 cm.

"The substance of the following pages was published a short time ago, as a series of separate communications, in the weekly medical journals [*The Lancet* and *London Medical Gazette*] and entitled 'An Inquiry into some of the Consequences, and Causes of occasional failure, attending the new operation for the cure of Strabismus'" (Preface, p. [xi]). The work was praised by a contemporary reviewer for its unusually moderate price considering the number of engravings with which it is illustrated.

BOA I:57; Hirschberg §495; Wellcome II:493.

119   Du Hamel, Jean Baptiste, 1624-1706.

De corpore animato libri quatuor: seu promotae per experimenta philosophiae specimen alterum. Paris: S. Michallet, 1673.

[24], 535, [13] p., [4] plates; 15 cm. (12mo)

Though usually designated as an anatomist, Du Hamel's inter-

ests ranged widely in the realms of scientific inquiry. His writings are regarded as representative of the increasing interest in experimental method that characterizes the progress of much of seventeenth century science. In the *De corpore animato* the author discusses the physiology of sensation, including nearly a hundred pages on vision (Ch. V, "De visus organo"; Ch. VI, "De visione").

DicSciBio IV:222; Thorndike VIII:210; Waller 2625; Wellcome II:495.

120   Du Laurens, André, 1558-1609.

Toutes les oeuvres . . . . Recueillies et traduittes en francois, par Me. Theophile Gelée. Rouen: J. Besongne, 1661.

[16], 572, [30], 488 (i.e. 288), [6] p.: ill., port.; 38 cm. (fol.)

The complete anatomical and medical works of the renowned French anatomist who was also physician to Henry IV and professor of physics at the University of Montpellier. In the anatomical works the author devoted ten chapters to the anatomy and physiology of the eye in an exposition and amplification of Vesalius. The author's principal ophthalmological work, *Le conservation de la veue*, is reprinted in this edition. An extended analysis of this treatise on the preservation of sight can be found in Percy Dunn's article, "A sixteenth century oculist," *Proceedings of the Royal Society of Medicine* 9 (2):120-142 (1916).

121   Eble, Burkard, 1799-1839.

Ueber den Bau und die Krankheiten der Bindehaut des Auges, mit besonderem Bezuge auf die contagiöse Augenentzündung. Nebst einem Anhange über den Verlauf und die Eigenthümlichkeiten der letzteren unter der Garnison von Wien vom Jahre 1817-1827. Vienna: F. Ullrich for J. G. Heubner, 1828.

xiv, 255, [3] p., 3 plates; 23 cm.

A detailed study of the gross and microscopic anatomy and the pathology of the conjunctiva based on the author's research and observations in dealing with trachoma. Eble, an Austrian military physician, signed the plates which illustrate this work. Appended to the study are observations on the Egyptian ophthalmia as it occurred in the Vienna garrison between 1817 and 1827.

Hirschberg §490.

122   Edmondston, Arthur, 1776?-1841.

A treatise on the varieties and consequences of ophthalmia. With a preliminary inquiry into its contagious nature. Edinburgh: G. Caw for W. Blackwood & Longmans (London), 1806.

[4], ix, [1], 85-86 [cancellans], 319 p.; 22 cm. (8vo)

Edmondston, a Scottish surgeon of the Second Regiment of the Argyleshire Fencibles, published in 1802 the first account in English of Egyptian ophthalmia. That work proved to be the first of more than twenty English publications dealing with ophthalmia that appeared between 1806 and 1820. In the present treatise the author establishes his claim as the first to demonstrate the contagious nature of ophthalmia. Although Edmondston was not in Egypt, his researches were based on his experience with an outbreak among troops at Gibralter and on a Paris epidemic in 1803. In dividing inflammations of the eye into idiopathic and symptomatic ophthalmias, he anticipated William Mackenzie's approach by some thirty years.

Hirschberg §629A.

122.1   Edridge-Green, Frederick William, 1863-1953.

Colour-blindness and colour-perception. London: K. Paul, Trench, Trübner & Co., 1891.

viii, 311, [1]; 89, [7] p., 3 plates: ill., diagrs.; 19 cm.

Bound with publisher's catalog (89, [7] p. at end).

Series: International scientific series; v. 71.

The book contains the author's theory of vision and color "based on the careful examination of 116 colour-blind people" (Pref.). Following a short historical introduction, the text discusses "the physical basis of colour, the psycho-physical perception of colour, normal colour-perception, the composition of colour, acquired colour-blindness, and tests for colour-blindness" (BOA III:57). Edridge-Green's lantern test officially replaced the Holmgren test in Great Britain in 1915, and he introduced a new kind of color perception spectrometer as well (cf. AmEncOph IV:2410-2412, VI:4157-4158).

BOA III:57; G-M 5937; Waller I:2694.

122.2   Eisenach, Heinrich.

Dissertatio inauguralis sistens observationem irideremiae partialis, nec non vis vitae maternae in conformationem foetus humani. . . . Kassel: H. Hotopius, 1836.

[4], 18 p., [1] plate; 22 cm.

An inaugural dissertation about partial irideremia, especially from the congenital aspect. This work was publicly presented to the physicians of Marburg on the 6th of February, 1836. In the 1870s, Heinrich Eisenach also published in the field of

biology, namely on the flora and fauna of the area around Kassel, Germany.

NUC 157:323.

Engelbrecht, Martin, 1684-1756, engr.

See Prints 2, 3.

123   The English impostor detected.

Or, the history of the life and fumigation of the renown'd Mr. J— T—, occulist. Dublin: s.n., 1732.

16 p.; 16 cm. (12mo)

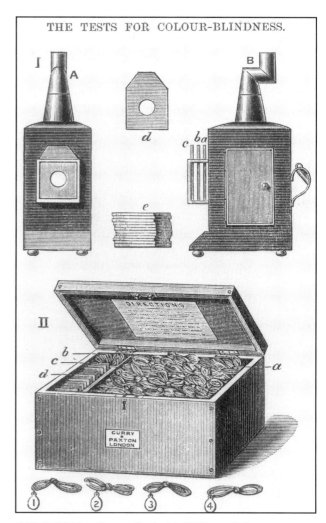

(122.1) Edridge-Green, Frederick William. *Colour-blindness...*, 1891, p. 263: I. The lantern test; II. The color classification test. (8 x 13 cm.)

An early attack on John Taylor, known as the "Chevalier" (370-72). This satire, which seems not to have been reprinted, was written in a mock heroic style and concludes with a long poem in Latin that is translated into English. The tract gives an account of the "fumigation" of Taylor, a practical joke played upon him by some young men of Dublin. The author refers to his pseudonym, "Dionysius Querpoides," in the note to the reader. Taylor is described as "the grand Antiluminary of his Age" (p. 9).

124   Ens, Sicco, 1779-1842.

Historia extractionis cataractae. . . . Franeker: Verweijan, 1803.

xii, 313, [7] p., V plates; 23 cm. (8vo)

The author's dissertation for his medical degree from the University of Franeker in Friesland. Divided into two sections, the first presents a very thorough historical review of the operation for cataract extraction from Daviel to Ens's own time. The second section is the author's *epicrisis* or synthesis of the best procedure and instruments to be used in the extraction of cataract. The historical utility of this unusual dissertation has been noted by both Hirsch and Hirschberg. Lacking the errata slip after page 313.

Callisen VI:513; Hirsch II:417; Hirschberg §830; Waller 2762; Wellcome II:526.

125   Euclid, fl. ca. 300 B.C.

La prospettiva di Euclide, nella quale si tratta di quelle cose, che per raggi diritti si veggono: & di quelle, che con raggi reflessi nelli specchi appariscono. Tradotta dal R. P. M. Egnatio Danti ....Con alcune sue annotationi de' luoghi piu importanti. Insieme con La prospettiva di Eliodoro Larisseo cavata della Libreria Vaticana, e tradotta dal medesimo nuovamente data in luce. Florence: Stamperia de'Giunta, 1573.

[8], 110, [38] p.: diagrs.; 23 cm. (4to)

Contents: La prospettiva di Euclide [Optica]; — Gli specchi di Euclide [Catoptrica]; — La prospettiva di Eliodoro Larisseo; — Ηλιοδωρου Λαρισσαιου κεφαλαια των οπτικων; Heliodori Larissaei capita opticorum.

The first vernacular and only sixteenth century Italian edition of Euclid's *Optica* and the spurious *Catoptrica*. Included is the first publication of the *Capita opticorum* of Heliodorus of Larissa, in Italian, followed by the Greek original and its Latin translation.

Euclid's was the first mathematical exposition of a theory of vision. Ignoring the physical and psychological aspects of seeing, Euclid restricted himself to what could be expressed mathematically. Thus, in positing rectilinear visual rays, Euclid was able to develop a theory of vision along strictly geometrical lines. The sixty-one propositions of the *Optica*, modeled on the geometrical system of the *Elements*, remained authoritative until the time of Kepler. The *Capita opticorum* of Heliodorus of Larissa is the only work of this second century Greek mathematician to have survived. Both Euclid and Heliodorus were rendered into Italian by Ignatio Danti (1537-1586).

BM Italian, p. 239; Wellcome I:2085.

126   Euler, Leonhard, 1707-1783.

Dioptricae pars prima, continens librum primum, de explicatione principiorum, ex quibus constructio tam telescopiorum quam microscopiorum est petenda; pars secunda, continens librum secundum, de constructione telescopiorum dioptricorum . . . ; pars tertia, continens librum tertium, de constructione microscopiorum tam simplicium, quam compositorum. St. Petersburg: Academia Imperialis Scientiarum, 1769-71.

3v. ([4], 337 p., III plates; [8], 592 [i.e. 584] p., III plates; [8], 440 p.): ill.; 26 cm. (4to)

One of the most important mathematicians of the eighteenth century, Euler's work was ever related to its applications to the other sciences and to problems of technology. In the first part of the *Dioptrica* Euler discusses the properties of lenses as an introduction to the construction of dioptric instruments. The second and third parts describe the construction of the telescope and microscope.

Blake, p. 139; BOA I:65.

127   Fabini, Johann Gottlieb, 1791-1847.

Doctrina de morbis oculorum. Budapest: J. T. Trattner de Petróza, 1823.

[8], 355, [1] p.; 22 cm.

The author obtained his medical degree at Vienna in 1817 and served as an assistant in Beer's clinic before receiving his appointment by the University of Pest. Hirschberg considered this work to be probably the last ophthalmology text written in Latin.

Hirschberg §480-481.

128   Fabini, Johann Gottlieb, 1791-1847.

Doctrina de morbis oculorum. Editio altera, denuo elaborata. Budapest: K. Trattner for O. Wigand, 1831.

[8], 370, [2] p.; 23 cm.

An Italian translation of this work was issued at Treviso in the same year as this second edition which is augmented by the inclusion of formulas and a bibliography.

Hirschberg §480-481.

129   Fabre, Antoine François Hippolyte, 1797-1854.

Némésis médicale illustrée, recueil de satires . . . rev. et corr. avec soin par l'auteur; contenant trente vignettes dessinées par M. Daumier. Paris: Béthune & Plon for Bureau de la Némésis Médicale, 1840.

2 v. (xxxii, 278 p.; 360 p.): ill.; 25 cm.

Originally published in parts (1836-1838?), this collection of twenty-five satires in verse is the first collected edition of Fabre's work. It contains the first issue of Daumier's famous illustrations and is one of the few books illustrated by Daumier. Passages in "Les Specialities" (2:[51]-74) refer to ophthalmology and to such notable practitioners as Sanson, Sichel, and Rognetta.

Waller 2876; Wellcome III:2.

130   Fabri, Honoré, 1606-1688.

Synopsis optica, in qua illa omnia quae ad opticam, dioptricam, catoptricam pertinet, id est, ad triplicem radium visualem directum, refractum, reflexum, breviter quidem, accurate tamen demonstrantur. Lyons: H. Boissat & G. Remeus, 1667.

[8], 246 p., 6 plates; 23 cm. (4to)

A significant work on optics, which though carefully read by Fabri's contemporaries, has been regarded with mixed feelings by historians of science. It was described as "copié des écrivains les moins recommendables" by the compiler of the *Biographie médicale* (IV:89), yet was regarded as one of Fabri's most important works by Poggendorf (I:711).

Fabri is one of the more interesting characters in the annals of seventeenth century science. A man of science, he was nonetheless a member of the Inquisition for thirty-four years. A voluminous writer on the sciences, he could yet be described by Thorndike (VII:665) as one who "attempted to meet developing modern science on its own ground, to fight against it with its own weapons, or . . . to accost it with diplomatic cour-

tesy and seeming friendliness, to yield a few minor points, and to try to outwit it on more important issues."

131   Fabri, Honoré, 1606-1688.

Tractatus duo: quorum prior est de plantis, et de generatione animalium; posterior de homine. Nuremberg: W. M. Endter & heirs of J. A. Endter, 1677.

[12], 582, [14] p., [1] plate; 23 cm. (4to)

Originally published in Paris in 1666, this second edition is divided into two parts. The first discusses plants and animal generation; the second human physiology. Thirty-five pages of the *De homine* are given to the eye and a discussion of the physiology of vision (p. 287-321). The book's only plate illustrates this section. It is also here that Fabri claims to have publicly taught the circulation of the blood long before a copy of Harvey's *De motu cordis* ever came into his hands.

Wellcome III:3.

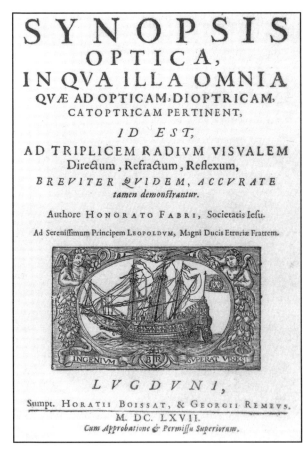

(130) Fabri, Honoré. *Synopsis optica*, 1667. Title page. (16 x 23 cm.)

132 Fabricius, Hieronymus, ab Aquapen-dente, 1537-1619.

Opera chirurgica in pentateuchum, et operationes chirurgicas distincta. Editio quinta et vigesima. Padua: M. de Cadorinis, 1666.

[8], 364, 31 p., 9 plates; 31 cm. (fol.)

Fabricius, a pupil of Fallopius at Padua and one of the greatest teachers of anatomy, succeeded his teacher, and built, at his own expense, the famous anatomical theater at Padua. His work on the valves of the veins allowed Harvey, his pupil, to finish his concept of the heart as a pump and present a complete theory of the circulation of the blood. "His ocular operations are all essentially taken from the Greeks and Arabians—chiefly Celsus, Paulus and Albucasis—and he even admits that he himself performed the cataract operation only twice or thrice all told. Later, he renounced this operation absolutely, recommending for cataract the use of a certain collyrium in an eye-cup" (AmEncOph VII:5132-33).

Hirschberg §316; Wellcome III:4.

133 Fabricius von Hilden, Wilhelm, 1560-1634.

Selectae observationes chirurgicae quinque & viginti. Item, De gangraena et sphacelo tractatus methodicus. Geneva: G. Cartier, 1598.

[16], 168 p.: ill.; 17 cm. (8vo)

This selection of twenty-five case histories by the "Father of German Surgery" was translated from the French by Joannes Rheterius and edited by Jean Antoine Sarrasin (1547-1598). In its format it is a precursor of the author's famous *Observationum et curationum chirurgicarum centuriae I-VI*, published between 1606 and 1641. The cases reported here are all reprinted in *Centuria I* (Basel, 1606). Among the cases of eye surgery is an account of a boy whose eye was pierced by an arrow with the loss of the aqueous humor. Fabricius reported that the fluids were quickly restored and the patient's sight recovered. This observation was significant as the loss of this fluid, greatly feared by earlier writers, came to be recognized as relatively inconsequential.

Durling Suppl 69 (Basel); Hirschberg §321; Wellcome I:2127 (Basel).

133.1 Farrar, John, 1779-1853, comp.

An experimental treatise on optics, comprehending the leading principles of the science, and an explanation of the more important and curious optical instruments and optical phenomena. Cambridge, Mass.: Hilliard & Metcalf, 1826.

vii, [1], 350, [2] p., VI folded plates; 26 cm.

Provenance: Samuel May, July 20, 1827, Harvard University, Cambridge; Hilliard, Gray; Elmer A. Harrington (inscriptions).

John Farrar was professor of mathematics and natural philosophy at Harvard University. He selected and compiled the content of this work from J.-B. Biot's *Précis élémentaire de physique expérimentale*, to be the third part of his course on natural philosophy. Jean-Baptiste Biot (1774-1862), a French physicist and geodesist, was especially interested in questions relating to the polarization of light, and his observations in this field gained him the Rumford medal of the Royal Society in 1840.

This copy of Farrar's book was obviously used for practical teaching, as the handwritten marginal notes bear witness to it. One of the notes manifests the user's appreciation of the phenomenon of light saying: "Light comes to us from the Sun . . . 96 millions of miles; about 12 millions of miles in a minute, about 200,000 miles in a second" (title page).

BM 71:95; BOA I:66; NUC 167:257.

Farre, John Richard, 1774-1862.

See Saunders (326).

134 Feller, Christian Gotthold, 1755-1785.

De methodis suffusionem oculorum curandi, a Casaamata et Simone cultis. Leipzig: S. L. Crusius, 1782.

[2], 29 p., [1] plate; 19 cm. (8vo)

Feller, a Leipzig physician, witnessed and here described the public demonstrations of cataract extraction performed by Simon in Paris in 1777 and by Casa Amata in Leipzig two years later. This dissertation is the only source which describes the procedures of these two surgeons. Casa Amata, ophthalmic surgeon to the Royal Court at Dresden from 1779 to 1806, was probably the first to attempt the surgical correction of aphakia with intraocular lenses. Cf. D P. Choyce, "Intraocular lenses," [Letter to the Editor], *The Lancet* 2 (8035):451 (August 27, 1977).

Hirschberg §442.

Fernel, Jean, 1497-1558.

See Bailey (30.1).

134.1 **Festschrift zur Feier des siebzigsten Geburtstages von Hermann von Helmholtz.** Stuttgart: Union Deutsche Verlagsgesellschaft, 1891.

[8], 91, [1] p., VIII plates: ill.; 40 x 33 cm.

A collection of essays by eighteen prominent ophthalmologists of England, Germany, France, and Italy published in honor of Hermann von Helmholz's 70th birthday. The topics include: hemorrhagic disease of the retina, retinal embolism, diagnostic ophthalmoscopy, strabismus, sciascopy, choroiditis, ocular motions, and cataract operation. "These papers are abstracted in the *Centralb. f. Augenheilk.* 1892, page 74 and following and page 236 and following" (Hirschberg §1037).

Helmholz is responsible for several advancements in ophthalmology, including the invention of the ophthalmometer, the development of the telestereoscope (1852), and new findings about accommodation (1854). His most important contribution, the invention of the ophthalmoscope (1851), may be considered the greatest event in the history of ophthalmology, since it vastly extended the means for study, diagnosis, and treatment. In particular, the instrument made it possible to see the fundus of the living eye. Helmholz received many honors, and his collected works became standard and were extensively translated.

Gorin, p. 126; Hirschberg §1037; NUC 141:338 (1891 Hamburg ed.); Poggendorff IV:612; Waller 4298.

135 **Feyens, Thomas, 1567-1631.**

Libri chirurgici XII. De praecipuis artis chirurgicae controversiis. . . . Opera posthuma, Hermanni Conringii, cura nunc primum edita. Frankfurt am Main: T. M. Goez, 1649.

[12], 108 p.; 19 cm. (4to)

The surgical writings of Thomas Feyens (or Fienus), professor of medicine at Louvain, edited for posthumous publication by Hermann Conring (1606-1681). Among the twelve treatises included here, the second ("De depositione," p. 25-32) describes the treatment of cataract by depression; and the third ("De depositione ungulae," p. 33-34) describes the operation for pterygium. The final treatise is on rhinoplasty. Feyens was a student of Tagliacozzi's at Bologna and witnessed the success of many of his teacher's rhinoplastic operations.

Hirsch II:512; Waller 3022; Wellcome III:24.

136 **Fischer, Johann Nepomuk, 1777-1847.**

Klinischer Unterricht in der Augenheilkunde. Prague: C. W. Medau (Leitmeritz) for Borrosch & Andre, 1832.

lxvii, [1], 416, [2] p., 7 plates; 20 cm.

Considered the founder of modern ophthalmology in Bohemia, Fischer was professor of ophthalmology at the University of Prague and the first physician appointed to the Prague Ophthalmic Institute.

Hirschberg §477.

Flechsig, Paul Emil, 1847-1929.

See Ramón y Cajal (309.1).

137 **Florio, Pierre, fl. 1840.**

Description historique, théorique et pratique, de l'ophthalmie purulente observée de 1835 à 1839 dans l'Hopital militaire de Saint-Pétersbourg. Paris: Guiraudet & Jouaust for H. Cousin, 1841.

[8], iii, [1], 320 p., 5 plates; 21 cm.

A prefatory note informs readers that by order of the Emperor of Russia this work was printed in the Russian language at government expense and distributed to all military physicians to guide and instruct them in the treatment of purulent ophthalmia. The second chapter provides an introduction to the history of trachoma which was rampant in the armies during the Napoleonic era.

Hirschberg §719.; Wellcome III:34.

138 **Florio, Pierre, fl. 1840.**

Descrizione istorica teorica e pratica dell'ottalmia purolenta osservata dal 1835 al 1839 nell'ospedale militare di Pietroburgo. Tradotta in italiano dal dottor Emmanuele Cangiano. Naples: Filiatre-Sebezio, 1842.

232 p., 5 plates: port.; 21 cm.

The Italian translation includes a portrait of the author not present in the original French edition of 1841.

Hirschberg §719.

139 **Follin, François Anthyme Eugène, 1823-1867.**

Leçons sur l'exploration de l'oeil et en particulier sur les applications de l'ophthalmoscope au diagnostic des maladies des yeux. . . . Rédigées et publiées par Louis Thomas. Paris: A. Delahaye, 1863.

vii, [1], xxiii, [1], 304 p., II plates: ill.; 23 cm.

The greatly enlarged and improved second edition of Follin's *Leçons sur l'application de l'ophthalmoscopie* (Paris, 1859), the earliest work in the French language devoted entirely to the ophthalmoscope.

Hirsch II:559; Hirschberg §1028, 1031.

140   Fontana, Felice 1730-1805.

Dei moti dell' iride. Lucca: J. Giusti for V. Landi, 1765.

xii, 106 p.; 20 cm. (8vo)

An important book in the history of physiological optics in which the author described the lymphatic vessels in the crystalline lens, confirmed Haller and Caldani in associating the pupillary reflex with the reactions of the retina to light, and noted the effect of cerebral excitement upon the dilation of the pupil. The channels in the ciliary body of the eye are named after Fontana.

Hirschberg §731; Wellcome III:37.

140.1   Fournier, Bernard.

De l'appareil des voies lacrymales. Montpellier: J. Martel, 1803.

45, [1] p.; 25 cm. (4to)
Bound with Baudet-Dulary (35.2).

A treatise concerning the anatomy and pathology of the lacrimal passages as well as the therapeutics of lacrimal apparatus diseases. Bernard Fournier, a former army surgeon, was a member of the Society of Medicine, Arts and Sciences in Grenoble and taught anatomy at the School of Surgery in the same city.

BM 76:449; Callisen 2538.

Fraas, Christoph Friedrich, respondent.

"De pupillae phthisi ac synizesi."

In Dissertationes medicae selectae Tubingenses (112) 2:73-114.

France, John Frederick, 1818-1900, ed.

See Morgan (264).

141   Franz, Joann Christoph August, 1807-ca. 1859.

The eye: a treatise on the art of preserving this organ in a healthy condition, and of improving the sight; to which is prefixed, a view of the anatomy, and physiology of the eye; with observations on its expression as indicative of the character and emotions of the mind. London: J. Churchill, . . . et al., 1839.

xix, [1], 296 p., [l] plate; 19 cm.

Franz received his medical education in Leipzig and later emigrated to England where he settled at Brighton. The present work is divided into two parts. The first deals with the anatomy and physiology of the eye (with a curious final chapter on the expression of the eye as indicative of moral disposition). The second part discusses the care of the eyes and the preservation of sight.

BOA I:72; Hirsch II:607; Hirschberg §470; Wellcome III:64.

142   Frick, George, 1793-1870.

A treatise on the diseases of the eye; including the doctrines and practice of the most eminent modern surgeons, and particularly those of Professor Beer. London: C. Smith for J. Anderson, 1826.

xii, [13]-308 p., 1 plate; 22 cm.

"First important American text-book of ophthalmology" (G-M 5844, citing 1823 Baltimore edition). Frick's work, a compendium based largely on G. J. Beer's lectures, was so highly regarded in England that it was re-published there with notes by Richard Welbank.

G-M 5844 (1823 Baltimore ed.); Hirschberg §746.

142.1   Froriep, Robert, 1804-1861.

Dissertatio medica de corneitide scrofulosa . . . die II mensis Decembris A. MDCCCXXX. publice auctor defendet auctor Robertus Froriep. Jena: s.n., 1830.

[2], 18 p., [1] col. plate: ill.; 26 cm.

A doctoral dissertation describing scrofulous keratitis and its therapeutics. Two years after publishing this treatise, Robert Froriep was appointed professor at the University of Jena, and the following year at the University of Berlin. He also taught anatomy at the Art Academy of Brandenburg province, where his knowledge of anatomy complemented his not inconsiderable artistic talent. This work contains a color plate that was made from Froriep's original drawing.

Hirsch II:635; NUC 187:578.

(6) Aguilon, François d'. *Opticorum libri sex philosophis iuxtà ac mathematicis utiles*, 1613. Copperplate illustration on p. 356. (14.3 x 10 cm.)

143　Frost, William Adams, 1853-1935.

The fundus oculi with an ophthalmoscopic atlas illustrating its physiological & pathological conditions. Edinburgh and London: Y. J. Pentland, 1896.

xviii, [2], 228 p., XLVII plates: ill.; 29 cm.

Noting in the preface that the great ophthalmoscopic atlases of earlier years were both difficult to come by and included no account of more recent developments in the field, Frost proposed his own atlas as a remedy to the situation. Indeed, the *Fundus oculi* is the worthy successor to the atlases of Liebreich and Jaeger. The superb plates, lithographed after the drawings of A. W. Head, made this atlas the best available until the electric ophthalmoscope made possible more finely detailed illustration. W. Adams Frost succeeded R. Brudenell Carter as senior ophthalmic surgeon at St. George's Hospital. His renown rests principally on this excellent atlas.

BOA I:73; Chance, p. 171; Hirschberg §650, 1029.

143.1　Fuchs, Ernst, 1851-1930.

Lehrbuch der Augenheilkunde. Dritte vermehrte Auflage. Leipzig; Vienna: F. Deuticke, 1893.

xvi, 832 p.: ill. (194 woodcuts); 24 cm.

Arlt's successor at Vienna, Fuchs happens to be better known for this textbook than for any other of his considerable scientific activities. He wrote the *Lehrbuch* in order to provide his students with the substance of his teaching in a permanent form, relieving them of the need to take copious notes, thus enabling them to concentrate on his lectures. The result was one of the classics on the pathology of the eye. The *Lehrbuch* went through eighteen German editions between 1889 and 1945, and ten British and American editions between 1892 and 1933.

BOA I:73 (1894 ed.); Fischer I:461 (1889 ed.); G-M 5935 (1889 ed.); NUC 187:177.

144　Fuchs, Ernst, 1851-1930.

Text-book of ophthalmology. . . . Authorized translation from the second enlarged and improved German edition by A. Duane. New York: D. Appleton & Co., 1896.

xiii, [1], 788 p.: ill.; 24 cm.

The 1896 printing of the first American edition (lst printing., New York, 1892). This English translation of Fuch's *Lehrbuch der Augenheilkunde* (2. Aufl., Leipzig & Wien, 1891) was often referred to in America as "the Bible of the ophthalmologist." The work was also translated into French,

Spanish, Japanese, and Chinese.

145　Fuchs, Leonhart, 1501-1566.

Tabula oculorum morbos comprehendens, 1538. A facsimile. Palo Alto: privately printed, 1949.

[6] leaves, 1 folding broadsheet; 32 cm., broadsheet 63.3 x 40.5 cm.

Facsimile of a 'fugitive sheet' drawn up by the author for his students at Tübingen which survives in possibly a unique copy at the Lane Medical Library, University of California at Los Angeles. Karl Sudhoff published the text of this sixteenth century synopsis of eye diseases in *Archiv für Augenheilkunde* 97:493-501 (1926).

Hirschberg §143.

146　Fuchs, Samuel, 1588-1630.

Metoposcopia & ophthalmoscopia. Strasbourg: T. Glaser for P. Ledertz, 1615.

[16], 140 p.: ill.; 17 cm. (8vo)

Samuel Fuchs, a native of Koslin in Pomerania, was professor of rhetoric at Königsberg. In this curious and little known work the author suggests a system for the estimation of character based on the shape of the head and the eyes which is linked by Garrison (p. 273) to the work of Carden and Lavater. Among the finely executed engravings and woodcuts are portraits of Cosimo Medici, Andrea Doria, Christopher Columbus, and Philip II, Duke of Pomerania. A. de Neuille published a detailed analysis of this work, "Une precurseur de Lambroso au XVIIe siecle," in *La Revue des Revues* (15 June 1896). Cf. L. Stieda, "Samuel Fuchs, der Verfasser der Metoposcopia und Ophthalmoscopia," *Janus* 4:134-136 (1899).

Garrison, p. 273; Hirschberg §483; Waller I:3303; Wellcome I:2468.

Fullenius, Bernardus 1640-1707, ed.
See Huygens (199).

147　Furnari, Salvatore, 1808-1866.

Essai sur une nouvelle méthode d'opérer la cataracte. Paris: Crochard & Co., 1839.

16 p., 2 plates; 23 cm.

The author's description of his method for the extraction of cataract using instruments of his own devising, described and illustrated with two lithographic plates.

148   Furnari, Salvatore 1808-1866.

Traité pratique des maladies des yeux contenant 1° l'histoire de l'ophthalmologie; 2° l'exposition et le traitement raisoné de toutes les maladies de l'oeil et de ses annexes; 3° l'indication des moyens hygiéniques pour préserver l'oeil de l'action nuisible des agens physiques et chimiques mis en usage dans les diverse professions; 4° les nouveaux procédés et les instrumens pour la guérison du strabisme; 5° des instructions pour l'emploi des lunettes et l'application de l'oeil artificiel, suivi de conseils hygiéniques et thérapeutiques sur les maladies des yeux qui affectent particulièrement les hommes d'état, les gens de lettres et tous ceux qui s'occupent de travaux de cabinet et de bureau. Paris: P. Baudouin for J. B. Baillière, 1841.

[2], viii, 440 p., 4 plates; 21 cm.

Written by a graduate of the University of Palermo who achieved a certain reputation in the treatment of eye diseases in Paris where he founded a clinic and dispensary with Carron du Villards (70-71). Furnari returned to Sicily in 1848 to accept the chair of clinical ophthalmology at Palermo which he held until his death. The dedication of this work to Scarpa and Ramazzini reveals the author's interest in occupational diseases and hygiene as they relate to the eye.

Hirschberg §569.

148.1   Furnari, Salvatore, 1808-1866.

De la tonsure conjonctivale, et de son efficacité contre les lésions panniformes et chroniques de la cornée et contre les ulcérations vascularisées et les opacités interlamellaires de cette membrane. Paris: J. B. Baillière & Sons, 1862.

43, [1] p.: ill.; 23 cm.

Provenance: Inscribed by the author to Dr. Brochin.

Furnari's much debated article about his method of peritomy operation was published first in the *Gazette médicale* (1862) and then as a monograph. "Furnari reports in this article that he had performed his first operation of the kind . . . in Africa; he claims that nobody before him had performed this operation, though 'a partial or circular peritomy of the conjunctiva from the limbus had been performed since time immemorial.' His operation is identical to the one performed by the ancient Arabs against pannus. They had exactly described it; Furnari only adds a cauterization of the bared sclera and this step was severely criticized by his colleagues" (Hirschberg §735). An Italian translation of this work by Angelo Pace was published in 1864.

Hirschberg §735; NUC 188:150 (1864 Italian ed.).

Galenus.

Littere ad Corisium de morbis oculorum et eorum curis.

In Collectio ophthalmologica veterum auctorum (82), fasc. 7.

Galenus.

See Ḥunayn ibn Isḥāq al-Ibādī (197).

149   Gataker, Thomas, d. 1769.

Essays on medical subjects, originally printed separately: to which is now prefixed an introduction relating to the use of hemlock and corrosive sublimate: and to the application of caustic medicines in cancerous disorders. London: R. & J. Dodsley, 1764.

[4], lii, [2], 284 p.; 19 cm (8vo)

The final work in this collection of separate treatises, "An account of the structure of the eye, with occasional remarks on some disorders of that organ," first published in 1761, was based on a course of lectures delivered at the theatre of London's Surgeon's Hall. Gataker was surgeon to Westminster Hospital and St. George's Hospital and he was succeeded at the latter by the famous John Hunter. An account of the author is provided by R. R. James, "Thomas Gataker: an 18th century English surgeon with ophthalmological leanings," *Archives of Ophthalmology* 64:171-179 (1932).

Hirsch II:695.

150   Gauss, Carl Friedrich, 1777-1855.

Dioptrische Untersuchungen. Göttingen: Dieterich, 1841.

[2], 30, 25-34 p.; 27 cm.

"In the same year [Gauss] finished *Dioptrische Untersuchungen* (1841), in which he analyzed the path of light through a system of lenses and showed, among other things, that any system is equivalent to a properly chosen single lens. Although Gauss said that he had possessed the theory forty years before and considered it too elementary to publish, it has been labelled his greatest work by one of his scientific biographers (Clemens Schäfer, in *Werke*, XI, pt. 2, sec. 2, 189ff.). In any case, it was his last significant scientific contribution" (DicSciBio V:306).

The peculiarity in the pagination is due to the fact that leaf Dl (p. 25-26) is a cancel. The cancelled leaf is also present however, along with the other three leaves of this gathering, thus duplicating the pagination.

DicSciBio V:306.

Geiger, Matthaeus Abraham Martin, respondent.

"De fistula corneae."

In Dissertationes medicae selectae Tubingenses (112) 2:195-232.

Gelée, Théophile, d. 1650, trans.

See Du Laurens (120).

151   Geminus, Thomas, ca. 1500-ca. 1570.

Compendiosa totius anatomie delineatio. A facsimile of the first English edition of 1553 in the version of Nicholas Udall, with an introduction by C. D. O'Malley. London: Dawson's of Pall Mall, 1959.

39, [l] p., [100] leaves: facsims.; 44 cm.

The *Compendiosa* of Geminus, translated into English by Nicholas Udall and present here in a facsimile edition from a copy in the Wellcome Historical Medical Library, was a skillful and successful plagiarism of Vesalius's two great anatomical treatises. The illustrations, among the earliest English copperplate engravings, were copied from Calcar's woodcuts which appeared first in Vesalius's *De humani corporis fabrica* (387). The text is made up from a fifteenth century manuscript or from Vicary's digest of it, mingled with passages from the work of Louis Vasse and from Vesalius's *Epitome*. Geminus's purpose in issuing this pirated work was not to promote or extend anatomical knowledge but to provide the barber-surgeons with a practical dissection manual. The illustrations of the eye on the final plate are from the *Fabrica* (p. 643-644).

Hirschberg §100.

Genth, Carl Philipp, 1844-1904, jt. author.

See Pagenstecher (281.1).

Georgius, Ferdinand Gottfried, respondent.

"De corneae oculi tunicae examine anatomico-physiologico."

In Dissertationes medicae selectae Tubingenses (112) 2:328-367.

Gerardus Cremonensis, 1114-1187, ed.

See Alhazen (8).

151.1   Gerold, Jakob Hugo, 1814-1898.

Die Lehre vom schwarzen Staar und dessen Heilung. Nach eigenen Erfahrungen am Krankenbette und pathologisch-anatomischen Untersuchungen für practische Aerzte. Magdeburg: E. Fabricius for Rubach'sche Buchhandlung, 1846.

[4], viii, [2], 377, [1] p., [1] plate: ill.; 21 cm.

Provenance: Signed by the author for Rudolph Mannl in Carlsbad; Karlsbader Stadtbibliothek (bookplate).

Jakob Hugo Gerold (originally: Gerson), a well-known ophthalmologist of Aken on the Elbe and later district physician in Delitzsch, was a professor at the University in Giessen. He taught physiological optics, ophthalmoscopy, and ocular surgery and published several works in ophthalmiatrics specializing in amblyopia, cataract, and diseases of the retina. *"Die Lehre vom schwarzen Staar . . .* [contains Gerold's] concept of amaurosis or glaucoma and its cure. Wilhelm Roser (1817-1888) called this work *'a chaos of nonsequiturs'* (*Arch. f. Physiol. Heilk.* 1847, p. 96) and recommended the author to use a Latin dictionary so that in the future he would not confuse softening with sclerosis" (Hirschberg §498). Gerold's terminology is sometimes confusing indeed. He calls himself *"ein umfassender Kritik der Nomenklatur"* and describes his unique system of terms in the third chapter of the book.

AmEncOph VII:5369; BM 85:27; Hirsch II:727; Hirschberg §498; NUC 197:246; Pagel, col. 595-596.

Gerson, Jacob Hugo, 1814-1898.

See Gerold (151.1).

Gesner, Konrad, 1516-1565.

See Houllier (195).

152   Gibson, Benjamin, 1774-1812.

Practical observations on the formation of an artificial pupil, in several deranged states of the eye; to which are annexed, remarks on the extraction of soft cataracts, and those of the membraneous kind, through a puncture in the cornea. London: J. Haddock (Warrington) for Cadell & Davies, 1811.

[iii]-xiv, [2], [17]-155 p., 2 plates; 22 cm. (8vo)

In 1799, at the age of twenty-five, Gibson was called to

Manchester to become Charles White's assistant. White (1728-1813) was a distinguished Manchester surgeon whose midwifery text contained many original observations on the true nature of puerperal fever which anticipated the later work of Semmelweiss. Written late in the author's life and the only monograph published by Gibson, this work includes a valuable account of the history of the operation for artificial pupil. James Wardrop (400) published a biographical account of the author in the *Edinburgh Medical and Surgical Journal* 10:1-12 (1814).

Hirschberg §675-676.

153   Gibson, John Mason, fl. 1825-1835.

A condensation of matter upon the anatomy, surgical operations and treatment of diseases of the eye, together with remarks. Baltimore: W. R. Lucas, 1832.

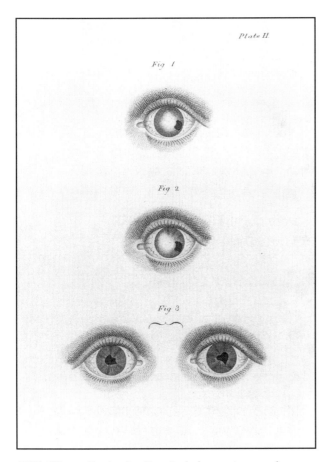

(152) Gibson, Benjamin. *Practical observations on the formation of an artificial pupil...*, 1811. Plate II. (13 x 22 cm.)

[2], 203, [13] p., 12 plates; 27 cm.

This is the second American book on ophthalmology, preceded only by Frick's *Treatise on the diseases of the eye* (Baltimore, 1823). Gibson admits the derivative nature of his work in the preface: "The work is one of compilation [and] the author's claims to originality do not extend father [*sic*] than too [*sic*] the construction of the plates." Historians of the eye are unanimous in their characterization of this book as a poorly written, ill-arranged and inaccurate work "that is scarcely ever heard of, and deserves oblivion" (Hubbell, p. 98-99). Cf. Harry Friedenwald, "The early history of ophthalmology and otology in Baltimore 1800-1850," *Johns Hopkins Hospital Bulletin* 8:184-189 (1897).

Hirschberg §749.

Gifftheil, Christoph Friedrich, respondent.

"De ulceribus corneae."

In Dissertationes medicae selectae Tubingenses (112) 2:141-174.

154   Gleize, Jean François, fl. 1763-1811.

Nouvelles observations pratiques sur les maladies de l'oeil et leur traitement; ouvrage fondé sur une nouvelle théorie; dans lequel l'auteur explique & concilie plusieurs méthodes d'opérer la cataracte, & propose différens instrumens nouveaux pour cette opération, ainsi que pour les diverses maladies qui affectent l'oeil. Paris: P. F. Didot, 1786.

vi, [xi]-xvi, 238 p., [3] plates: port.; 22 cm. (8vo)

One of the more reputable of the roving oculists of eighteenth century France, Gleize was an advocate and successful practitioner of the extraction operation in cases of cataract. His works are generally free from the pretentious claims which often characterize the writings of these itinerent oculists; however, he was not above using the popular press to extol his achievements. Laid into this copy is a broadside advertising his services in Paris where he undertook to operate for cataract gratuitously in cases of the genuinely poor. Also inserted is a tract by Gleize on the artificial nourishment of newborns.

Hirschberg §383; Wellcome III:125.

155   Gleize, Jean François, fl. 1763-1811.

Réglement de vie, ou comment doivent se gouverner ceux qui sont affligés de la foiblesse de la vue, avec les moyens de s'en préserver. Orléans: Jacob for Didot & Méquignon (Paris), 1787.

[4], vi, 180 p.; 22 cm. (8vo)

A treatise on ocular hygiene, originally bound as the second volume of a set which included the preceding work. The author was oculist to members of the French nobility and numbered among his patients the Count of Artois and the Duke of Orleans.

A tract against duelling by the same author is inserted in this volume.

Hirschberg §383; Wellcome III:125.

Gmelin, Johann Georg, 1709-1755, respondent.

"Ophthalmoxysis nov-antiqua."

In Dissertationes medicae selectae Tubingenses (112) 1:[1]-47.

Gmelin, Philipp Friedrich, 1721-1788, respondent.

"De hypopyo."

In Dissertationes medicae selectae Tubingenses (112) 1:48-110.

156 Goethe, Johann Wolfgang von, 1749-1832.

Beyträge zur Optik. [Facsimile.] Hildesheim: G. Olms, 1964 (Weimar: Industrie-comptoirs, 1791-92).

2 pts. in 1 v. ([4], 62; [4], 30, [2] p.): ill.; 17 cm. + 2 folding sheets (55 x 38 cm.) + 1 packet of 27 cards (10 x 6 cm.) + 1 booklet.

Issued in a case with Schuster (336).

"Goethe, in spite of his inadequate mathematical knowledge, opposed the Newtonian theory of colour and light. In this volume he outlines his own theories on the origin of light and colour and the principles of light. He carried out many experiments with the help of a prism and beams of light" (BOA I:78).

BOA I:78; Hirschberg §1010.

156.1 Gondret, Louis François, 1776-1855.

Mémoire sur le traitement de la cataracte. Deuxiéme édition. Paris: Ladvocat, Crévot, Gabon, 1826.

[4], xv, [1], [5]-38 p.; 21 cm.

Louis François Gondret is remembered chiefly as a disreputable figure in the history of ophthalmology, despite having been a physician to the Court of Justice in Paris, a member of

the Royal Academy of Medicine, and an author of numerous ophthalmological works. His reputation stems from his having introduced a *traitement syncipital* of the cataract, i.e. cauterization of the occiput with red hot copper or with his ammoniac ointment. For this he has been branded a "scoundrel" (Gilbert Breschet, 1835; cf. Hirschberg §555) and a "charlatan" (AmEncOph, p. 5605). This volume contains fifteen of Gondret's cataract case reports, including several instances for the use of his *pommade ammonicale.* An English translation was published in 1838.

Callisen VII:298; Hirsch II:795; Hirschberg §555; NUC 205:528 (1828, 1829 eds.).

Gosselin, Leon, 1815-1887, jt. author.

See Denonvilliers (98).

Gouan, Antoine, 1733-1821.

See Pellier de Quengsy (292).

157 Gouillin, Jean Antoine.

Hygiène des yeux ou traité des moyens d'entretenir la vue, de fortifier la vue faible, et de conserver la santé en général; précédé d'un abrégé de l'Exposé de la méthode résolutive, publié en 1838, pour la guérison des maladies des yeux, même de celles qui sont réputées incurables, sans opération et sans l'emploi des instruments tranchants . . . deuxième édition, considérablement augmentée. Paris: for the author, 1843.

[4], 256 p.; 22 cm.

Explanation of the author's *méthode résolutive*, in which he proposes to cure heretofore incurable maladies of the eye by the local application of liquid medicaments which "stimulent en même temps les vaisseaux lymphatiques absorbans, et les rendent propres à débarrasser les membranes et les humeurs de l'oeil des fluides épanchés et de l'albumine concrétée qui troublent leur transparence" (p. 6). A second part deals with ocular hygiene in general.

Hirschberg §470; Wellcome III:141.

Gowers, Sir William Richard, 1845-1915, trans.

See Pagenstecher (281.1).

158   Gowers, Sir William Richard, 1845-1915.

A manual and atlas of medical ophthalmoscopy. London: J. & A. Churchill, 1879.

xi, [1], 352 p., XVI plates: ill.; 23 cm.

Almost from the beginning Gowers's principal medical interests lay in neurology, culminating in his great work on the diseases of the nervous system in 1886. His first book of any real importance, however, was this manual on ophthalmoscopy. The plates were all prepared after the author's own sepia drawings, which, according to the *Dictionary of National Biography* (1912-21, p. 222), "made them for long the standard illustrations on the subject." Ten of the sixteen plates are autotypes, which Gowers preferred, since "by it a more exact representation of delicate pathological appearances can be obtained than by chromolithography" (Pref., p. [iii]).

BOA I:80; DicNatBio 1912-21, p. 222; Hirsch II:814.

159   Gowers, Sir William Richard, 1845-1915.

A manual and atlas of medical ophthalmoscopy. . . . Third edition revised throughout, with numerous additions and additional illustrations. Edited with the assistance of Marcus Gunn. Philadelphia: P. Blakiston, Son & Co., 1890.

xi, [1], 330 p., XII plates: ill.; 22 cm.

In the preface to the third edition Gowers writes, "The whole work has been subjected to a revision sufficiently thorough to involve additions and alterations on almost every page and in almost every paragraph" (p. [v]). In this edition the four lithographic plates that followed the autotypes in the first edition have been engraved as illustrations in the text.

Osler 2786.

Graefe, Albrecht von, 1828-1870.

Three memoirs on iridectomy in certain forms of iritis, choroiditis, and glaucoma.

In Selected monographs (338.1).

Graefe, Albrecht von, 1828-1870.

See Jaeger (204.1).

160   Graefe, Albrecht von, 1828-1870.

Clinical lectures by Professor A. von Graefe, on amblyopia and amaurosis and the extraction of cataract. Boston: D. Clapp & Son, 1866.

iv, [5]-86, [2] p.; 23 cm.

Provenance: Inscribed by the translator to Dr. A. A. Gould; —Medical Society of the County of Kings (bookplate).

The *Clinical lectures* were translated by Hasket Derby from the *Klinische Monatsblätter für Augenheilkunde* for the *Boston Medical and Surgical Journal* in 1865. "Its publication is undertaken for the two-fold object of introducing Albrecht von Graefe to the American medical public as a clinical teacher, and of exhibiting the progress which has been made in the exploration of one of the most obscure departments of the ophthalmic science, and for which we are indebted to his genius and industry" (Pref., p. iii-iv).

"Albrecht von Graefe . . . [is generally considered] the creator of the modern surgery of the eye, and indeed the greatest of all eye surgeons. . . . [He] introduced the operation of iridectomy in the treatment of iritis, iridochoroiditis, and glaucoma (1855-62), made the operation for strabismus viable (1857), and improved the treatment of cataract (1865-68). . . . He applied the ophthalmoscope to the study of the amblyopias in functional disorders . . . ; made a brilliant diagnosis of the retinal artery as the cause of the case of sudden blindness (1859), and proceeded to point out that most cases of blindness and impaired vision connected with cerebral disorders are traceable to optic neuritis rather than to paralysis of the optic nerve (1860). . . . Graefe was also the founder of modern knowledge of sympathetic ophthalmia (1866) and the semeiology of ocular paralyses (1866), described conical cornea (1854), . . . and first noted the stationary condition of the upper eyelid, when the eyeball is rolled up and down in exophthalmic goiter (Greafe's sign, 1864)" (Garrison, p. 608-609).

BM 90:156; NUC 209:228.

161   Graefe, Albrecht von, 1828-1870.

Sehen und Sehorgan. Berlin: C. G. Lüderitz'sche Verlagsbuchhandlung (A. Charisius), 1867.

48 p.: ill.; 22 cm.

Issued as part of the *Sammlung gemeinverständlicher wissenschaftlicher Vorträge* (Serie II, Heft 27).

Graefe, Alfred Karl, 1830-1899, ed.

See Handbuch der gesammten Augenheilkunde (176).

162   Grassus, Benvenutus, fl. 12th cent.

De oculis eorumque egritudinibus et curis. Translated with notes and illustrations from the first printed edition, Ferrara, 1474 A.D. Stanford: Stanford University Press, 1929.

xiii, [l], 101, [3] p., [5] plates; 23 cm.

English translation of the earliest printed book on ophthalmology. "Grassi was the most celebrated ophthalmic surgeon of the Middle Ages" (G-M 5816).

Hirschberg §291.

162.1   Gregoris, Luigi de.

Delle cateratte dei ciechi nati e della diversità della loro specie osservazioni teorico-cliniche del professore di chirurgia e di oftalmiatria Luigi de Gregoris Romano. Rome: Tipografia Perego-Salvioniana, 1826.

viii, 73, [1] p., [1] plate; 20 cm. (8vo)

Wellcome III:162.

162.2   Griffiths, Elijah, d. 1847.

An essay on ophthalmia, or inflammation of the eyes. Philadelphia: H. Maxwell, 1804.

26 p.; 23 cm.

A doctoral dissertation on endophthalmitis submitted to the University of Pennsylvania June 1, 1804. Elijah Griffiths, an honorary member of the Philadelphia Medical Society, was a physician in the Philadelphia Almshouse, which later became the Philadelphia General Hospital.

Austin 845; NUC 218:580; Reynolds 1732; Shaw 6424.

162.3   Grimaldi, Francesco Maria, 1618-1663.

Physico-mathesis de lumine, coloribus et iride. Bologna: Heirs of V. Benatius, 1665.

[20], 535, [17] p.: diagrs.; 24 cm. (4to)

The first and only edition of Grimaldi's work on the discovery of the diffraction of light was edited by Girolamo Bernia and published two years after the author's death. Grimaldi, a Jesuit professor of mathematics at Bologna, summarized his optical observations in this work which is a classic in the history of optics. This work marks the first scientific attempt to establish a comprehensive wave theory of light.

Hirschberg §451.

163   Grimaldi, Francesco Maria, 1618-1663.

Physico-mathesis de lumine coloribus et iride 1665. Facsimile reprint. London: Dawsons of Pall Mall, 1966 (Bologna: Heirs of V. Benatius, 1665).

[24], 535, [17] p.: diagrs.; 27 cm.

Grosseteste, Roger.

See Lacepiera (222).

164   Grossius, Thomas.

Lectiones de morbis capitis, et thoracis, in quibus infinita problemata, plures etiam Hyppocratis, Galeni, Avicennae, & aliorum auctorum controversiae explicantur, concilianturve. Accessit quaestio, an vinum nive refrigeratum propinari debeat. Ferrara: F. Succius, 1628.

[16], 516 p.; 23 cm.

Grossius wrote this treatise on diseases affecting the parts of the head while professor of medicine at Ferrara. The *De morbis capitis* includes sections on the maladies of the brain, ears and nose, as well as the eyes (p.281-323). References to Greek and Arabic medical authorities abound on every page. In accordance with this medical tradition, Grossius maintains that affections of the eye result from either a want or too great an abundance of the *spiritus visiuus*, a humor that proceeds from the brain. Thus, cataract is the concretion of such a humor before the lens; inflammations result from its collection in the eye and subsequent heating, etc.

165   Guépin, Ange, 1805-1873.

Nouvelles études théoriques & cliniques sur les maladies des yeux, l'oeil et la vision. Paris: Germer-Baillière, 1857.

88 p.; 22 cm.

Guépin intended to publish five fascicules in a series entitled *Nouvelles études théoriques et cliniques sur les maladies des yeux, l'oeil et la vision.* Only this first fascicule appears ever to have been published.

166   Guérin, Pierre, 1740-1827.

Traité sur les maladies des yeux, dans lequel l'auteur, après avoir exposé les différentes méthodes de faire l'opération de la cataracte, propose un instrument nouveau qui fixe l'oeil tout à la fois & opere la section de la cornée. Lyons: V. Reguilliat, 1769.

xvi, 445, [7] p., [l] plate; 17 cm. (12mo)

This first published work by Guérin has been characterized by Julius Hirschberg as *eine taube nuss* ("an empty nut"). As with so many works on cataract of this period the author proposed a modification of the extraction operation using an instrument of his own design. Haller (Haller Chir II:551) observed that while the arrangement of the book was less than satisfactory, the author possessed much experience. An extended obituary of Guérin was published in *Notice des travaux de la Soçiété de Médecine de Bordeaux*, 83-113 (1827).

BOA I:84; Hirschberg §377; Waller 3804; Wellcome III:176.

Guérin, Pierre, 1740-1827.
See Pellier de Quengsy (292).

167   Guillemard, Pierre-Louis.

Dissertatio medica de suffusione. . . . Praeside . . . Francisco Boissier de Sauvages. . . . Avignon: Joseph Tilan, 1760.

27 p.; 23 cm. (4to)

The Latin *suffusio* is usually translated "cataract", but is used in this work to refer to the phenomenon we term photopsia. This dissertation was submitted under the supervision of François Boissier de Sauvages de la Croix (1706-1767) and published at Avignon.

168   Guillemeau, Jacques, 1550-1613.

Traité des maladies de l'oeil, qui sont en nombre de cent treize, ausquelles il est suject. Paris: C. Massé, 1585.

[18], 101 (i.e. 100), [1] leaves; 17 cm. (8vo)

"His book was an epitome of the existing knowledge on the subject, chiefly from Greek and Arabian sources" (G-M 5818). A sonnet by Ambroise Paré addressed to the author praises his pupil and recalls their collaboration at the Hotel Dieu, on the battlefield, and as surgeons to the King.

G-M 5818; Hirschberg §319; Waller 3855.

169   Guillié, Sébastien, 1780-1865.

Essai sur l'instruction des aveugles, ou exposé analytique des procédés employés pour les instruire. Paris: 'les aveugles', 1817.

224 p., 22 plates: diagrs.; 20 cm. (8vo)

Guillié established the first ophthalmological clinic in France and became director of the Institution Royale des Jeunes Aveugles in Paris. The Institution, founded by Haüy (181) in 1785, was the first such school for the blind in the world. The author chronicles the philanthropic deeds directed toward the blind up to that time and describes the first attempts at special graphic methods for the use of the blind. Of particular interest is the account of his methods of instructing the blind in various crafts. The plates show blind craftsmen engaged in a variety of skilled occupations. Guillié endeavored to understand and encourage the communication which he observed between blind and deaf-mute children at the time when the two institutions were united (p. 170-177). There is a correction by the author handwritten in the margin on p. 97.

Hirschberg §554; Waller 3858; Wellcome III:180.

170   Gullstrand, Allvar, 1862-1930.

Allgemeine Theorie der monochromatischen Aberrationen und ihre nächsten Ergebnisse für die Ophthalmologie. Uppsala: Akademische Buchdruckerei (E. Berling), 1900.

[6], 204 p.: ill.; 29 cm.

Professor of ophthalmology at the University of Uppsala at the time this work was written, Gullstrand later became professor of physics and physical optics, until retiring in 1927. The author offers here his general theory of monochromatic aberrations. For his work on the diffraction of light by lenses applied to the eye Gullstrand was awarded the Nobel Prize in 1911, the only ophthalmologist yet to receive this honor. Charles Snyder has remarked that "next to Helmholtz, Gullstrand contributed more than anyone else to a mathematical understanding of the human eye as an optical system" (Snyder, p. 149).

G-M 5945; Hirschberg §868; Pybus 853; Waller 3872.

Gunn, Robert Marcus, 1850-1909, ed.
See Gowers (159).

171   Guthrie, George James, 1785-1856.

A treatise on the operations for the formation of an artificial pupil; in which the morbid states of the eye requiring them, are considered; and the mode of performing the operation, adapted to each peculiar case, fully explained; with an account of the opinions and practice of the different foreign and British authors who have written on the subject. London: F.

(6) Aguilon, François d'. *Opticorum libri sex philosophis iuxtà ac mathematicis utiles*, 1613. Copperplate illustration on
p. 452. (14.3 x 10 cm.)

Dutton for Longmans and Callow, Burgess & Hill, 1819.

xix, [1], 209, [3] p., 2 plates; 23 cm. (8vo)

In 1817 the author, who had accompanied Wellington in the Napoleonic campaigns, presented a course of lectures on the anatomy and the diseases of the eye, the first such systematic lectures in England on this subject. Guthrie wrote this book to provide students with a conspectus of both English and European opinions with respect to the operations for artificial pupil. Guthrie's introduction takes the form of a careful overview of the history of this surgical procedure.

BOA I:86; Hirschberg §655-656.

172 Guthrie, George James, 1785-1856.

Lectures on the operative surgery of the eye or, an historical and critical inquiry into the methods recommended for the cure of cataract, for the formation of an artificial pupil, &c. &c. &c. containing a new method of operating for cataract by extraction, which obviates all the difficulties and dangers hitherto attendant on that operation: being the substance of that part of the author's course of lectures on the principles and practice of surgery which relates to the operations on that organ. 2d ed. London: C. Wood for Burgess & Hill, 1827.

xxvii, [1], 554 p., 7 plates; 23 cm.

"Guthrie founded the Royal Westminster Ophthalmic Hospital, London, in 1816. He was the earliest teacher of the subject in the British Isles. The above includes important work on the artificial pupil" (G-M 5845). The first edition appeared in 1823.

Hirschberg §655-656; Waller 3884; Wellcome II:182.

173 Haase, Johann Gottlob, 1739-1801.

Ordinis medicorum. . . procancellarius D. Ioannes Gottlob Haase. . . panegyrin medicam. . . indixit et de narium morbis alteram commentationem scripsit. Leipzig: S. Linck, 1797.

xi, [1] p., [2] plates; 24 cm. (4to)
Bound with Rosenmüller (314).

Haase, Rosenmüller's teacher, published this panegyric and dissertation on the diseases of the nose to accompany Rosenmüller's dissertation. The plates were designed by Rosenmüller and the work includes his vita.

Hackley, Charles Elihu, 1836-1925, ed. & trans.

See Stellwag von Carion (354, 355).

174 Haguenot, Henri, 1687-1775.

Tractatus de morbis capitis externis. Geneva: H. A. Gosse & 'socios', 1751.

[6], 280 p.; 18 cm. (12mo)

Haguenot, professor of medicine at Montpellier, wrote this work on the diseases of the external parts of the head for the use of his students. Considerable attention is given to diseases of the eye (p. 2-134), but it was a work of secondary interest and Haguenot failed to cite those authors on whose work he so heavily drew. The Becker Library (Goldstein Collection) also holds a copy of the duodecimo edition published in Avignon in the same year.

Hirschberg §385.

175 Hall, John Charles, 1816-1876.

On the nature and treatment of some of the more important diseases, medical & surgical, including the principal diseases of the eye. . . . Second edition, enlarged. London: J. Churchill, 1844.

[6], [v]-viii, 247 p.; 23 cm.

Physician to the Sheffield Public Hospital and lecturer at the Sheffield School of Medicine, Hall was a frequent contributor to the *British Medical Journal* and the author of half a dozen medical monographs. The present work was originally published in 1843 under the title *Clinical remarks on the diseases of the eye.* It is divided into two parts: the first on the diseases of the eye, and the second on non-ocular maladies.

Hirsch III:31.

Haller, Albrecht von, 1708-1777, ed.

See Boerhaave (53).

Hampel, E.

See Stellwag von Carion (356).

176 Handbuch der gesammten Augenheilkunde.

Herausgegeben von Prof. Arlt in Wien . . . [et al.]. . . . Redigirt von Prof. Alfred Graefe und Prof. Theodor Saemisch. Leipzig: W. Engelmann, 1874-80.

7 v.: ill.; 23 cm.

"In the literature of ophthalmology there stands as a monument of greatness unequalled by any other work, the *Handbuch der gesammten Augenheilkunde*" (Chance, p. 155). The *Handbuch* was the collaborative effort of some of the greatest German-speaking ophthalmologists of the nineteenth century, under the editorship of Alfred Graefe and Theodor Saemisch.

Chance, p. 155; Hirschberg §1102.

177 Hannover, Adolph, 1814-1894.

Das Auge. Beiträge zur Anatomie, Physiologie und Pathologie dieses Organs. Leipzig: L. Voss, 1852.

[4], 159, [1] p., IV plates; 21 cm.

Danish born, Hannover received his medical education at Paris and in Berlin. He was a prolific author of works on microscopic technique and on the anatomy and physiology of the eye. The present work is a collection of previously published articles originally offered in book form in a Danish edition of 1850. In 1856 and again in 1878 Hannover received the Monthyon Prize of the Institut de France for his investigations into the anatomy and pathology of the eye.

Hirsch III:54.

178 Harder, Matthaeus.

De cataracta, seu suffusione. Basel: J. Bertsche, 1675.

[24] p.; 19 cm. (4to)

An early dissertation on cataract, presented at the University of Basel. Harder, a native of Schaffhausen (Switzerland) was a relative of J. J. Harder (1656-1711), who distinguished himself as an anatomist and who here added a poem in praise of the author.

Hirschberg §1168.

179 Hartmann, Johann, 1568-1631.

Anthropologia physico-medico-anatomica … in qua totius humani corporis mechanica structura describitur, partiumque usus, atque operandi modus examinatur. Opus non inutile, maximè medicinam exercentibus cum indice rerum notabilium, quae pertractantur. Venice: J. B. Tramontini, 1696.

[14], 350, [2] p.; 24 cm. (4to)

The first to hold an established chair of chemistry at a European university, Hartmann, a chemist in the Paracelsian tradition, sought to introduce chemical therapeutics into the practice of medicine. The use of mercury in cases of cataract and incurable blindness is mentioned in the chapter on the eye (p. 295-315). The work is essentially a compendium of anatomy with physiological hypotheses.

179.1 Hasner, Josef, Ritter von Artha, 1818-1892.

Klinische Vorträge über Augenheilkunde. Prague: F. A. Credner, 1860-65.

3 pts. in 1 v. (vi, [2], 119; [2], [121]-217; [2], [219]-324 p.): ill.; 23 cm.

Joseph Hasner, born and educated in Prague, succeeded Ferdinand Arlt as first assistant in Johann Fischer's eye clinic, and was professor of ophthalmology at the University of Prague from 1852 to 1884. He discovered "the valve of Hasner" (i.e., plica lacrimalis), and introduced the theory that myopia is caused by a stretching of the eyeball due to pulling on the posterior pole by the optic nerve. Hasner was on the editorial board of the *Prager Medicinische Vierteljahrschrift*, and published numerous ophthalmological journal articles and monographs. This volume contains his clinical lectures in three parts: I. diseases of the sclera and the eyeballs; lectures on eye glasses and ophthalmoscopy; II. diseases of the cornea; III. diseases of the system of lenses.

AmEncOph VIII:5704; BM 99:294; Hirsch III:82; NUC 234:164.

Haug, Philipp Adam, respondent.

"De ocul [*sic*] artificiali, ekblepharo & ypoblepharo." *In* Dissertationes medicae selectae Tubingenses (112) 1:250-282.

180 Haugsted, Frederik Christian, 1804-1866.

Læren om Øiets Sygdomme, overeenstemmende med Videnskabens nyeste Fremskridt, efter de berømteste Øienlægers Værker paa Dansk bearbeitet. Copenhagen: P. R. Jørgensen for C. A. Reitzels, 1834.

viii, 331 p., [1] plate; 18 cm.

A compendium on the diseases of the eye from the writings of some of the most important contemporary German, English, French and Italian authors. Haugsted was *Privat-Docent* at the University of Copenhagen. This particular work was intended as a manual for his students in ophthalmology.

Callisen XXVIII:411; Hirsch III:89; Hirschberg §863.

181 Haüy, Valentin, 1745-1822.

Essai sur l'éducation des aveugles, ou exposé de différens moyens, vérifiés par l'expérience, pour les mettre en état de lire, à l'aide du tact, d'imprimer des livres dans lesquels il puissent prendre des connoissances de langues, d'histoire, de géographie, de musique, &c., d'exécuter différens travaux relatifs aux métiers, &c. Paris: Clousier, 1786.

vii, [1], 126, 15, [37] p.; 25 cm. (4to)

"Haüy founded the first school for the blind. To him belongs the honour of being the first to emboss paper as a means of reading for the blind. His *Essai* originated modern methods of teaching and caring for blind persons" (G-M 5833). The *Essai* is printed on only one side of each leaf, the blank sides being pasted together. The type is the disconnected "caractères en relief" used at the Institution for teaching the "enfans aveugles." At a special audience at Versailles on December 26, 1786, Haüy and his pupils presented a number of specially bound copies of this work to Louis XVI and members of the royal family. This copy was presented to Madame Adélaïde (1732-1800), daughter of Louis XV and Marie Leczinska and Louis XVI's aunt. Madam Adelaïde's library of more than 10,000 volumes was sold at the time of the French Revolution. Her books were uniformly bound in red morocco by Fournier of Versailles and Pierre Vente of Paris with her coat-of-arms in gold on the covers.

Hirschberg §407; Olivier, 26. ser., 3. pt.

Haüy, Valentin, 1745-1822.

An essay on the education of the blind; or, an explication of the different means, confirmed by successful experiments, to render them capable of reading by the assistance of touch, and of printing books, in which they may obtain the knowledge of languages, of history, of geography, of music, &c. of performing the different offices necessary in mechanical employments, &c. Paris: Printed in the original by blind children, 1786.

In Blacklock (51), p. [217]-262.

Haüy, Valentin, 1745-1822.

See also Do you want a friend? (114.1).

Hays, Isaac, 1796-1879, ed.

See Jones (213) and Lawrence (233).

181.1 Heister, Lorenz, 1683-1758.

De cataracta glaucomate et amaurosi tractatio in qua multae novae opiniones & inventa contra vulgatas medicorum, chirurgorum, philosophorum nec non mathematicorum sententias continentur. . . . Altdorf: J. G. Kohles, 1713.

[16], 368 p., II plates; 17 cm. (8vo)

Heister, the founder of scientific surgery (as well as of ophthalmology) in Germany, is erroneously credited in the *Dictionary of scientific biography* as having discovered the true

(181.1) Heister, Lorenz. *De cataracta glaucomate et amaurosi tractatio*, 1713. Frontispiece. (8 x 14 cm.)

cause of cataract. That cataract is an opacity of the lens had been maintained by a few physicians even before Maître-Jan adopted this thesis or Brisseau published his classic monograph (63) establishing cataract's true nature. To Heister, however, belongs the credit of being the first German physician to support the startling new theory, while giving full credit for its re-discovery to the *duo industrii Galli*, Maître-Jan and Brisseau. This book was immediately swept into the vortex of the controversy between the supporters of the two Frenchmen and their opponents, notably Woolhouse (423), Hecquet and Hovius.

Blake, p. 204; DicSciBio VI:231; Hirsch III:141; Hirschberg §331, 410.

182   Heister, Lorenz, 1683-1758.

Apologia et uberior illustratio systematis sui de cataracta glaucomate et amaurosi contra Wolhusii ocularii Parisiensis cavillationes & objectiones itemque Parisiensis eruditorum diarii iniquam censuram. Altdorf: J. G. Kohles, 1717.

[30], 307, [1] p., [1] plate; 17 cm. (8vo)

Heister was the first German physician to support the thesis of Maître-Jan (243-44) and Brissseau (63) that the true nature of cataract was an opacity of the crystalline lens. Heister's opinion dates from 1711 when his first dissertation on the subject appeared. He published supporting works in 1712 and 1713 and in the present work he defended this view against his critics, notably Woolhouse (423) and Andry. Woolhouse held that cataract consisted of a "thickened humor" or membrane in a purely imaginary cataract space between the pupil and the lens. An engraved frontispiece presents a classic illustration of couching for cataract in a richly appointed eighteenth century drawing room.

Hirschberg §410; Waller 4235.

183   Heister, Lorenz, 1683-1758.

Institutiones chirurgicae, in quibus quidquid ad rem chirurgicam pertinet, optima et novissima ratione pertractatur. . . . Opus quadraginta fere annorum, nunc demum, post aliquot editiones germanica lingua evulgatas, in exterorum gratiam latine altera vice longe auctius atque emendatius publicatum. Amsterdam: Jansson-Waesberge, 1750.

2 v. ([4], viii, 56, [8], 599, [1] p., 19 plates; [2], 603-1187, [52] p., 21 plates): port.; 25 cm. (4to)

Heister emerged as the outstanding German surgeon of the first half of the seventeenth century and his textbook of sur-

gery was accepted throughout Europe. An extensive section on surgery of the eye and the eye lids (p. 507-599) presents a full picture of early eighteenth century ophthalmic surgery. This work first appeared in 1718 and was reissued frequently in Latin and the major European languages until the last edition in 1779.

Hirschberg §410; Wellcome III:237.

184   Heister, Lorenz, 1683-1758, praeses.

De tunica oculi choroidea . . . publice defendet Joannes Sigismundus Leincker. . . . Venice: A. Bortoli, 1764.

xvi, 64 p., [l] plate; 17 cm. (8vo)

Third edition of a dissertation by Johann Sigismund Leincker (1724-1788), much augmented by Heister, for his medical degree at Helmstaedt. Heister himself published a dissertation on the anatomy of the choroidea of the same title in 1708. The second edition of this dissertation was published in Venice in 1752.

Blake, p. 204.

Heliodorus of Larissa, 2nd cent.

See Euclid (125).

185   Helmholtz, Hermann Ludwig Ferdinand von, 1821-1894.

Handbuch der physiologischen Optik. Leipzig: L. Voss, 1867.

xiv, 874, [4] p., XI plates: ill.; 23 cm.

The great classic of nineteenth century physiological optics, the *Handbuch* was issued in three parts between 1856 and 1866, prior to being published as a whole in 1867. The first part, issued when Helmholtz was professor of anatomy and physiology at Bonn, gives a detailed treatment of the dioptrics of the eye, the various imperfections of the lens system, his theory of accommodation, and a description of the ophthalmoscope. In the second part, issued in 1860, two years after Helmholtz had gone to Heidelberg, he revives Thomas Young's theory of color vision (423.1), and discusses the phenomena of irradiation, after images and contrast phenomena. The third part, issued toward the end of 1866, is an extended defense of his empiric theory of visual perception, an epistemological corollary to his physiology of vision.

Cushing H231; G-M 1513; Heirs 1010; Hirsch III:151; Hirschberg §1021; Waller 4299.

Helmholtz, Hermann Ludwig Ferdinand von, 1821-1894.

See also Festschrift (134.1).

Herz, Ludwig.

See Stellwag von Carion (357).

186   Heurne, Johan van, 1543-1601.

Praxis medicinae nova ratio, qua, libris tribus methodi ad praxin medicam, auditus facillimus aperitur ad omnes morbos curandos. Recognita & emendata ab auctore, & auctior ac melior reddita: ita ut iam extrema manu ficta, & manumissa ab eo fit. Leyden: F. Raphelengien for Officina Plantiniana, 1590.

[8], 518, [20] p., [3] tables; 21 cm. (4to)
Bound with Heurne (187, 188).

187   Heurne, Johan van, 1543-1601.

De morbis pectoris liber, editus post mortem auctoris, ab ejus filio Othone Heurnio. Leyden: F. Raphelengien for Officina Plantiniana, 1602.

Bound with Heurne (186, 188).

188   Heurne, Johan van, 1543-1601.

De morbis oculorum, aurium, nasi, dentium et oris, liber, editus post mortem auctoris, ab ejus filio Othone Heurnio. Leyden: F. Raphelengien for Officina Plantiniana, 1608.

[8], 96 (i.e. 66), [6] p.; 21 cm. (4to)
Bound with Heurne (186, 187).

Heurne studied medicine at Louvain, Paris, and Padua where he took his medical degree in 1571. A student of Fabricius ab Aquapendente, Heurne was a devoted admirer of Hippocrates and one of the restorers of Hippocratic medicine in the sixteenth century. As professor of medicine at Leyden he introduced clinical teaching of medicine as early as 1591 and was the first to undertake anatomical demonstrations on human cadavers. This work was edited and published posthumously by his son, Otto, who succeeded him at Leyden. The section on diseases of the eye (p. 1-33) is drawn for the most part from the writings of the ancients. While the provenance of this volume is uncertain, due to the partial obliteration of the title page inscription, this copy once belonged to a Jos. Barth of Vienna,

perhaps the oculist to Joseph II of the House of Hapsburg.

Heurne, Otto van 1577-1652, ed.

See Heurne (186, 187, 188).

189   Hewson, Thomas, 1783-1831.

Observations on the history and treatment of the ophthalmia accompanying the secondary forms of lues venerea. London: R. and A. Spottiswoode for Longmans, 1824.

xi, [1], 117 p., [1] plate; 21 cm.

A little-known treatise on venereal ophthalmia by a member of the Royal College of Surgeons in Ireland, professor of materia medica and pharmacy, and surgeon to Meath Hospital in Dublin. Despite unfavorable reviews in the leading journals the work went through three editions, the last appearing in 1836 under the title *Practical observations on the history, nature & treatment of the venereal diseases of the eye.* An extended review appeared in the *Edinburgh Medical and Surgical Journal* 23:358-378 (1825).

Hirschberg §637.

190   Heymann, Mme. Alfred.

Lunettes et lorgnettes de jadis. Paris: J. Leroy & Co., 1911.

x, [4], 65, [3], 58, [2] p., 24 plates: ill.; 34 cm.

"A limited edition [this is copy 286 of 300 numbered copies] of a work dealing with the history of spectacles, tracing their successive forms, and showing their anachronistic representation by medieval painters. A great number of historic and interesting examples are shown of spectacles, lorgnettes, quizzers, cases, etc." (BOA II:47).

Included is a facsimile of a seventeenth century treatise by Jacques Bourgeois on the preservation of sight, entitled "Advis aux curieux de la conservation de leur veüe" (Paris, 1645).

BOA II:47.

Himly, Ernst August Wilhelm, 1800-1881, ed.
See Himly (191).

191   Himly, Karl, 1772-1837.

Die Krankheiten und Missbildungen des menschlichen Auges und deren Heilung. Nach den hinterlassenen Papieren desselben herausgegeben und mit Zusätzen versehen von E. A. W. Himly. Berlin: B. G. H. Schmidt (Nordhausen) for A. Hirschwald, 1843.

2 v. ([2], xvi, 585, [1] p., [1] plate; viii, 521 p., 5 plates); 23 cm.

"Himly was professor of ophthalmology at Jena and later at Göttingen. He introduced clinical teaching in ophthalmology" (G-M 5857). This work was published posthumously by the author's son, Ernst August Wilhelm Himly (1800-1881), professor of physiology, comparative anatomy and legal medicine at Göttingen.

G-M 5857; Hirschberg §482; Waller 4483; Wellcome III:268.

Himly, Karl, 1772-1837.

See also Weiss (410.2).

192   Hippel, Eugen von, 1867-1939.

Ueber Siderosis Bulbi und die Beziehungen zwischen siderotischer und hämotogener Pigmentirung. Leipzig: W. Engelmann, 1894.

161 p.; 22 cm.

Hippel's *Habilitationsschrift* for the medical faculty at Heidelberg, while he was an assistant at the university eye clinic. It was published the same year as an article in Albrecht von Graefe's *Archiv für Ophthalmologie* (Bd. XL, Abt. 1:123-279, 1894).

Hoelder, Philipp Friedrich Benjamin, respondent.

"De staphylomate, vexato nomine, affectuque oculi difficili as intricato."

In Dissertationes medicae selectae Tubingenses (112) 1:168-250.

193   Hogg, Jabez, 1817-1899.

The ophthalmoscope; its mode of application explained, and its value shown, in the exploration of internal diseases affecting the eye. London: J. Churchill, 1858.

[6], 107 p., [1] plate: ill.; 20 cm.

"I believe the instrument destined to open out a new era in ophthalmic medicine," wrote Hogg in the preface to this book, the first monograph on ophthalmoscopy to be published in the English language. It originally appeared as a series of articles

in *The Lancet* for 1857. A second edition was also published in 1858.

BOA I:100; Hirschberg §659.

194   Hogg, Jabez, 1817-1899.

A manual of ophthalmoscopic surgery; being a practical treatise on the use of the ophthalmoscope in diseases of the eye. . . . Third edition, re-written and enlarged. London: J. Churchill & Sons, 1863.

xii, 296 p., 4 plates; 23 cm.

The third edition of Hogg's *The ophthalmoscope* (193). Considerably larger than the previous two editions, the *Manual* received mixed reviews in the British medical press. Both the *British Medical Journal* and *The Lancet* gave the book favorable reviews, the latter's only criticism being that the plates "compare disadvantageously with those of other authors, continental and English." The *Ophthalmic Review* however was not so favorable. "The book is so utterly and unutterly bad," wrote the reviewer, "that we almost despair of being able to impart anything like a correct impression of its demerits." Fair or unfair, we offer one last quote, ". . . he pursues his way, breaking through concords, tumbling over relative pronouns, misquoting, mistaking, misspelling, ignoring optics, trampling upon physiology, and all the while sustained by an unconsciousness of his own ignorance, and by a serene faith in his own destiny, that unite to impart to his eccentricities an audacity that borders upon the sublime."

BOA I:100; Hirsch III:271; Hirschberg §659.

Hoin, Jean Jacques Louis, 1722-1772.

"Sur une espèce de cataracte nouvellement observée."

In Académie Royale de Chirurgie, *Mémoires* (2).

Holmes, Timothy, 1825-1907, trans.

See Selected monographs (338.1).

194.1   Holmgren, Alarik Frithiof, 1831-1897.

Om färgblindheten i dess förhållande till jernvägstrafiken och sjöväsendet. Uppsala: E. Berling, 1877.

[4], 172, [2] p., [1] color plate: ill.; 22 cm.

Alarik Frithiof Holmgren was professor of physiology at the

Gio. Batta Piazzetta inv.   Marco Pitteri Scolp.

(7) Algarotti, Francesco. *Il Newtonianismo per le dame ovvero dialoghi sopra a luce e i colori*,
1737. Frontispiece. (13 x 19 cm.)

University of Uppsala and also the founder of the first physiological research laboratory in Sweden. One of the first Swedish medical educators specializing in optics, he gave special consideration to color-blindness and stimulated an entirely new branch of literature on defective vision. His test for color vision, the Holmgren test, consisted of selecting skeins of woolen yarns of various colors, shades, tints, and grays to match three standard test skeins. "A serious railway accident in Sweden in 1875 was believed by Holmgren to be due to colour-blindness, and resulted in the above important paper dealing with the condition and its relation to railway and maritime traffic" (G-M 5916).

G-M 5916 (cited as an article in *Upsala Läkaref. Förh.* 12:171-251, 267-358; 1876-77); Hirsch III:280 (1878 German ed.); Hirschberg §869 (1878 German ed.); Waller 4856.

Holscher, Georg Philipp, 1792-1852.
See Neue Bibliothek (272.1).

194.2   Horner, William Edmonds, 1793-1853.

Description of a small muscle at the internal commissure of the eyelids. Philadelphia: W. Fry, 1824.

14 p., [1] plate; 22 cm.

After serving as army surgeon in the war of 1812, Horner was an anatomy prosector under Caspar Wistar, J. S. Dorsey, and P. S. Physick at the University of Pennsylvania. In 1831 he succeeded Physick as professor of anatomy, and later was appointed dean of the medical school. His *Treatise on the descriptive anatomy of the human body* became a generally used textbook, and his *Treatise on pathological anatomy* is considered the first work on the subject written in the United States. "He made several advances in anatomy including the discovery of the *tensor tarsi* (Horner's muscle), a muscle in the lachrymal apparatus" (Heirs 1499), although both Hirschberg and Morton point out that this muscle was first described by J. F. M. Du Verney in 1749 and later by J. C. Rosenmüller in 1805 (G-M 1494, Hirschberg §751).

This work is Horner's second treatise on the *tensor tarsi* which was reprinted from the *Philadelphia Journal of the Medical and Physical Sciences* (May, 1824) and won the author acclaim for improvements over the observations of Du Verney and Rosenmüller (Hirschberg §751). The volume contains a plate, drawn and engraved by J. Drayton, illustrating the Horner's muscle.

AmEncOph VIII:6010 (cited as an article; see G-M); G-M 1494 (cited as an article in *Philad. J. Med. Phys. Sci.* 8:70-80; 1824); Hirsch III:301 (cited as an article; see G-M).

195   Houllier, Jacques, d. 1562.

Viaticum novum. De omnium fere particularium morborum curatione, liber, authoris innominati quidem, sed longè doctissimi, verè aureus & incomparabilis, nunc primùm in lucem editus per Casparum Wolphium. Zurich: C. Froschauer, 1565.

[8], 142, [1] leaves; 16 cm. (8vo)

A sixteenth century handbook for medical practitioners which contains three chapters on diseases of the eye—"De ophthalmia," "De debilitate visus," and "De cataracta" (leaves 32-40).

Caspar Wolf (1532-1601) discovered, edited, and published this work from a manuscript of unknown authorship. A Paris edition of the same year, however, was published as the work of Jacques Houllier whose manuscripts passed at his death to his students Didier Jacot, Louis Duret, and Antoine Valet for publication. Wolf acknowledged Houllier's authorship in the second Zurich edition (1578) which he also edited. The notice to the reader is by Konrad Gesner, an intimate friend of the author and a distinguished zoologist, physician and bibliographer.

Durling 2494.

196   Hovius, Jacobus, fl. 1702.

De circulari humorum ocularium motu. Utrecht: G. van de Water, 1702.

44 p., 3 plates; 21 cm. (4to)

The author's doctoral dissertation, defended at the University of Utrecht, which contains the discovery of the circle of anastomoses between the anterior branches of the *venae vorticosae*, present in the eyes of many mammals but not usually occurring in man. Ruysch described the same circuit in 1706 and Hovius, in defense of his prior discovery of what is now eponymously known as the "canal of Hovius," published his *Epistola apologetica.*

This dissertation also contains observations on the influx and efflux of the ocular humors as well as a method of measuring these fluxions.

BOA II:50; Hirschberg §330.

196.1   Hueck, Alexander Friedrich, 1802-1842.

Das Sehen, seinem äussern Processe nach entwickelt. Riga: J. F. Deubner; Göttingen: Dieterische Buchhandlung, 1830.

146, [2] p.; 21 cm.
Provenance: Goethe-Sammlung, Günther Schmid (book-plate).

Completing his studies in Berlin, München, and Paris, A. F. Hueck became a professor of anatomy at the University of Tartu, Estonia, where he taught anatomy until his early death in 1842. In addition to several anatomical and physiological works, he published in the fields of paleontology, anthropology, and archeology. His ophthalmological investigations specialized in the crystalline lens and in ocular rotation.

This work is a systematic treatise on the visual process involving optical, physical, and physiological aspects. However, the author's general approach to his topic is somewhat philosophical as he talks about objective and subjective sight and discusses the phenomenon of vision in an almost existentialistic manner. References to classics of medicine and natural philosophy also bear witness to Hueck's unique "optical philosophy," as well as the motto of his book:

> Wär' nicht das Auge sonnenhaft,
> Wie könnten wir das Licht erblicken?
> Läg' nicht in uns des Gottes eigne Kraft,
> Nie würd' uns Göttliches entzücken.
>
> Goethe

AmEncOph VIII:6061; BM 108:445; Hirsch III:324; NUC 258:233.

Huette, Charles, jt. author.
See Bernard (46).

197 Ḥunayn ibn Isḥāq al-Ibādī, 809?-873.
The book of the ten treatises on the eye, ascribed to Hunain ibn Is-haq (809-877 A.D.). The earliest existing systematic text-book of ophthalmology. The Arabic text edited from the only two known manuscripts, with an English translation and glossary by Max Meyerhof. Cairo: Government Press, 1928.

[2], liii, [3], 227, [3], [230] p., [3] plates: ill.; 25 cm.

The Arabs were the first to make a speciality of ophthalmology and much of their work remained authoritative until the early modern period. Ḥunayn's treatise, written over a period of thirty years, was the first systematic textbook in Arabic literature. He has been called the "Erasmus of the Arabic Renaissance," for much of our present knowledge of Greek medicine, and particularly Galen's works, is dependent on his critical collations and translations. Meyerhof was the first to collate and publish Ḥunayn's *Ten treatises* in its entirety.

These treatises contain extracts of all the passages from the works of Galen concerning the eye. The last treatise contains collyrium prescriptions taken from the books of Galen and from his compilers, Oribasius and Paulus Aegineta.

198 Huygens, Christiaan, 1629-1695.
Traité de la lumière. Avec un discours de la cause de la pesanteur, 1690. Facsimile reprint. London: Dawsons of Pall Mall, 1966 (Leyden: P. van der Aa, 1690).

[10], 180 p.: ill.; 19 cm.

The classical formulation of the wave theory of light and the explanation of reflection, refraction, and polarization. Overshadowed by the corpuscular theory of Newton (273), it was largely neglected until 1802, when Thomas Young (423.1) recovered and exploited it to explain optical interference. Two states of the two title pages are known. This facsimile is the state with Huygens's name in full on both title pages; the other issue carries only the initials C. H. D. Z. in place of the full name.

Hirschberg §452-454.

199 Huygens, Christiaan, 1629-1695.
Opuscula postuma, quae continent Dioptricam, Commentarios de vitris figurandis, Dissertationem de corona & parheliis, Tractatum de motu, De VI centrifuga, Descriptionem automati planetarii. Leyden: C. Boutesteyn, 1703.

[20], 460 p., [24] plates: ill.; 20 cm. (4to)

Six posthumous works by the great physicist and mathematician, edited by professors De Volder of Leyden and Fullenius of Franeker in accordance with Huygens's will. The bulk of the work consists of *Dioptrica*, an exhaustive study of optics, published just one year before Newton's epoch-making work (273). A large part of this treatise is devoted to the theory of telescopes and microscopes and, next to his *Traité de la lumière* (198), it stands as Huygens's most important contribution to optics. The author was the first to propound and develop what is now known as the wave theory of light.

Hirschberg §452-454.

Ivanov, Aleksandr, 1836-1880.
See Wecker (408.1).

200 Jackson, Edward, 1856-1942.
Skiascopy and its practical application to the study of refraction. Philadelphia: The Edwards &

Docker Co., 1895.

112 p.: ill.; 23 cm.

Edward Jackson's work on skiascopy, an obsolete term for retinoscopy, is one of the best productions of nineteenth century American ophthalmic literature. Although as early as the 1860s the mirror of the ophthalmoscope was used to detect regular astigmatism, the shadow test itself was not introduced until 1873, in an article by Ferdinand Cuignet in the *Recueil d'ophthalmologie*, in which he gave an account of the test using the plane mirror as a practical means of measuring errors of refraction. Jackson himself popularized the use of the plane mirror rather than the concave.

Chance, p. 106; Hirschberg §1031.

201   Jackson, Edward, 1856-1942.

A manual of the diagnosis and treatment of the diseases of the eye. Philadelphia: W. B. Saunders, 1900.

604 p.: ill.; 21 cm.

While convalescing from an attack of diphtheria, which caused him prolonged paralysis of one leg and the focusing muscles of the eyes, Jackson became interested in the disorders of vision. Upon resuming his medical practice in 1884, he devoted himself largely to ophthalmology, becoming professor of ophthalmology at the Philadelphia Polyclinic and surgeon to the Wills Eye Hospital. Jackson moved to Denver in 1899 where he continued his professional activities. He founded the *Ophthalmic Yearbook* in 1909, which he edited until 1917.

Jacque, Charles, 1813-1894.

See Print 12.

202   Jaeger, Eduard, Ritter von Jaxtthal, 1818-1884.

Ueber die Behandlung des grauen Staares an der ophthalmologischen Klinik der Josephs-Akademie. Vienna: C. Ueberreuter, 1844.

x, 11-70 p.; 20 cm.

A statistical and descriptive analysis of the treatment of cataract at Vienna's principle ophthalmological clinic during the years 1826 to 1844, presented as Jaeger's inaugural dissertation. The author, son of Friedrich von Jaeger and grandson of G. J. Beer (37-40), was the first to describe the ophthalmoscopic appearances in cases of diabetes.

Hirschberg §1235-1240.

203   Jaeger, Eduard, Ritter von Jaxtthal, 1818-1884.

Ueber Staar und Staaroperationen nebst anderen Beobachtungen und Erfahrungen. Vienna: L. W. Seidel, 1854.

[iii]-viii, [2], 128 p., VIII plates; 23 cm.

Jaeger's work on cataract and its surgical treatment is also one of the earliest books in which the descriptions of pathological states are based upon ophthalmoscopic examination. Pages 89 to 109 describe the ophthalmoscope and the ophthalmoscopic illustrations on plates II thru VIII.

Hirschberg §1241.

204   Jaeger, Eduard, Ritter von Jaxtthal, 1818-1884.

Beiträge zur Pathologie des Auges. Vienna: Kaiserlich-königliche Hof- und Staatsdruckerei, 1855-70.

2 v. (56 p., XXI plates; [4], 57-219 p., XXII-LXXVII plates); 35 cm.

A collection of seventy-seven chromolithographic plates issued in parts between 1855 and 1870, illustrating the varying appearances of the fundus in health and disease. About this work Julius Jacobsen commented, "Ed. Jäger in seinem seit 1855 erscheinenden *Beiträge zur Pathologie des Auges* bis jetzt unbestritten die besten bildlichen Darstellungen der ophthalmoskopischen Veränderungen geliefert hat" (*Königsberger Med. Jahrb.* I:301). Hirschberg saw the original drawings of Jaeger's ophthalmoscopic views in 1871. He later remarked that the chromolithographic reproductions failed to capture the brilliance of the originals, testifying to Jaeger's artistic abilities, his powers of observation, and the limitations of color printing in the third quarter of the nineteenth century. A concordance of the plates in this first edition, the 1870 second edition (207), and the *Hand-Atlas* (206) follows the text.

Hirschberg §1031, 1240.

204.1   Jaeger, Eduard, Ritter von Jaxtthal, 1818-1884.

Augenspiegel nach Jaeger. Manuscript, ca. 1860.

[14] leaves; 15 cm.

A medical manuscript containing notes about Jaeger's observations on the human eye with the aid of the ophthalmoscope. Jaeger introduced direct ophthalmoscopy, and with this new method he determined objectively the refractive error in the eye, as well as describing and illustrating the diseases of the ocular fundus. Hirschberg valued Jaeger's contributions very highly, and claimed that "Jäger was the greatest ophthalmoscopist of the world, and it seems doubtful whether anybody could follow him who would achieve this level of expertise" (Hirschberg §1236).

This manuscript written by an unknown hand also contains an abstract of an article on glaucoma by Albrecht von Graefe, which appeared in the *Archiv für Ophthalmologie* (Bd. 3, Abt. 2). Unfortunately, the manuscript is a fragment. The second gathering may have contained more text, before it was almost entirely cut out, leaving in place only its first two leaves.

205 Jaeger, Eduard, Ritter von Jaxtthal, 1818-1884.

Über die Einstellungen des dioptrischen Apparates im menschlichen Auge. Vienna: L. W. Seidel & Son; Paris: V. Masson, 1861.

viii, 283 p., V plates; 23 cm.

Published before either Donders's (115) or Helmholtz's (185) classic works on physiological optics, Jaeger's book contained many new and important observations in the field of dioptrics. In his own book, Donders credits the work of A. von Graefe, Jaeger and Helmholtz as being the most influential in the formation of his own ideas.

Hirschberg §1241.

206 Jaeger, Eduard, Ritter von Jaxtthal, 1818-1884.

Ophthalmoskopischer Hand-Atlas. Vienna: Kaiserlich-königliche Hof- und Staatsdruckerei, 1869.

[4], xviii, 236 p., XXIX plates; 27 cm.

Its clear verbal and graphic descriptions made this atlas one of the several most important ophthalmoscopic atlases to be published in the nineteenth century. The *Hand-Atlas* includes many views not contained in either the first or second editions of his *Beiträge zur Pathologie des Auges* (204 & 207). An English translation was published in 1890, and a second German edition in 1894.

Chance, p. 171; G-M 5904; Hirschberg §1032; Pybus 1070; Waller 5103.

207 Jaeger, Eduard, Ritter von Jaxtthal, 1818-1884.

Beiträge zur Pathologie des Auges. . . . Zweite Auflage. Vienna: Kaiserlich-königliche Hof- und Staatsdruckerei, 1870.

[4], 223 p., LXXIII plates; 35 cm.

The second edition, published the same year as the last part of the first edition. The commentary and plates have been arranged in an entirely different numerical sequence than in the previous edition. Also, four plates present in the first edition have not been included here. A concordance of the plates in the *Hand-Atlas* (206) and in the two editions of the *Beiträge zur Pathologie des Auges* (1st ed., 204) follows the text.

Hirschberg §1240.

207.1 Jakob, Christfried, 1866-1956.

Atlas des gesunden und kranken Nerven-system, nebst Grundriss der Anatomie, Pathologie und Therapie desselben. Munich: J. F. Lehmann, 1895.

xxiii, [1]-26, [3], 33-89, (p. 39 misnumbered as 66), 78 plates; 197, [1], 10 p.: ill.; 18 cm.

A richly illustrated handbook on the nervous system and its diseases. The author, C. Jakob, practiced medicine in Bamberg, Germany, and was also an assistant at the medical clinic in Erlangen. He published several other works in the fields of physiology, pathology, and neurology, and his *Atlas des gesunden und kranken Nervensystem* went through two French and an English edition as well. In this first German edition, the color lithographs (by F. Reichhold) and the black and white woodcuts (by M. Toller) were made from Jakob's original drawings and photographs. The first two plates—cross sections of the brain showing different layers with the aid of superimposed flaps—recall those published three hundred years earlier in Georg Bartisch's *Augendienst* (34).

BM 114:401 (1896 English ed.); NUC 276:278.

Jallat, L. P., 1792-1864, ed.

See Weller (412).

208 Janin de Combe-Blanche, Jean, 1731-1799.

Mémoires et observations anatomiques, physiologiques et physiques sur l'oeil, et sur les maladies qui affectent cet organe; avec un précis des opérations & des remedes qu'on doit pratiquer pour les guérir. Lyons: Perisse & Roche for P. F. Didot (Paris), 1772.

x1, 474, [6] p.; 20 cm. (8vo)

The eighteenth century was a period of significant scientific advances in ophthalmology and the heyday of ophthalmic quackery. The worlds of Jacques Daviel and the Chevalier

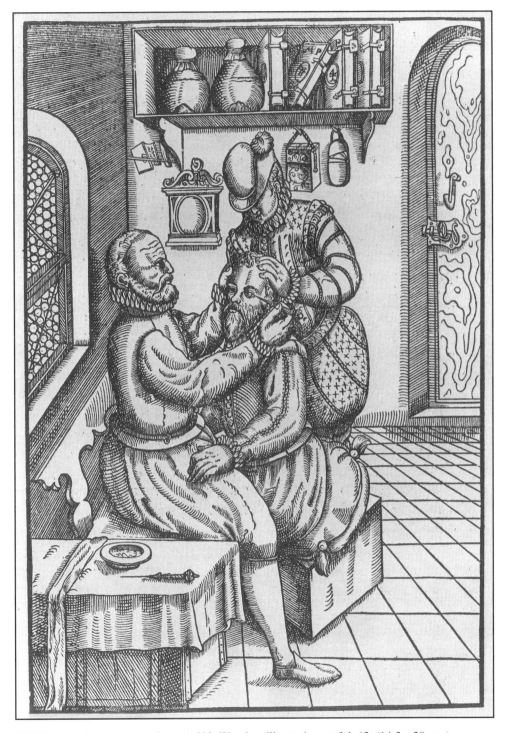

(35) Bartisch, Georg. *Augendienst*, 1583. Woodcut illustration on fol. 62. (14.5 x 20 cm.)

Taylor are easily distinguishable; and yet, there was a great gray area inhabited by men such as Jean Janin who had the ability and inclination to move in and out of these two worlds of medical respectability and quackery. Janin, the charlatan, appears in the boastful advertisements which were published in Montpellier and Avignon in 1757 and 1760 and which Truc and Pansier have reprinted. However, he also published this valuable collection of memoirs which shows him to have been both a skilled surgeon and a careful observer. According to Hirsch (III:418) this book contains an account of the first experiments with glasses of complementary colors before both eyes. In the final section (p. 429-432) Janin gives the first published account of hypermetropia. Janin performed a cataract operation on the Duke of Modena who subsequently ennobled him under the name Combe-Blanche. The grateful nobleman also named Janin honorary professor at the University of Modena at an annual pension of 2,400 livres.

BOA II:53; Hirsch III:418; Hirschberg §378; Waller 5116; Wellcome III:345.

al-Jayyānī, Abū ʿAbd Allāh Muhammad ibn Muʿādh, 11th cent.

See Alhazen (8).

209 Jeffries, Benjamin Joy, 1833-1915.

Enucleation of the eyeball. . . . Section of the ciliary nerves and optic nerve. . . . Some unnecessary causes of impaired vision. Boston: D. Clapp & Son, 1868.

[2], [281]-300, 6, 17 p.: ill.; 23 cm.

A collection of three papers, the first of which was originally read before the Massachussetts Medical Society, and the latter two previously published in the *Boston Medical & Surgical Journal.*

210 Jeffries, Benjamin Joy, 1833-1915.

The eye in health and disease: being a series of articles on the anatomy and physiology of the human eye, and its surgical and medical treatment. Boston: A. Moore, 1871.

119 p.: ill.; 24 cm.

Hirsch III:426.

211 Jeffries, Benjamin Joy, 1833-1915.

Color-blindness: its dangers and its detection. Boston: Houghton, Osgood & Co.; Cambridge: The

Riverside Press, 1880 (c1879).

xvii, [1], 316 p., [1] plate: ill.; 20 cm.

The first monograph and significant contribution on color-blindness by an American author. At a time when European governments were already taking steps to guard against the occupational hazards of color-blindness, Jeffries was the only American voice to direct attention to the perils of color-blindness in railway engineers, ship's pilots, etc. One of the earliest books on the subject, Jeffries draws heavily on the writings of his two most important predecessors, George Wilson (422) and Frithiof Holmgren (194.1). Appropriately, the book is bound in linen with broad horizontal bands of red, green and blue.

Hirsch III:426; Waller 5134.

Johannis de Casso, fl. 1346.

Tractatus de conservatione visus. Editus anno 1346. Publié pour la première fois d'après les manuscrits de la Bibliothèque Nationale de Paris et de la Bibliothèque de Metz.

In Collectio ophthalmologica veterum auctorum (82), fasc. 1.

212 Jones, Thomas Wharton, 1808-1891.

A manual of the principles and practice of ophthalmic medicine and surgery. London: G. J. Palmer for J. Churchill, 1847.

xxxvi, [8], 570 p., 4 plates: ill.; 17 cm.

Jones, an outstanding English ophthalmologist and physiologist, failed to comprehend the value of a prototype ophthalmoscope which Charles Babbage showed him in 1847, four years before Helmholtz first introduced his instrument. Writing in 1854 in the *British and Foreign Medico-Chirurgical Review* (14:549-557), Jones acknowledged Babbage's invention and admitted his part in discouraging its development: "It is with justice that I should here state, however, that seven years ago Mr. Babbage showed me the model of an instrument which he had contrived for the purpose of looking into the interior of the eye." Babbage (1792-1871) is remembered today not for his ophthalmoscope or his "analytical machine," a mechanical computer which suffered a similar neglect, but for his "Table of Logarithms."

An unattractive book typical of a series of stumpy thick octavo manuals brought out by John Churchill, Jones's work stands at the watershed of old and new ophthalmology for it is the last English textbook published before the introduction of the ophthalmoscope. Cf. Charles Snyder, "Charles Babbage and his rejected ophthalmoscope," *Archives of Ophthalmology* 71:591-593, (1964).

213 Jones, Thomas Wharton, 1808-1891.

The principles and practice of ophthalmic medicine and surgery. Edited by Isaac Hays. Philadelphia: T. K. & P. G. Collins for Lea & Blanchard, 1847.

xxxvi, [17]-509 p., 4 plates: ill.; 20 cm.

Both the English and American editions of 1847 contain an extended account of inflammation of the eye which illustrates Jones's interest in pathology. This section disappeared from later editions as the introduction of the ophthalmoscope stripped the term of any specific meaning. A full biographical sketch of the author by Sir Rickman Godlee appeared in the *British Journal of Ophthalmology* 5 (3):97-117 and 5 (4): 145-156 (1921).

Hirschberg §671.

214 Juler, Henry Edward, 1866-1921.

A handbook of ophthalmic science and practice. Philadelphia: H. C. Lea's Son & Co., 1884.

xv, [16]-467 p., [31] plates: ill.; 24 cm.

Juler was a London ophthalmologist with a successful practice on Cavendish Square. His *Handbook* became one of the standard ophthalmic textbooks of the period, going through three British and three American editions between 1884 and 1904. This is the first American edition, with additions by Charles A. Oliver of Philadelphia.

215 Jüngken, Johann Christian, 1793-1875.

Die Lehre von den Augenkrankheiten. Ein Handbuch zum Gebrauche bei Vorlesungen, und zum Selbstunterrichte für angehende Aerzte. Berlin: J. F. Starcke for Schüppel, 1832.

xx, 960 p.; 21 cm.

The author was a respected Berlin ophthalmologist who studied under and was an assistant to Carl Ferdinand Graefe. He was the first to perform an ophthalmic operation employing general anesthesia. A ten-page classified bibliography precedes the text of this work.

Hirschberg §487-488.

Jüngken, Johann Christian, 1793-1875.

See also Weiss (410.2).

215.1 Jung-Stilling, Johann Heinrich, 1740-1817.

Methode den grauen Staar auszuziehen und zu heilen, nebst einem Anhang von verschiedenen andern Augenkrankheiten und der Cur-Art derselben. Marburg: Neue Akademische Buchhandlung, 1791.

134, [2] p., 5 plates; 17 cm. (8vo)

A modification of the method of cataract extraction and the extremely good results which attended it are reported by the author who, at the time of publication, occupied the chair of economy, finance and statistical science at the University of Marburg. Jung, a contemporary and acquaintance of Goethe and Herder, continued his ophthalmology practice while holding this academic post and writing the novels and poems for which he is remembered. His life is well described in Goethe's *Dichtung und Wahrheit*, and his biography was translated into English in 1938 by R. O. Moon (London: Foulis, 1938).

Hirschberg §421.

Jurin, James, 1684-1759.

"An essay upon distinct and indistinct vision."
In Smith (345, 346).

216 Keck, Egidius Crato, respondent.

Dissertatio medica de ectropio. Vom überstülpten, umgekehrten Auglitt, oder Plarr-Aug. Accedunt, in praefatione, de cataracta membranacea observationes . . . . Praeside . . . Johanne Zellero . . . publice defendet Autor & respondens Egidius Crato Keck. Tübingen: G. F. Pflicke, 1733.

28 p.; 20 cm. (4to)

A thesis on ectropium, the eversion or turning out of the edge of the eyelid. Hirschberg (§413) points out that it was actually written by the famous ophthalmologist B. D. Mauchart. It introduces the term "entropium" for the inversion of the edge of the eyelid, crediting J. T. Woolhouse, Mauchart's teacher, with the distinction between the two conditions.

Hirschberg §43, No. 4.

216.1 Kepler, Johannes, 1571-1630.

Ad Vitellionem paralipomena, quibus astronomiae pars optica traditur; potissimùm de artificiosa observatione et aestimatione diametrorum deliquiorum[que]; solis & lunae. Cum exemplis

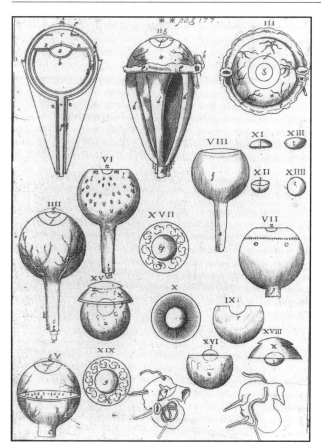

(216.1) Kepler, Johannes. *Ad Vitellionem paralipomena*, 1604. Plate [1]. (12 x 17 cm.)

insignium eclipsium. Habes hoc libro, lector, inter alia multa noua, tractatum luculentum de modo visionis, & humorum oculi vsu, contra opticos & anatomicos. Frankfurt am Main: C. Marnius and heirs of J. Aubrius, 1604.

[14], 449, [19] p., [3] plates (2 folding): ill.; 20 cm. (4to)

"The physical theory of vision, which might be styled the ground-bass [sic] of ophthalmology, owes its development mainly to the work of great astronomers and physicists. The *Ad Vitellionem paralipomena*, of the astronomer Kepler (Frankfort, 1604), contains a treatise on vision and the human eye in which is shown for the first time how the retina is essential to sight, the part the lens plays in refraction, and that the convergence of luminous rays before reaching the retina is the cause of myopia" (Garrison, p. 260). The volume includes an index and printed marginal notes, as well as several geometrical figures and tables. It is decorated with floriated initials and headpieces; its pages 395 and 412 are misnumbered "359" and "417." The Becker Library's copy is bound in its original vel-lum binding.

Kepler made several other contributions to optics. He introduced the terms "prism," "lens," "meniscus," and many others, computed the angle of incidence of light, and explained the formation of a rainbow. Gorin notes that "it is remarkable that he created the whole system of optics in the eye with one pair of lenses" (p. 34).

BM 122:344; Chance, p. 45; Garrison, p. 260; Hirschberg §308; Krivatsy 6343; NUC 294:54.

217   Kircher, Athanasius, 1602-1680.

Ars magna lucis et umbrae in decem libros digesta. Quibus admirandae lucis et umbrae in mundo, atque adeò universa natura, vires effectusq. uti nova, ita varia novorum reconditiorumq. speciminum exhibitione, ad varios mortalium usus, pandantur. Rome: H. Scheus, 1646.

[40], 411, 404-405, 414-568, 567-935, [15] p., 39 plates: ill.; 31 cm.

One of the most remarkable intellectual figures of the seventeenth century, Kircher at different periods held professorships of Greek, Hebrew, Syriac, mathematics and philosophy, while simultaneously carrying on his intensive investigations into Egyptian hieroglyphics, geography, astronomy, optics, acoustics, medicine and orientology. He was the author of forty-four authoritative works on all these subjects.

The *Ars magna lucis et umbrae* is regarded by many as the most important of Kircher's encyclopedic works. It contains important observations on the nature of light, lenses, astronomy and related topics. It also includes early descriptions of the camera obscura and the magic lantern. The text is illustrated with numerous woodcuts. The thirty-nine leaves of copperplate engravings typify the quality of illustration found in so many of Kircher's works. A second edition was published at Amsterdam in 1671.

BOA I:113; DicSciBio VII:375-76; Hirsch III:529; Wellcome III:394.

Kirmisson, Edouard, 1848-1927, ed.
See Panas (287).

218   Kitchiner, William, 1775?-1827.

The economy of the eyes: precepts for the improvement and preservation of the sight. Plain rules which will enable all to judge exactly when, and what spectacles are best calculated for their eyes, observations on opera glasses and theatres, and an account of the pancratic magnifier, for double stars, and day telescopes. London: Hurst, Robinson, & Co., 1824.

viii, 246 p., [2] plates; 18 cm.

The son of a wealthy London coal merchant, Kitchiner's medical degree from Glasgow assured that he would never have to practice in London, where he opted to settle after receiving his inheritance. A renowned gourmet, Kitchiner's lunches and dinners were famous. His culinary experiences resulted in his best known work, *Apicius redivivus, or, the cook's oracle.* Describing itself as "a culinary code for the rational epicure," this work went through at least twenty editions between 1817 and 1855. The present work, the fruit of the author's avid interest in optics, is a popular work on lenses and the hygiene of the eye. A German translation was made in 1825. In 1826 a second edition appeared, followed in the same year by a sequel, *The economy of the eyes. Part II.*

Knapp, Arnold Herman, b. 1869, trans.

See Oeller (278)

219 Knapp, Herman, 1832-1911.

A treatise on intraocular tumours. From original clinical observations and anatomical investigations. . . . Translated by S. Cole. New York: W. Wood & Co., 1869.

xii, [17]-323 p., XVI plates; 23 cm.

A translation of one of Knapp's most important works, *Die intraocularen Geschwülste* (Karlsruhe, 1868). Knapp has been described by Burton Chance as "perhaps the most remarkable figure in American ophthalmology." He was born in Germany, and began his medical studies the same year Helmholtz published his description of the ophthalmoscope. Admitted to the medical faculty at Heidelberg, Knapp established its first eye clinic, and later succeeded Chelius as professor of ophthalmology. In 1868 Knapp emigrated to America, where he established the New York Ophthalmic and Aural Institute, modelled upon von Graefe's clinic in Berlin. The year after he arrived in New York, Knapp founded, with Salomon Moos, the *Archiv für Augen- und Ohrenheilkunde* and its simultaneously published English version.

219.1 Knapp, Herman, 1832-1911.

Cocaine and its use in ophthalmic and general surgery . . . with supplementary contributions by Drs. F. H. Bosworth, R. J. Hall, E. L. Keyes, H. Knapp and Wm. M. Polk. New York; London: G. P. Putnam's Sons, 1885.

[4], 87 p.; 23 cm.

Knapp's treatise on the use of cocaine as a local anesthetic was originally published in the *Archives of Ophthalmology* (December, 1884). It "includes his own translation of Carl Koller's second account of Koller's discovery of the uses of cocaine in ophthalmic surgery, first published in vol. 34 of the *Wien. Med. Wochenschrift* on 25 October [cols. 1276-78] and 1 November 1884 [cols. 1309-11]" (Norman 1224).

BM 124:610 (1883 ed.); G-M 5678; Hirsch III:556; Norman 1224; NUC 299:692; Waller 5322.

219.2 Kranichfeld, Friedrich Wilhelm Georg, 1789-1850.

Anthropologische Uebersicht der gesammten Ophthalmiatrie; nebst einer anthropologischen Zusammenstellung der Augenkrankheiten und Grundzüge der anthropologischen Methode, sie zu heilen. Berlin: J. Naumann, 1841.

[2], xv, [1], 158, [2] p.; 22 cm.

A summary of ophthalmiatrics systematized from an anthropological perspective. The diseases of the eye and their different treatments are organized in a chart, and then in chapters and several levels of sub-chapters and sub-divisions. The whole system is very complicated and subjectively arranged, or—as Hirschberg pointed out—"deranged." According to Hirschberg, some of Kranichfeld's "students thought that he was somewhat deranged . . . [and] when trying to read his *Ophthalmiatrie*, one is inclined to share their opinion" (§485).

F. W. G. Kranichfeld practiced in Vienna, then was physician to the Austrian Embassy in Constantinople, and later to the imperial Russian court. He was appointed professor at the University of Berlin and founded a private institute for ophthalmic outpatients in the University building. In 1834 he established another private hospital named Hygiocomium.

AmEncOph IX:6870; Hirsch III:601; Hirschberg §485; NUC 305:329.

Küfner, Johann, ed.

See Vittori (391).

219.3 Kühne, Willy, 1837-1900.

Lehrbuch der physiologischen Chemie. Leipzig: W. Engelmann, 1868.

viii, 605 p.: ill.; 23 cm.

A general textbook on physiological chemistry published as

one of the earliest works of W. Kühne. It appeared in the year when he was appointed professor of physiology at the University of Amsterdam.

Hirsch III:627; Hirschberg §1154; NUC 308:43; Pagel, col. 922-923.

220 Kühne, Willy, 1837-1900.

Zur Photochemie der Netzhaut. Heidelberg: C. Winter, 1877.

14 p.; 24 cm.

This paper was originally read before the Naturhistorisch-medicinische Vereins zu Heidelberg on the 5th of January, 1877, and published in the society's *Verhandlungen* (I:484-92) the same year. The significance of this paper is explained in the annotation to the next entry (221). Kühne succeeded Helmholtz to the chair of physiology at Heidelberg in 1871.

221 Kühne, Willy, 1837-1900.

Ueber den Sehpurpur. Heidelberg: C. Winter, 1878?.

89 p., 1 plate; 24 cm.

"In 1876 Boll had established that the layer of rods of the retina contain a purple pigment that disappears on exposure to light. On this basis Kühne supposed that there was a primarily chemical process that preceded excitation of the optic nerves. He demonstrated that the retina works like a photographic plate, with light bleaching out the visual purple, which is regenerated in darkness. He succeeded in producing his famous 'optograms'—the reproduction of the pattern of crossbars of a window on the chemical substance of the retina of a rabbit. . . . Kühne was thus the first to perceive the migrating pigments in the living retina" (DicSciBio VII:520).

A separately printed offprint of an article which was published with his *Zur Photochemie der Netzhaut* (220) in the *Untersuchungen aus dem physiologischen Institute der Universität Heidelberg* (Bd. I, Heft 1, p. 1-14 [*Netzhaut*], p. 15-103 [*Sehpurpur*]) in 1878. Together they represent Kühne's earliest complete statement regarding his researches on rhodopsin. Both papers were again published together in an English translation in 1878.

Kürner, Georg Andreas, respondent.

"De lapsu palpebrae superioris."

In Dissertationes medicae selectae Tubingenses (112) 3:229-277.

Küssmaul, Adolf, 1822-1902.

See Selected monographs (338.1).

221.1 La Caille, Nicolas Louis de, 1713-1762.

Leçons elementaires d'optique. Paris: Guerin Brothers, 1750.

[8], 119, [1] p., [4] folding plates: ill.; 19 cm. (8vo)

The rare first edition of a textbook on basic optics by the French mathematician and astronomer, Nicolas de la Caille. La Caille was professor of mathematics at Collège Mazarin, Paris and published several works on astronomy, physics, trigonometry, and geometry. From 1741 he was a member of the Académie des Sciences, and between 1750 and 1753 he participated in an expedition to the Cape of Good Hope to carry out astronomical mensurations.

Leçons élémentaire was translated into Latin and went through at least five editions during the eighteenth century. It discusses the principles and properties of light, vision, color, and perspective; the laws of dioptrics and catoptrics; as well as the theory of telescopes and microscopes.

BM 128:210 (1756 ed.); BOA II:58 (1766 French and Latin eds.); NUC 310:328 (1756, 1764, 1766 eds.); Poggendorff I:1338; Wellcome III:329, 424 (1756, 1757, 1764 eds.).

222 Lacepiera, Petrus, d. 1306.

Libro de locchio morale et spirituale vulgare. Venice: Joannes Rubeus Vercellensis, 21 May, 1496.

[64] leaves; 22 cm. (4to)

An Italian translation of the second earliest printed work on the eye, Grassus's *De oculis* (1474) being the first. Often ascribed to the English Franciscan John Peckham, it seems established now that the author of this text was Peter of Limoges, canon of Evreux, who flourished at the Sorbonne in Paris in the late thirteenth century and is named in the colophon. Sarton writes: "The purpose of the *De oculo morali* is purely ethical but it contains a description of the eye, together with a brief account of eye diseases and their treatment" (Sarton II:1029). The work is translated into Italian by Fra Teofilo Romano. A title page woodcut depicts a monk preaching to a group of disciples and pointing to his eye.

BM 15th c. 5:419; Goff J393; Hain 9805.

223 La Chambre, Marin Cureau de, 1594-1669.

La lumière. Paris: P. Rocolet, 1657.

[20], 64, 67-368, 379-414, [l0] p.: ill.; 25 cm. (4to)

(222) Lacepiera, Petrus. *Libro de locchio morale et spirituale vulgare*, 1496. Title page illustration. (7.5 x 7.7 cm.)

"Ainsi, toute la théorie de Démocrite sur les corpuscules ou atomes lucides, se retrouve dans un traité de la lumière" (*Nouvelle biographie générale* XXVIII:504). La Chambre's principal work on optics, in which he discusses the nature of light, the origin of colors, refractions, etc. Largely ignored by historians, this work was nonetheless consulted by such figures as Grimaldi and Huygens.

224 La Chambre, Marin Cureau de, 1594-1669.

Nouvelles observations et conjectures sur l'iris. Paris: J. Langlois for J. d'Allin, 1662.

[8], 340, [6] p.: ill.; 24 cm. (4to)

The author, one of the founders of the Académie des Sciences, physician to Louis XIII and XIV, and a celebrated physiognomist, was held to be an acute judge of character. A secret correspondence on this subject was initiated with him by Louis XIV and conducted for several years. This volume is an optical treatise which deals with rainbows, the origin and nature of colors, and the refraction of light. The properties of colors are related to the theory of harmonics in music.

225 La Charrière, Joseph de, fl. 1680.

Nouvelles operations de chirurgie: contenant leurs causes fondées sur la structure de la partie, leurs signes, leurs simptomes & leur explication; avec plusieurs observations. Et une idée generale des playes. Paris: D. Horthemels, 1692.

[24], 331 p.; 13 cm. (12mo)

Little is known of the life of Joseph de La Charrière beyond what is recorded in his two books, though from the preface it is apparent that he quarrelled with a Mr. Du***, probably Joseph Guichard Duverney (1648-1730), professor of anatomy in Paris. The present work enjoyed a degree of popularity, went through many editions, and was translated into German (1700) and English (1705). The author presents a description of the disease in each case and the surgical procedure necessary to cure it, but he gives no details of the operations. Cataract was attributed to a small pellicle which detached itself from the crystalline lens, thickened, floated into the aqueous humor and was rendered opaque. This was a common understanding of cataract in the late seventeenth century. La Charrière borrowed heavily from both the writings of Duverney and the surgical lectures which Dionis (111) presented at the Jardin-du-Roi from 1672 to 1680.

Hirschberg §328; Wellcome II:425.

226 La Charrière, Joseph de, fl. 1680.

Anatomie nouvelle de la tête de l'homme, et de ses dépendances; avec l'usage de ses parties, suivant leurs structure et la physique moderne. Paris: Widow of D. Hortemels, 1703.

[20], 436 p., 2 plates; 16 cm. (12mo)

An anatomy of virtually every part of the human head. Pages 267 to 352 are devoted to the anatomy of the eye and the physiology of vision, including a discussion of the nature of light, the perception of color and the correction of visual defects by lenses. Both copperplate engravings in the volume illustrate this section.

Blake, p. 250; Hirsch I:890.

La Faye, Georges de, 1669-1781.

"Pour servir à perfectionner la nouvelle méthode de faire l'opération de la cataracte."
In Académie Royale de Chirurgie, *Mémoires* (2).

La Forest (de).

"Nouvelle méthode de traiter les maladies du sac lacrymal, nommées communement, fistules lacrymales."

In Académie Royale de Chirurgie, *Mémoires* (2).

227 Lambert, Johann Heinrich, 1728-1777.

Les propriétés remarquables de la route de la lumière, par les airs et en general par plusieurs milieux refringens spheriques et concentriques, avec la solution des problèms, qui y ont du rapport, comme sont les refractions astronomiques et terrestres, et ce qui en depend. The Hague: N. van Daalen, 1759.

116 p., 2 plates; 20 cm. (8vo)

The first published work of this famous Alsatian scientist whose later researches in the field of photometry provided a scientific basis for the measurement of light. This work contains important researches on the refraction of light, including atmospheric refraction, which greatly influenced Arago in his researches on polarization. Cf. Steck, Max. "Ein unbekannter Brief von Johann Heinrich Lambert und Johannes Gessner [Johann Rudolf Iselin]," *Gesnerus* 8:245-248 (1951) and 11:36-40 (1954).

Hirschberg §452.

Lancisi, Giovanni Maria, 1654-1720.

"Dissertationes duae anatomico-medicae: . . . De vena sine pari; altera De gangliis nervorum."

In Morgagni (263).

227.1 Landi, Pasquale, 1817-1895.

Della ottalmia catarrale epidemica nelle milizie austriache stanziate in Firenze. Florence: M. Cecchi, 1850.

96, [4] p., 2 color plates; 22 cm.

A treatise on a catarrhal ophthalmia epidemic among the Austrian militia stationed in Florence in 1849. The work was written by the Italian surgeon Pasquale Landi. Born in Porrona, Landi received his doctoral degree in Siena in 1841. He first practiced surgery in Florence, then was a professor at the surgical clinic in Siena, and later the director of the surgical clinics of Bologna and Pisa. He was the first in Italy to perform a successful ovariotomy operation. *Della ottalmia* is Landi's only ophthalmological publication, which he dedicated to Antonio Scarpa.

AmEncOph IX:7006 (1851 ed.); Hirsch III:660 (1851 ed.); NUC 314:101.

228 Landolt, Edmund, 1846-1926.

The refraction and accommodation of the eye and their anomalies. . . . Translated, under the author's supervision, by C. M. Culver. Edinburgh: Y. J. Pentland, 1886.

xi, [3], 600 p.: ill.; 24 cm.

Swiss born, Landolt studied at Zurich and later worked in physiological optics with Snellen and Donders at Utrecht, where he doubtless laid much of the groundwork on which the present volume is based. Landolt's eye clinic on the Rue Saint-André-des-Arts was world famous. With Panas and Poncet he founded the *Archives d'ophtalmologie* in 1881.

BOA I:119; Fischer II:856; Hirschberg §1273.

Landolt, Edmond, 1846-1926, jt. author.

See Wecker (408.1).

229 Langenbeck, Bernhard Rudolph Conrad von, 1810-1887.

De retina. Observationes anatomico-pathologicae. Göttingen: Dieterich, 1836.

x, [2], 188 p., 4 plates; 25 cm.

The publication of this "Habilitationschrift" marked Langenbeck's admission as an unsalaried university lecturer ("Privatdozent") at Göttingen. The significance of this work to ophthalmology is the author's microscopic proof that retinal neoplasms consist essentially of a hyperplasia of the normal retinal cells.

Hirschberg §484.

Langenbeck, Konrad Johann Martin, 1775-1851, ed.

See Neue Bibliothek (272.1).

L'Armessin, Nicholas de, III, 1640-1725, engr.

See Print 4.

Lasseré, François, 1613-1697.

See Chérubin d'Orléans (75.1).

230 Lattier de Laroche, Thomas Michel Antoine Amédée de, 1785-1836.

Mémoire sur la cataracte, et guérison de cette maladie,

sans opération chirurgicale. 2. éd., augm. de neuf nouvelles observations. Paris: Carpentier-Méricourt for the author, Delaunay & Béchet, 1833.

236 p.; 22 cm.

Bound with Lattier de Laroche (231).

A summary view of the anatomy of the eye and the nature of cataract precedes forty-eight case histories of the medical treatment and proclaimed cure of numerous forms of cataract. The author reveals none of the details of his medical secrets in these cases.

231 Lattier de Laroche, Thomas Michel Antoine Amédée de, 1785-1836.

Suite au mémoire sur la cataracte, et guérison de cette maladie sans opération chirurgicale. Tome deuxième. Paris: F. Malteste & Co. for the author, Delaunay & Béchet, 1835.

xvi, 204 p.; 22 cm.

Bound with Lattier de Laroche (230).

The benefits of the author's secret medical treatment of cataract are extolled and forty-three additional cases are presented, but details of this charlatan's secret cure remain unrevealed.

Lawrence, Sir William, 1783-1867.

See also Neue Bibliothek (272.1).

231.1 Lawrence, Sir William, 1783-1867.

A treatise on the venereal diseases of the eye. London: J. Wilson, 1830.

xiii, [1], 337, [1] p.; 23 cm.

Provenance: Inscribed "Dr. Bethune, with the author's compliments."

A treatise on "the nature, symptoms, and treatment of venereal diseases affecting the eye, including gonorrheal inflammation of the conjunctiva, the external tunics, and the iris, [as well as] syphilitic diseases of the eye" (BOA I:124). Hirschberg considered it the first monograph on the subject. A German edition was published in 1831.

William Lawrence was a student of Abernethy, then prosector at St. Batholomew's Hospital, London. In 1817 he became director of the London Ophthalmic Hospital, Moorfields (according to Gorin, the first special eye hospital in the world, founded in 1805). Lawrence, dubbed by some "Nestor of British surgery," was a prolific writer, a noted lecturer, and a member of several prestigious societies. He was also active in poli-

tics and was knowledgeable in foreign languages and literature. His work on natural history (*Lectures on physiology, zoology, and the natural history of man*) was controversial for advocating the doctrine of evolution.

BM 132:35; BOA I:124; Dawson 4076; Gorin, p. 75; Hirsch III:700; Hirschberg §359; NUC 319:511; RoyMedSoc I:691; Wellcome III:462.

232 Lawrence, Sir William, 1783-1867.

A treatise on the diseases of the eye. Washington: D. Green for the Register & Library of Medical & Chirurgical Science, 1834.

xii, 582 p.; 22 cm.

"This comprehensive work marks an epoch in ophthalmic surgery" (G-M 5849). It is based on lectures delivered by Lawrence at the London Ophthalmic Hospital. In 1819 Lawrence succeeded Abernethy as lecturer on surgery at St. Bartholomew's Hospital where he contributed significantly to the advancement of eye surgery.

G-M 5849; Hirschberg §637.

233 Lawrence, Sir William, 1783-1867.

A treatise on the diseases of the eye. A new edition. Edited, with numerous additions . . . by Isaac Hays. Philadelphia: T. K. & P. G. Collins for Lea & Blanchard, 1847.

xxxii, 33-55, [1], 49-858, [2] p., 12 plates: ill.; 24 cm.

The second Lea and Blanchard edition edited by Isaac Hays, a famous American ophthalmologist, who also edited the *American Journal of Medical Sciences* for over fifty-two years.

Hirschberg §637.

233.1 Lawson, George, 1831-1903.

Injuries of the eye, orbit, and eyelids: their immediate and remote effects. London: Longmans, Green, and Co., 1867.

xiv, 430 p.: ill.; 22 cm.

A systematic description of injuries of the visual apparatus and their treatment. The work discusses topics including injuries from burns, scalds, and chemical agents, as well as penetrating wounds, gunshot wounds, traumatic cataract, capsular opacities, dislocation of the lens, and treatment of foreign bodies in the eye. The volume is illustrated with almost one hundred fine woodcuts. An American edition of this book also appeared in 1867. Lawson wrote another successful work on the subject, entitled *Diseases and injuries of the eye*, which went through five editions in less than twenty years.

Student and assistant to the famous surgeon, W. Fergusson, George Lawson started his practice in London in 1856. He became a surgeon and an instructor of surgery at the Middlesex Hospital and later at Moorfields Hospital. Achieving a great reputation as an ophthalmologist, he became surgeon oculist to Queen Victoria in 1886, and received many other honors.

BM 132:61; BOA I:124; Hirsch III:701; Hirschberg §650; NUC 319:581.

234   Le Cat, Claude Nicolas, 1700-1768.

Traité des sens. Nouvelle éd., corr., augm., & enrichie de figures en taille douce. Amsterdam: J. Wetstein, 1744.

[16], 328 p., 19 plates; 20 cm. (8vo)

Le Cat, a prominent French surgeon, better known for his surgical ability than as a writer in the field of ophthalmology, so consistently won the prizes offered by the Académie de Chirurgie in Paris that the members of that society felt obliged to beg him not to compete anymore so as not to intimidate others. The present work, illustrated by an unusual set of anatomical plates, treats the anatomy and physiology of the sense organs in a philosophical context.

Hirschberg §330; Wellcome III:468.

Le Cerf, Christoph, 1696-1755, trans.

See Woolhouse (423).

235   Le Clerc, Sébastien, 1637-1714.

Discours touchant le point de veue, dans lequel il est prouvé que les choses qu'on voit distinctement, ne sont veuës qu'd'un oeil. Paris: T. Jolly, 1679.

[12], 86, [2] p., [1] plate: ill.; 15 cm. (12mo)

An unusual work on the physiology of vision, with special regard to its implications for artistic perspective. A well-known engraver and geometrician, Le Clerc was professor of perspective at the Académie Royale de Peinture for thirty years. During this period he produced an estimated 4,000 different copperplate engravings. His explanations in this treatise are illustrated with twenty-four engravings of his own devising. Later editions were published at Paris under the title *Système de la vision* in 1712 and 1719.

Le Dran, Henri François, 1685-1770.

"Sur un oeil éraillé."

In Académie Royale de Chirurgie, *Mémoires* (2).

235.1   Lefébure de Saint-Ildephont, Guillaume Réné, baron, 1744-1809.

Histoire anatomique, physiologique et optique de l'oeil. Pour servir d'introduction aux autres ouvrages sur les maladies et les opérations des yeux, du même auteur, et d'examen à ceux qui se destinent à cette pratique. Paris; Strasbourg: A. Koenig, 1803.

xii, 252 p.; 21 cm. (8vo)

Medical doctor, military officer, historian, and literary author, Lefébure was the city physician of Versailles, where he also lectured on syphilitic diseases and obstetrics. Later he served as court physician to Louis XVIII. He fled the Revolution in 1790 and continued to practice and teach in Holland, Germany, Italy, and Hungary. During the Franco-Austrian War of 1809 he joined the French army, and died of typhoid fever in the same year.

This general work on ophthalmology is one of Lefébure's medical writings, which form only a small part of his multidisciplinary oeuvre. Hirschberg does not discuss this work specifically, but after listing Lefébure's medical publications, he points out several examples of nonsense in them and considers the author a "bombastic quack . . . [and an] imposter."

BiogMed V:564; Hirsch III:720; Hirschberg §480; NUC 323:385.

235.2   Lehnberg, Carl.

Tal om optiken, hållit för Kongl[iga] Vetensk[aps] Academien. Stockholm: L. Salvius, 1756.

[2], 32 p.; 19 cm. (8vo)

An address on optics delivered by Carl Lehnberg on the 28th of August, 1756, when he became a member of the Royal Academy of Sciences in Stockholm.

Leincker, Johann Sigismund, 1724-1780, defendant.

See Heister (184).

Leonides, 1st cent.

See Aetius, of Amida (5).

Levistal, Alfred, 1838-1874, ed.

See Verdet (386.1).

Die Candidaten.

(38.1) Beer, Georg Joseph. *Das Auge, oder Versuch das edelste Geschenk der Schöpfung vor dem höchst verderblichen Einfluss unseres Zeitalters zu sichern,* 1813. Frontispiece. (10 x 18 cm.)

236 Liebreich, Richard, 1830-1917.

Atlas der Ophthalmoscopie. Darstellung des Augengrundes im gesunden und krankhaften Zustande enthaltend 12 Tafeln mit 59 Figuren in Farbendruck, nach der Natur gemalt und erläutert .... Dritte Auflage. Berlin: A. Hirschwald, 1885.

[2], viii, 31 p., XII plates; 35 cm.

The first atlas of the fundus and one of the most important ophthalmoscopical atlases of the nineteenth century. In the preface to the first edition Liebreich states that it was from Helmholtz himself that he first learned of the ophthalmoscope in 1851. It was while an assistant at von Graefe's Berlin clinic (1854-62) that Liebreich took his initial steps in the practical application of the new instrument, resulting in the present work. The twelve lithographic plates are after Liebreich's own paintings, and were first published at Berlin in 1863. Although more than a hundred textbooks and atlases of ophthalmoscopy were to appear in the nineteenth century, the unusually detailed and comprehensive accuracy of Liebreich's work assured it a lasting place both in nineteenth century practice and in the history of ophthalmoscopic literature. The text of this third edition is identical with that of the previous edition; the quality of the plates, however, is improved. "A comparison of the illustrations of the third edition with those in both former ones shows evidence of advances in the technique of color printing: the backgrounds of the fundi are more luminous, the vessels and hemorrhages of a more natural transparent blood color, the blood deposits have a much deeper hue" (Paul Tower, "Richard Liebreich and his atlas of ophthalmoscopy," *Arch. of Ophth.* 65:792).

In 1862 Liebreich migrated to Paris where he remained until the outbreak of the Franco-Prussian War. From 1871 to 1878 he was ophthalmic surgeon at St. Thomas Hospital in London. His career may be said to have culminated with the publication of this atlas. After his return to Paris in 1878, Liebreich continued his private practice, but devoted an increasing amount of time to the serious study of painting. He died in Paris in 1917.

Hirsch III:782; Hirschberg §1032.

237 Littell, Squier, 1803-1886.

A manual of the diseases of the eye. Philadelphia: J. Van Court for J. S. Littell, 1837.

xiv, [2], 255 p.; 20 cm.

The third American book on diseases of the eye, preceded only by the monographs by Frick (142) and Gibson (153), this work is based on the author's experience in Philadelphia's Wills Hospital and in private practice. "At a time when Lord Jeffrey sneeringly asked, 'Who reads an American book?' it received the honor of republication in England a year after it came out here" (A.D. Hall, "Memoir of Squire Littell, M.D." *Transactions of the College of Physicians of Philadelphia*, 3. ser., 9: [cdxlix]-cdlx [1887]). The London edition of 1838 was edited by Hugh Houston, one of England's most eminent surgeons. Cf. Burton Chance, "Squier Littell, M.D." *Annals of Medical History* 1:50-56 (1929).

Hirschberg §748.

237.1 Littrow, Joseph Johann, Edler von, 1781-1840.

Dioptrik, oder Anleitung zur Verfertigung der Fernröhre. Vienna: J. B. Wallishausser, 1830.

xviii, 494 p., 2 folding plates: tables; 22 cm.

Provenance: Jakob Merz (inscription).

After having been professor of astronomy at the Universities of Crakow (Poland) and Kazan (Russia), Joseph Littrow was appointed co-director of the observatory in Pest (Hungary) in 1816. From 1819 he was professor of astronomy at the University of Vienna, where he directed the local observatory. He was knighted by the Emperor of Austria in 1837.

Littrow published numerous works on astronomy, geometry, chronometry, and physics, and he wrote a few works on optics as well. This volume is an optical handbook discussing the theory of objectives, telescopes, mirrors, and microscopes. The last chapter is a comprehensive history of optics from ancient Greece to the 1810s.

BM 138:819; NUC 336:368.

237.2 Lloyd, Humphrey, 1800-1881.

A treatise on light and vision. London: Longman, Rees, Orme, Brown, and Green, 1831.

xxx, [2], 402 p.: ill.; 23 cm.

Bound with publisher's catalog (16 p.) dated May, 1833.

A comprehensive work on optics containing in three parts: 1. the theory of simple or homogeneous light and the principles of reflection and refraction; 2. the theory of compound or solar light, the dispersion of light, and the phenomena of colors; 3. the laws of vision, the description of the human eye, and the principles of optical instruments, such as lenses, telescopes, and microscopes. The author, Humphrey Lloyd, was the provost of Trinity College, Dublin. He published several works on topics in physics, especially on magnetism and the properties of light.

BM 140:367; BOA I:127; NUC 337:218.

238 Losen de Seltenhoff, Edouard de.

La macrobiotique des yeux ou l'art de conserver la vue jusqu'a l'age le plus avancé, précédé d'un coup d'oeil historique sur l'ophthalmologie, et suivi: 1° d'une note sur les mouches volantes; 2° des expériences de Sir Everard Home sur les changements qu'éprouve la cornée pour s'adapter aux divers degrés de vision; 3° de considérations pratiques sur l'exploration des yeux malades; 4° du traitement de l'ophthalmie par la méthode hydriatrique. Brussels: Société Encyclographique . . . de Mortier, 1841.

xxxix, [1], 300 p.; 23 cm.

A popular work on the hygiene of the eyes drawn largely from the writings of Beer, Weller, Jungken, Carron du Villards, and Reveillé-Parise, described elsewhere in this catalogue. The author divides his treatise into four sections and treats the structure of the eye; light and the physiology of vision; rules to maintain the eye in health; the regimen for weak eyesight; and the care of diseased eyes. A brief review of the history of ophthalmology precedes the body of the work.

Hirschberg §470; Waller 6023.

Louis, Antoine, 1723-1792.

"Mémoire sur plusieurs maladies du globe de l'oeil; où l'on examine particulièrement les cas qui exigent l'extirpation de cet organe, & la méthode d'y procéder."

In Académie Royale de Chirurgie, *Mémoires* (2).

Louis, Antoine, 1723-1792.

"Précis historique de la doctrine des auteurs sur l'opération qu'ils ont proposee pour remédier au renversement des paupières."

In Académie Royale de Chirurgie, *Mémoires* (2).

Louis, Antoine, 1723-1792.

"Réflexions sur l'opération de la fistule lacrymale."

In Académie Royale de Chirurgie, *Mémoires* (2).

239 Lusardi, Christophe Mathieu, b. 1778.

Traité de l'alteration du cristallin et de ses annexes; précédé d'un précis sur l'anatomie de l'oeil, et suivi de l'extrait d'un mémoire inédit sur la pupille artificielle. Paris: J. Roger (Lyons) for Menard & Desenne, and Million (Lyons), 1819.

xii, 220 p., [1] plate; 20 cm. (8vo)

The operation of depression for cataract is advanced as superior to that of extraction by this Parisian oculist of Italian origin. Lusardi received medical degrees from both Duisburg and Montpellier and studied for a time at Pavia under Scarpa, one of the foremost exponents of the extraction procedure.

Hirschberg §352; Wellcome III:561

240 Mackenzie, Sir Stephen, 1844-1909.

Retinal haemorrhages and melanaemia as symptoms of ague. London: Pardon & Son, printers, 1877.

16 p.: ill.; 21 cm.

The brother of Morrell Mackenzie, the author was a dermatologist and ophthalmologist of considerable importance. This work was originally published in the *Medical Times and Gazette*.

241 Mackenzie, William, 1791-1868.

A practical treatise on the diseases of the eye. London: E. Khull & Son (Glasgow) for Longman, 1830.

xvi, 861 p.; 23 cm.

"In this book, Mackenzie, one of the foremost ophthalmologists of his time, included a classical description of the symptomatology of glaucoma, and was probably the first to draw attention to the increase of intra-ocular pressure as a characteristic of the condition. He introduced the term 'asthenopia', and was the first to describe sympathetic ophthalmia as a distinct disease" (G-M 5848). Mackenzie's work in ophthalmology is commemorated today by the William Mackenzie Medal awarded by the University of Glasgow. Many of the books in this collection were once part of Mackenzie's own library.

G-M 5848; Hirschberg §680-683.

242 Magne, Pierre Alexandre Charles, 1818-1887.

Hygiène de la vue, ou conseils sur la conservation et l'amélioration des yeux, s'addressant a toutes les classes de la société et en particulier aux mères de famille, aux hommes d'état, aux gens de lettres et a toutes les personnes qui se livrent aux travaux de cabinet. Paris: A. Bailly for the author & Truchy, 1847.

[6], [ll]-323 p.; 21 cm.

A popular work on the care and hygiene of the eyes and the preservation of vision, introduced by a summary view of the history of French ophthalmology and a somewhat jingoistic examination of the German school with particular reference to the theories of Beer (37-40).

Hirschberg §575.

243   Maître-Jan, Antoine, 1650-1730.

Traité des maladies de l'oeil et des remedes propres pour leur guerison. Enrichy de plusieurs experiences de physique. Troyes: J. Le Febvre, 1707.

[14], 580, 561-573, [1] p.; 25 cm. (4to)

"Called the Father of French ophthalmology, Maître-Jan energetically supported Brisseau's doctrine [(163)], ensuring its acceptance. As far back as 1692 Maître-Jan had proved that the opaque lens is cataract, but before Brisseau's work appeared it had been regarded as a sort of skin or pellicle immediately inside the capsule of the lens" (G-M 5824). Maître-Jan called glaucoma a false cataract and never having dissected a glaucomatous eye, he viewed it as a disease of the lens. The present copy appears to be an unrecorded state of the first edition with a completely reset title page, clearly conjugate with leaf a4, and not a cancel. The work was published simultaneously in Rouen.

G-M 5824; Hirschberg §327; Waller 5824.

244   Maître-Jan, Antoine, 1650-1730.

Traité des maladies de l'oeil, et des remedes propres pour leur guérison; enrichi de plusieurs expériences de physique. Paris: Widow of L. d'Houry, 1740.

x, 554 p.; 17 cm. (12mo)

"The use of chemical fixatives was elaborated by the great French ophthalmologist, Antoine Maître-Jan (1650-1730), who thereby was able to dispel many misconceptions such as that the lens and vitreous were fluid humours which clotted after death, and to demonstrate the onion-like structure of the former and the fibrous-fluid consistency of the latter" (Duke-Elder 2:41).

Hirschberg §327.

244.1   Malus, Étienne Louis, 1775-1812.

Théorie de la double réfraction. S.l.: s.n., 1811.

303-508 p., 3 folding plates: ill.; 26 cm. (4to)

"An important memoir, which was awarded the prize of the French Institute, enlarging and treating mathematically the author's discovery of polarization by reflection" (BOA I:136). This copy of the *Théorie* is extracted from *Mémoires de l'Institut des Sciences*, no. 2 (1811), but the work was published in book format as well (Paris: Garnery, 1810).

The author, Étienne Malus, started his career in military engineering and during the Revolutionary and Napoleonic Wars served with the French army in Egypt and Germany. In 1809 he returned to Paris and devoted himself to optical research. His discovery of the polarization of light by reflection was first published in his paper, *Sur une propriété de la lumière réfléchie par les corps diaphanes (Bull. Soc. Philomat.* I:16) in 1809.

BM 151:331 (1810 ed.); BOA I:136 (1810 ed.); NUC 358:102 (1810 ed.); Poggendorff I:30 (1810 ed.).

Man, Jacobus de, b. 1688, engr.

See Print 7.

245   Manzini, Carlo Antonio, d. 1678.

L'occhiale all'occhio dioptrica pratica dove si tratta della luce; della refrattione de raggi; dell'occhio; della vista; e de gli aiuti, che dare si possono à gli occhi per vedere quasi l'impossibile. Dove in oltre si spiegano le regole pratiche di fabbricare occhiali à tutte le viste, e cannocchiali da osservare i pianeti, e le stelle fisse, da terre, da mare, et altri da ingrandire migliaia di volte i minimi de gli oggetti vicini. Bologna: Heirs of Benacci, 1660.

[2], 268, [4] p., [l], plate: port., ill., tables; 21 cm. (4to)

The rare first edition of an important work in the history of optics, valuable as one of the earliest detailed accounts of methods of grinding and polishing lenses. A large number of fine woodcuts illustrate the machinery and processes described by the author.

BOA I:137; Hirschberg §303.

246   Marescotti, Francesco, fl. 1770.

Saggi di operazioni chirurgiche, e mediche, eseguite con metodo della maggiore semplicità, di cui la stessa natura è maestra, e da esito felice quasi sempre accompagnate. Modena: Heirs of B. Soliani, 1777.

[4], 66, [2] p.; 22 cm. (8vo)

Pflege der Augen 1811.

(38.1) Beer, Georg Joseph. *Das Auge, oder Versuch das edelste Geschenk der Schöpfung vor dem höchst verderblichen Einfluss unseres Zeitalters zu sichern,* 1813. Plate [4]. (10 x 18 cm.)

Fifty-six surgical case histories are reported including eleven cases involving the eye in the treatment of cataract, corneal injuries, ophthalmia, and lachrymal fistula.

Marlé, engr.
See Print 1.

247   Martin, Benjamin, 1704-1782.

A new and compendious system of optics. In three parts, viz. Part I. Catoptrics, or the doctrine of vision by rays reflected from mirrors, or polished surfaces. Part II. Dioptrics, or the theory of vision by rays refracted through lenses, or transparent substances. Part III. A practical description of a great number of the most useful optical instruments and machines, and their construction shewn from the theory; viz. The eye, camera obscura, single and double microscopes, refracting and reflecting telescopes, perspective glasses, the magic lanthorn, &c. The manner of adapting micrometers to microscopes and telescopes of the reflecting sort. London: J. Hodges, 1740.

xxiv, 295, [1], p., 34 plates; 20 cm. (8vo)

The author, a mathematician, instrument maker, and general scientific compiler, drew up a new system of optics to "remove the Difficulties that have hitherto discouraged Persons from the Study of so excellent a Science" (Preface, p. xv). Among the difficulties enumerated by Martin were the perplexing algebraic solutions and geometric demonstrations in the works of Molyneaux and James Gregory (1638-1675) and the expense of Smith's treatise (345). Martin was an ardent champion of the Newtonian system.

BOA I:139.

Masselon, Julien, 1844-1917, ed.
See Wecker (408).

Matsuda, Kinsai.
See Plenk (300).

Mauchart, Burchard David, 1696-1751.
See Keck (216).

Mauchart, Burchard David, 1696-1751, praeses.

"De conjunctivae et corneae, oculi tunicarum, vesiculis ac pustulis."
In Dissertationes medicae selectae Tubingenses (112) 1:143-168.

"De corneae oculi tunicae examine anatomico-physiologico."
In Dissertationes medicae selectae Tubingenses (112) 2:328-367; 3:1-46.

"De empyesi oculi s[ive] pure in secunda oculi camera stagnante."
In Dissertationes medicae selectae Tubingenses (112) 2:175-195.

"De fistula corneae."
In Dissertationes medicae selectae Tubingenses (112) 2:195-232.

"De hydrophthalmia, & hydrope oculi."
In Dissertationes medicae selectae Tubingenses (112) 2:1-18.

"De hypopyo: dem Eyter-Aug, gravi ac intricato affectu oculi."
In Dissertationes medicae selectae Tubingenses (112) 1:48-110.

"De maculis corneae earumque operatione chirurgica, apotripsi."
In Dissertationes medicae selectae Tubingenses (112) 2:261-328.

"De mydriasi, pupillae seu p. n. dilatatione."
In Dissertationes medicae selectae Tubingenses (112) 2:18-72.

"De ocul [*sic*] artificiali, ekblepharo & ypoblepharo."
In Dissertationes medicae selectae Tubingenses (112) 1:250-282.

"De palpebrarum tumoribus cysticis casuque speciali magni tumoris steatomatico-scirrhosi e palpebra superiore et orbita feliciter nuperrime extirpati."

In Dissertationes medicae selectae Tubingenses (112) 1:283-312.

"De paracentesi oculi in hydrophthalmia, et amblyopia senum."

In Dissertationes medicae selectae Tubingenses (112) 1:341-370.

"De pupillae phthisi ac synizesi, s. angustia p. n. & concretione."

In Dissertationes medicae selectae Tubingenses (112) 2:73-114.

"De setaceo nuchae, auricularum, ipsiusque oculi."

In Dissertationes medicae selectae Tubingenses (112) 2:232-260.

"De staphylomate, vexato nomine, affectuque oculi difficili ac intricato."

In Dissertationes medicae selectae Tubingenses (112) 1:168-250.

"De synechia, sive praeternaturali adhaesione corneae cum iride."

In Dissertationes medicae selectae Tubingenses (112) 1:110-143.

"De ulceribus corneae."

In Dissertationes medicae selectae Tubingenses (112) 2:141-174.

"De ungue oculi, s. pure inter corneae lamellos collecto."

In Dissertationes medicae selectae Tubingenses (112) 2:114-140.

"Ophthalmoxysis nov-antiqua, s. Woolhusiano-Hippocratica nobilissima ocularia e textu graeco eruta & bis mille annos neglecta nunc demum penitus emergens."

In Dissertationes medicae selectae Tubingenses (112) 1:1-47.

"Oratio publica in D. D. Tayloris, angli, merita famamque habita cum fasces rectorales de poneret."

In Dissertationes medicae selectae Tubingenses (112) 2:368-392.

"Tobiae levcomata."

In Dissertationes medicae selectae Tubingenses (112) 1:312-340.

248 Mauchart, Burchard David, 1696-1751, praeses.

De ungue oculi seu pure inter corneae lamellas collecto. Permittente gratiosa facultate medica pareside Burc. David Mauchart. . . . Disputabit pro licentia summos in medicina honores & privilegia doctoris rite catessendi, respondens Carolus Ferdinandus Bilger, Esslingensis, Ad Diem ... Jul. MDCCXLII. Tübingen: G. F. Pflick & J. D. Bauhof, 1742.

24 p.; 20 cm. (4to)

Burchard David Mauchart, professor of anatomy and surgery at the University of Tübingen, was one of the outstanding ophthalmologists of his time. His publications appeared exclusively in the form of theses by his pupils, like this one which deals with the pus which collects between the layers of the cornea. It appears also in Haller's *Disp. Chir.*, Lausanne, 1755 (1:381-395); and also in *Dissertationes medicae selec-tae Tubingenses* (112).

Waller 6337.

Mauchart, David, 1735-1767, respondent.

"Novum problema chirurgicum de extractione cataractae ultra perficienda."

In Dissertationes medicae selectae Tubingenses (112) 3:278-323.

249 Mauclerc, John Henry.

Nomenclatura critica morborum ocularium: or, a critical index to the distempers of the eyes. London: Sold by F. Newbery . . . and C. Heydinger, 1768.

[4], iii, [1], 32 p.; 23 cm. (8vo)

A curious little dictionary of Latin names or latinized forms of Greek names given to diseases of the eyes. Most entries are accompanied by a definition, though no etymologies are provided. The whole is completed with an "Index graecus."

Blake, p. 293; Hirschberg §400.

250 Maunoir, Jean Pierre, 1768-1861.

Mémoires sur l'organisaiton de l'iris et l'opération de la pupille artificielle. Paris & Geneva: J. J. Paschoud, 1812.

[4], 69 p., [1] plate; 20 cm. (8vo)

The procedure for iridectomy modified by Maunoir, a Swiss surgeon and ophthalmologist, was widely adopted by other ophthalmic surgeons. It was incorporated into the ophthalmological textbooks of the period. Guthrie (171) [p. 25-27] summarizes Maunoir's technique and Scarpa's adaptation of it. The author continued to operate for cataract to the age of eighty with success using an ingenious system of mechanical supports to steady his arms.

Hirschberg §780.

251 Maunoir, Jean Pierre, 1768-1861.

Mémoire sur les causes de non-succès dans l'opération de la cataracte et des moyens d'y remédier. Bordeaux: H. Faye, 1842.

[2], 88 p., [2] plates; 22 cm.

Written in the author's seventy-fourth year and based on forty-five years of experience, this work treats the accidents which often compromise the success of the extraction operation for cataract. A full biographical notice of the author appeared in *Compte rendu des travaux de la Société Médicale de Genève pendant l'année 1861*, p. 17-33 (1862).

Hirschberg §780.

252 Mauthner, Ludwig, 1840-1894.

The sympathetic diseases of the eye. . . . Translated from the German by Warren Webster and James A. Spalding. New York: William Wood & Co., 1881.

iv, [5]-220 p.; 19 cm.

Translation of "Die sympathischen Augenleiden" which comprises Hefte I-II (1879) of Mauthner's *Vortraege aus dem Gesammtgebiete der Augenheilkunde* (Wiesbaden, 1878-89). Hirschberg ranks Mauthner with Arlt and Stellwag von Carion among the most important figures in Viennese ophthalmology in the second half of the nineteenth century.

253 May, Charles Henry, 1861-1943.

Manual of the diseases of the eye for students and general practitioners. New York: W. Wood and

Co., 1900.

xiii, [3], 406 p., VI plates: ill.; 19 cm.

The first edition of a text that went through twenty-four English editions between 1900 and 1974. It has been translated into German, Italian, French, Dutch, and Spanish as well.

254 Mead, Richard, 1673-1754.

The medical works of Richard Mead . . . with an account of the life and writings of the author. Edinburgh: A. Donaldson and J. Reid for C. Buglass (Berwick), 1765.

3 v. in 2 (18, 272 p., 4 plates; vii, [1], 255 p., [1] plate; vii, [1], 213, [73] p.); 17 cm. (12mo)

The eleventh chapter (3:99-105) of the author's *Medical precepts and cautions* is devoted to diseases of the eye and was considered authoritative in this field, even though it contained nothing original, because of the high standing of Mead. It is here incorporated into the last collected edition of Mead's works which includes many other proofs of his extensive practice and attentive observation.

Hirschberg §392; Osler 3362.

255 Melli, Sebastiano, fl. 1713-1750.

Delle fistole lacrimali il pro, e contra nel nuovo methodo di guarirle, proposto dal Sig. Domenico Anel Francese, ed impugnato dal Sig. Francesco Signorotti in Genova. Con riflessioni chirurgiche, et anatomiche. Venice: G. B. Recurti, 1717.

150, [6] p., [1] plate; 16 cm. (8vo)

In 1713 Anel (17, 18) successfully performed the first catheterization of the lachrymal duct, thereby revolutionizing the treatment of affections of the lachrymal apparatus. Melli and Francesco Signorotti (341) quickly emerged as the fiercest opponents to Anel's procedures. Originally published in 1713, this work contains a translation of Anel's work with Melli's own extensive comments and criticisms. Signorotti's objections to Anel's work are also reprinted here.

Hirschberg §361.

256 Mercuriale, Girolamo, 1530-1606.

De venenis, et morbis venenosis tractatus locupletissimi, variaque doctrina referti non solùm medicis, verum etiam philosophis magnopere utiles . . . in libros duos digesti: opera Alberti Scheligii.

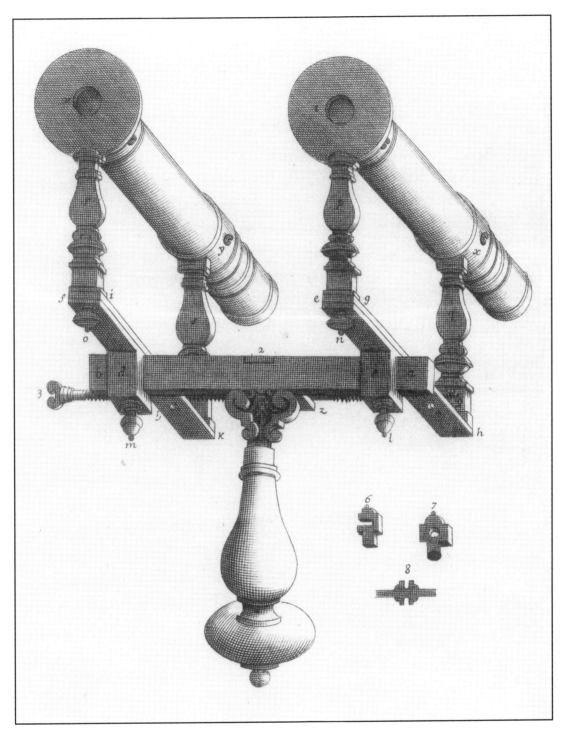

(75.1) Chérubin de Orléans. *La vision parfaite: ou le concours des deux axes de la vision en un seul point de l'objet*, 1677-81. Plate [3], figure J, following p. 100. (14 x 18 cm.)

Venice: Giunta, 1601.

[3], 47 leaves; 22 cm. (4to)

As with so many of Mercuriale's writings, this early treatise on toxicology was edited and published by one of his students, Albert Schlegel of Warsaw. Mercuriale of Forli, professor of medicine at Padua, Bologna, and Pisa, encouraged his students to publish his teachings but it has been noted that such works published after his lectures and with his approval were generally much inferior to his own writings.

Wellcome I:4245.

257   Metz, Abraham, 1828-1876.

The anatomy and histology of the human eye. Philadelphia: Medical and Surgical Reporter, 1868.

xvi, [17]-184 p.: ill.; 24 cm.

The most important work of a well-known American ophthalmologist of the third quarter of the nineteenth century. Most of the titles cited in the bibliography were published in Germany after 1851, indicating that the author was well abreast of the most recent developments in his field. From 1864 Metz was professor of ophthalmology at the newly founded Charity Hospital Medical College in Cleveland.

258   Meyer, Edouard, 1838-1902.

A practical treatise on diseases of the eye. . . . Translated, with the assistance of the author, from the third French edition, with additions as contained in the fourth German edition by Freeland Fergus. Philadelphia: P. Blakiston, Son & Co., 1887.

xi, [1], 17-647 p.: ill.; 24 cm.

The translation and first American edition of Meyer's most important work, the *Traité des maladies des yeux* (Paris, 1873; 3e éd., Paris, 1887). German born, Meyer spent three years in Berlin under von Graefe (1859-62) before migrating to Paris in 1863. There he remained until his death. The immensely popular *Traité* was also translated into German, Italian, Spanish, Greek, Russian, and Polish. A London edition was also published in 1887.

Hirschberg §1268.

Meyerhof, Max, 1874-1945, trans.

See Muḥammad ibn Kassūm ibn Aslam, al-Ghāfikī (266).

259   Michaelius, Joannes, 1578-1651.

Oculi fabrica, actio, usus, seu de natura visus libellus. Leyden: A. Wyngaerden, 1651.

[16], 84, [172] p.; 15 cm. (8vo)

A complete treatise on the anatomy and physiology of the eye that seems to have escaped the attention of bibliographers and historians of ophthalmology. The 84 numbered pages of the *Oculi fabrica* are followed by 22 unnumbered pages of notes, and another 150 unnumbered pages of poetry the author saw fit to append. The first edition was issued at Dordrecht in 1645 under the title *De oculo*. The author must have enjoyed some popularity, either as an anatomist or a poet, as a Leyden edition was published in 1649. Three separate issues of the 1651 edition appeared at Leyden, each with a different imprint.

259.1   Michel, Guillaume, proponent.

Quaestio medico-chirurgica, quodlibetariis disputationibus, manè discutienda, in Scholis Medicorum . . . anno Domini M. DCC. LXXVIII, M. Claudius-Antonius Caille, . . . praeside. An depressioni cataractae sua laus? Paris: Quillau, 1778.

4 p.; 26 cm. (4to)

260   Mohrenheim, Joseph Jakob, d. 1799.

Beobachtungen verschiedener chirurgischer Vorfälle. Vienna: R. Gräffer 1780 (vol. 2: Dessau: Kosten, 1783).

2 v. in 1 ([16], 214, [2] p., 2 plates; [16], 248 p.); 20 cm. (8vo)

The author of this collection of surgical cases was professor of medicine in Vienna and later at St. Petersburg. While better known for his work in obstetrics, he also specialized in ophthalmology and was widely known as a skilled cataract surgeon. Half of each of these volumes is devoted to observations on the surgery of the eye.

Hirschberg §430; Waller 6595.

261   Molinetti, Antonio, d. 1675.

Dissertationes anatomico-pathologicae quibus humani corporis partes accuratissimè describuntur morbique singulas divexantes explicantur. Opus philosophis utile, medicis verò necessarium. Venice: P. Balleoni, 1675.

[8], 338 p., [3] plates; 22 cm. (4to)

Molinetti, son of a Venetian surgeon, was the successor of

Vesling and the immediate predecessor of Morgagni as professor of anatomy at Padua. This work, first issued in 1669 but considerably augmented in this edition, gives a survey of the anatomy and physiology of the whole body. Of great importance are his investigations on the physiology of the senses and the brain, the sensitive and motoric nerves, and the refraction of the eye. The section on vision, the structure, and diseases of the eye comprise six chapters (p. 138-160) and includes two plates showing the enlarged anatomy and physiology of the eye.

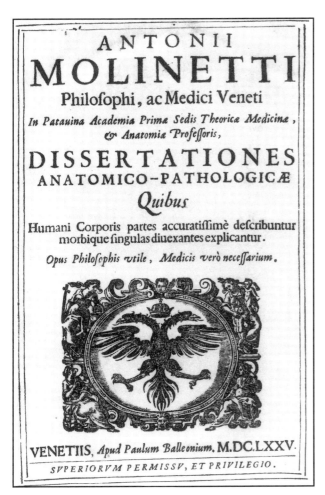

(261) Molinetti, Antonio. *Dissertationes anatomico-pathologicae*, 1675. Title page. (12 x 19 cm.)

262   Monro, Alexander, 1733-1817.

Three treatises. On the brain, the eye, and the ear. Edinburgh: Bell & Bradfute, 1797.

viii, [9]-32, 32*^{r-v}, [33]-263 p., 24 plates; 34 cm. (fol.)

Included in this collection of anatomical studies is the author's reiteration of his claim to the discovery of the interventricular foramen. However, J. A. Sharp [*Medical history* 5:83-93 (1961)] has argued that the "foramen of Monro" is misnamed, as Monro "added nothing of value to the pre-existing descriptions of the foramen, and secondly because he actually misinterpreted the nature of the communication between the third and lateral ventricles." The treatise on the structure and functions of the eyes is illustrated by nine copperplate engravings. Monro *Secundus* is considered the greatest of the family dynasty which monopolized the teaching of anatomy in Edinburgh for more than a century. Cf. Rex E. Wright-St. Clair. *Doctors Monro: a medical saga* (London: Wellcome Historical Medical Library, 1964).

Hirschberg §393; Waller 6646.

Mons, Charles Jacques van, jt. author.
See Vleminckx (392).

Monte, Giovanni Battista da, 1498-1551, trans.
See Aetius, of Amida (5).

Moore, William Daniel, 1813-1871, trans.
See Donders (115).

Morand, Sauveur François, 1697-1773, & César Verdier, 1685-1759.
"Rapport des opérations de la cataracte par l'extraction du cristallin, faites devant les Commissaires de l'Académie, par M. Poyet. . . ."
In Académie Royale de Chirurgie, *Mémoires* (2).

Morand, Sauveur François, 1697-1773.
See Devaux (108).

262.1   Morax, Victor, 1866-1935.
Recherches bactériologiques sur l'étiologie des conjonctives aiguës, et sur l'asepsie dans la chirurgie oculaire. Paris: Société d'Éditions Scientifiques, 1894.

144 p., [1] plate; 26 cm.

Series: Bibliothèque générale de médecine.

A systematic work on the different types and the etiology of conjunctivitis containing a final chapter on asepsis in oph-thalmic surgery. The volume is illustrated with a lithograph which was made from the author's original drawing.

Born in Switzerland, Victor Morax studied in Freiburg (Ger-many) and later in Paris, where he completed his medical doc-torate in 1849. In addition to being an ophthalmologist at La Riboisière Hospital, he was co-editor of the *Annales d'Oculistique* (cf. Hirschberg §1273). In 1896 Morax de-scribed—simultaneously with T. Axenfeld—the diplobacillus that causes chronic or acute blepharocojunctivitis in man (Hemophilus duplex).

Fischer II:1066; NUC 394:145.

263   Morgagni, Giovanni Battista, 1682-1771.

Adversaria anatomica omnia archtypis aereis tabulis Cominianis ab auctore ipso communicatis, & universali accuratissimo indice ornata. Opus nunc vere absolutum, inventis, et innumeris observation-ibus, ac monitis refertum, quibus universa humani corporis anatome, & . . . res medica, & chirurgica admodum illustrantur. Venice: Remondiniana, 1762.

[2], xvi, 108, [2], 109-244 p., 11 plates; 41 cm. (fol.)

Regarded as the founder of pathological anatomy and credited with introducing and propagating the correct doctrine on the nature of cataract in Italy, Morgagni here corrected many ana-tomical errors of his predecessors. The final "adversaria" con-tains major sections on the eyes and eyelids. Morgagni was the first to describe the condition now known as Morgagnian cataract. The author reviewed the text for this edition and cor-rected some typographical errors of the edition published by Comino in Padua in 1719. The preface to the original edition by Giovanni Battista Volpi is included.

Hirschberg §404.

264   Morgan, John, 1797-1847.

Lectures on diseases of the eye. . . . Second edition, carefully revised, and enlarged with notes, by John F. France. London: S. Highley, 1848.

xx, 222 p., 18 plates; 23 cm.

Morgan was engaged in the preparation of this second edition (lst ed., 1839) when he was taken seriously ill. Editorial re-sponsibility was then assumed by Morgan's friend and col-league, John Frederick France (1818-1900), who published the *Lectures* the year following Morgan's death. France added the biographical memoir of the author that had appeared in both the *Medical Gazette* and the *Gentleman's Magazine*. Surgeon

at Guy's Hospital from 1821, Morgan had limited himself in later years to ophthalmic surgery at the Guy's Hospital Eye Infirmary.

Hirsch IV:266; Hirschberg §668.

265   Morton, Andrew Standford, 1847-1925.

Refraction of the eye, its diagnosis and the correction of its errors with chapter on keratoscopy. Philadelphia: P. Blakiston, 1881.

viii, 57 p.: ill.; 20 cm.

The first American edition of a popular work on refraction intended for beginners. A London edition was published the same year.

265.1   Muck, Ferdinand, respondent.

Dissertatio anatomica de ganglio ophthalmico et nervis ciliaribus animalium . . . praeside Friderico Tiedemann . . . publico eruditorum examini submittit auctor Ferdinandus Muck Euerbacensis ad diem XVI. mart. MDCCCXV. Landshut: J. Thomann, 1815.

vi, [7]-94 p., 2 plates; 25 cm. (4to)

NUC 399:265.

266   Muḥammad ibn Kassūm ibn Aslam, al-Ghāfikī, 12th cent.

Al-Morchid fi'l-kohhl; ou, le guide d'oculistique. Ouvrage inédit de l'oculiste arabe-espagnol. . . . Traduction des parties ophtalmologiques d'après le manuscrit conservé à la bibliothèque de l'Escurial par Max Meyerhof. Barcelona: Laboratoires du Nord de l'Espagne, 1933.

225, [3] p., [2] plates; 29 cm.

A French translation of the ophthalmological section of a twelfth century Arabic manuscript from the library of the Escurial Palace. Nothing is known of the circumstances of the life of the author beyond the fact that he was a practicing ocu-list near Cordova and was well acquainted with Arabic medi-cal literature. A glossary of French and Arabic terms is in-cluded.

Hirschberg §271.

267   Müller, Johannes, 1801-1858.

Zur vergleichenden Physiologie des Gesichtssinnes des Menschen und der Thiere nebst einem Versuch über die Bewegungen der Augen und über den menschlichen Blick. Leipzig: C. Cnobloch, 1826.

xxxii, 462, [2] p., 8 plates; 20 cm.

Written at the age of only 25, this is one of Müller's earliest and most important publications. It "includes (p. 73) his explanation of the colour sensations produced by pressure upon the retina" (G-M 1495). Polyak (*Vertebrate visual system*) cites Müller as the "originator of the concept of 'specific energy of nerves' and of the 'theory of identical points' of two eyes in single binocular vision." Cf. Burton Chance, "Johannes Müller; a sketch of his life and ophthalmologic works," *Transactions of the American Ophthalmological Society* 42:230-242 (1944).

G-M 1495; Hirschberg §1015; Waller 6734.

Munk, Ole, ed.
See Soemmerring (347).

268   Muter, Robert.

Practical observations on various novel modes of operating on cataract, and of forming an artificial pupil. Wisbech: J. White for T. Underwood (London), 1811.

[4], ix, [1], 115, [3] p.; 23cm. (8vo)

Muter's only contribution to the literature of ophthalmology was this treatise on the formation of an artificial pupil, published in the small Cambridgeshire village of Wisbech and largely ignored by his contemporaries and by later historians and bibliographers in the field. Muter, a member of the Royal College of Surgeons in London, took his medical degree at Edinburgh two years after the publication of this work.

269   Muys, Jan, b. 1654.

Praxis medico-chirurgica rationalis, seu observationes medico-chirurgicae secundum solida verae philosophiae fundamenta resolutae. Decades duodecim. Amsterdam: J. Wolters, 1695.

[12], 419, [9] p., [1] plate: ill.; 15 cm. (12mo)

Included in this collection of medical and surgical case histories is an account (p. 394-398) of a tumor of the orbit in which the eyeball was successfully extirpated by a surgeon named Seelen using a knife of Fabricius von Hilden's design (133). The author practised at Leyden where he also held the post of mayor for a time.

Hirschberg §369.

270   Nannoni, Angelo, 1715-1790.

Dissertazioni chirurgiche . . . I. Della fistola lacrimale. II. Della cateratta. III. De medicamentis exsiccantibus. IV. De medicamentis causticis. Paris: s.n., 1748.

xii, 245, [1] p.; 19 cm. (8vo)

Nannoni, Benevoli's (43) pupil and successor as chief surgeon at the Hospital Santa Maria Nuova in Florence, was probably the most famous and skillful surgeon of his time in Tuscany. The first two sections of this work deal with ophthalmological subjects. They are followed by two Latin treatises which were prize winning essays at the Paris Academy of Surgery. Haller provides a detailed discussion of Nannoni's works (Haller Chir II:288-290).

Haller Chir II:289; Hirschberg §401.

271   Nannoni, Lorenzo, 1749-1812.

Dissertazione sulla cateratta. Milan: A. Magg, 1780.

61 p.; 21 cm. (8vo)

The only ophthalmological work by the son of Angelo Nannoni (270), this text treats the etiology of inflammations of the crystalline lens. At the age of twenty, Nannoni traveled to France, England, and Holland at the expense of Pietro Leopoldo, Archduke of Austria and Grand Duke of Tuscany, accompanied by Felice Fortana (140), Jean Fabroni and Georges Sancti. The importance of these travels to Nannoni is suggested by the fact that eleven years later he dedicated this work to his patron, the Austrian archduke.

Hirschberg §1114.

272   Nettleship, Edward, 1845-1913.

Student's guide to diseases of the eye. . . . Second American from the second revised and enlarged English edition. With a chapter on examination for color perception, by William Thomson. Philadelphia: Henry C. Lea's Son & Co., 1883.

xix, [1], [13]-416 p., [1] plate: ill.; 20 cm.

The first edition of this popular textbook on the diseases of the eye was published at London in 1879, and the first American edition at Philadelphia in 1880. Nettleship originally took a degree in veterinary medicine, later becoming a student at Moorfields Eye Hospital. Surgeon to the South London Ophthalmic Hospital, St. Thomas's Hospital and the Royal Ophthalmic Hospital, Nettleship earned a reputation as a skilled operator, teacher, and clinical researcher. After 1902 Nettleship devoted most of his attention to congenital disorders of the eye.

272.1 Neue Bibliothek für die Chirurgie und Ophthalmolgie.

Herausgegeben von C. J. M. Langenbeck. . . . Zweyter Band. Erstes Stück. . . . Hannover: Hahn Brothers, 1819.

[2], 146 p., 2 plates; 19 cm. (8vo)

Provenance: Dem Ärzl. Verein Bundens (inscription);—Graubünden Kantons Bibliothek (stamp).

Contents: Holscher, G. P., Ueber Verrenkungen von Astley Cooper . . . mitgetheilt aus dem ersten Theile der Surgical essays;—Schlagintweit, W. A. J., Ueber den gegenwärtigen Zustand der künstlichen Pupillenbildung in Teutschland;—' Articles & review by C. J. M. Langenbeck: Bemerkungen über das Gräf'sche Coreoncion mit doppelten Haken;—Abhandlung von den Brüchen . . . von William Lawrence ... nach der 3ten Ausgabe . . . 1818;—Mein Instrument zur künstlichen Pupillenbildung kann nun auch zerlegt werden.—Anatomische Untersuchungen der Gegend, wo die Schenkelbrüche entstehen.

A collection of surgical and ophthalmological essays, abstracts, and reviews. The entire series was published in four volumes between 1815 and 1828 and was edited by Conrad Johann Martin Langenbeck. "This noted German surgeon and anatomist became professor of anatomy and surgery at Göttingen, and was named surgeon-general of the Hanoverian Army in 1814. He founded the surgery and ophthalmology clinic at Göttingen in 1807, and is especially remembered for devising an operation to construct an artificial pupil by implanting a slip of iris in a corneal incision" (Heirs 1320).

Hirsch III:667; NUC 315: 96; NYAM 22:576.

Neuffer, Philipp Jacob, respondent.

"De mydriasi, pupillae seu p. n. dilatitione."

In Dissertationes medicae selectae Tubingenses (112) 2:18-72.

The New Sydenham Society.

See Selected monographs (338.1).

273 Newton, Sir Isaac, 1642-1727.

Opticks: or, a treatise of the reflexions, refractions, inflexions and colours of light. Also two trea-

tises of the species and magnitude of curvilinear figures. London: S. Smith and B. Walford, 1704.

41, 144, 211, [1], p., 19 plates; 24 cm. (4to)

The classical formulation and first full presentation of Newton's corpuscular or emission theory of light. Newton and Huygens (1989-199) are the two great founders of the modern science of optics. Newton delayed publication of this work for many years because of his wish to avoid unpleasant disputes over priority, like that which ensued with Robert Hooke after publication of Newton's paper on light and color in 1671. Only after the death of Hooke in 1703 did Newton allow publication of the *Opticks*.

Newton discovered the composition of white light; he explained the colors of the rainbow; speculated on the double refraction of Iceland spar; and attempted an explanation of 'Newton's rings.' His corpuscular theory of light remained the dominant theory well into the nineteenth century, when the work of Young (423.1) and Maxwell seemed to establish the wave theory. More recently however, important features of the corpuscular theory have revived, and with Planck's quantum theory, modern views now ascribe both corpuscular and wave properties to light. Appended to the *Opticks* are two highly important mathematical treatises which are not present in later editions. These treatises constitute Newton's first published works on calculus.

Babson 132; BOA I:104; Gray 174; Hirschberg §451.

273.1 Newton, Sir Isaac, 1642-1727.

Optical lectures read in the publick schools of the University of Cambridge, anno domini, 1669. . . . Never before printed. Translated into English out of the original Latin. London: F. Fayram, 1728.

xi, [1], 212 p., 13 plates; 20 cm. (8vo)

Contents: "The refrangibility of rays is different" (p. 1-45); —"Of the measure of refractions" (p. 46-96); —"Of the refractions of planes" (p. 97-172); —"Of the refractions of curve surfaces" (p. 173-212).

"Newton's Lucasian lectures of 1669 were divided into two parts, the second of which was published in improved form in the *Opticks* (273); the first part is here published for the first time" (Norman 1592).

Babson 154; BM 171:330; BOA I:151; Gray 190; More, p. 57-58; Norman 1592; NUC 417:466; Wallis 190.

273.2 Noethig, Franz Nicolaus.

Dissertatio inauguralis anatomica de decussatione nervorum opticorum . . . praeside . . .

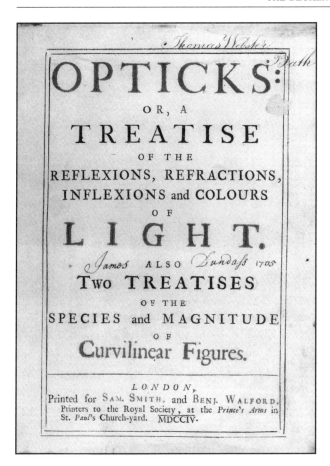

(273) Newton, Sir Isaac. *Opticks*, 1704. Title page.
(18 x 24 cm.)

Sam. Th. Soemmerring pro obtinensis summis publico eruditorum examini subiecit auctor Franc[iscus] Nic[olaus] Noethig. Mainz: I. I. Alef; heirs of Haeffner, 1786.

[10], [3]-48, [2] p., 1 folding plate; 19 cm. (8vo)

An inaugural dissertation on the cranial nerves, especially the optic nerve, publicly presented to the physicians of Mainz on the 17th of May, 1786. The praeses to the thesis was Samuel Thomas Soemmerring (cf. 348, 349). Included in this work is a plate depicting the optic nerve and chiasma which was engraved after Soemmerring's original drawing.

BM 172:594; Callisen XIV:39; NUC 420:581.

Norris, William Fisher, 1839-1901, ed.
See System of diseases of the eye (367).

Norton, Arthur Trehern, 1841-1912.
See Walton (399.1).

274   Noyes, Henry Drury, 1832-1900.

A treatise, diseases of the eye. New York: William Wood and Co., 1881.

xii, [2], 360 p., [2] plates: ill.; 23 cm.

Part of the *Wood's library of standard medical authors,* this work was later the basis for Noyes's famous *Text-book* (275). Like many Americans interested in ophthalmology in the mid-nineteenth century, Noyes spent several years in the clinics and lecture halls of the major figures in European ophthalmology. Noyes was one of the first to employ cocaine as a local anesthetic in eye operations, and the first to investigate the relation of retinitis to glycosuria. Under his direction, the New York Ear and Eye Infirmary developed into one of the finest specialist hospitals in the world.

275   Noyes, Henry Drury, 1832-1900.

A text-book on diseases of the eye. New York: William Wood & Co., 1890.

xiv, 733 p., 11 plates: ill.; 24 cm.

Noyes's principal work, the *Text-book* is the outgrowth of his *Treatise* (274) published nine years earlier. Though never translated or published outside the United States, the *Text-book* is noted in Hirsch as "eins der besten und am meisten gebrauchten in jener Zeit."

BOA I:154; Hirsch IV:389; Hirschberg §763; Waller 6911.

276   Nuck, Anton, 1650-1692.

Sialographia et ductuum aquosorum anatome nova, priori auctior & emendatior. Accedit defensio ductuum aquosorum, nec non fons salivalis novus, hactenus non descriptus. Leyden: P. van der Aa, 1690.

[14], 158, [16] p., 6 plates; 16 cm. (8vo)

Published originally in 1685 under the title *De ductu salivali novo, saliva, ductibus oculorum aquosis, et humore oculi aqueo* (G-M 1101), this revised and enlarged edition contains some of the author's most important observations on the salivary glands and the glands and ducts of the eye. The second part of the work (p. [77]-155) treats the aqueous chamber and the aqueous humor of the eye and includes surgical case histories.

Hirschberg §324; Waller 6919.

277   Nuck, Anton, 1650-1692.

Operationes et experimenta chirurgica...Editio novissima. Leyden: S. Luchtmans, 1733.

[2], 170, [10] p., [4] plates; 16 cm. (8vo)

A collection of fifty surgical observations, seven of which are given to the treatment of ocular disorders: strabismus (VI), depression of cataract (VII), symphisis of the eyelids (VIII), leukoma (IX), artificial glass eyes (X), hordeolum (XII), and hypopyon (XIII). This popular little work went through five Latin editions between its original publication in 1692 and this final edition. A German translation was published at Lübeck in 1709, and a Dutch translation at Leyden in 1740.

Blake, p. 328.

278 Oeller, Johann Nepomuk, 1850-1932.

Atlas der Ophthalmoskopie. Wiesbaden: J. F. Bergmann, 1896-99.

5 pts. ([38] p., 12 plates; [30] p., 15 plates; [30] p., 15 plates; [30] p., 15 plates; [42] p., 18 plates); 41 cm.

In Oeller's opinion the finest ophthalmoscopic atlas that had yet appeared was Jaeger's *Beiträge zur Pathologie des Auges* (204). Because of the expense involved in color reproduction, few atlases of the period could approach the quality of Jaeger's plates. It was Oeller's intention in publishing the present atlas to provide lithographic plates of greater detail and more intense color, and to update the text with the most recent observations made since the publication of the first part of Jaeger's *Beiträge* more than forty years before. The plates were lithographed after Oeller's own oil sketches by the art institute and press of the University of Würzburg under the supervision of H. Stürtz. The explanatory text for each plate is provided in both German and English. Extra title-page: Atlas of ophthalmoscopy. . . . The text translated into English by A. H. Knapp.

BOA I:155; Fischer II:1139; Hirschberg §1029 (52).

279 Oeller, Johann Nepomuk, 1850-1932.

Atlas seltener ophthalmoskopischer Befunde. Zugleich Ergänzungstafeln zu dem Atlas der Ophthalmoskopie. Wiesbaden: J. F. Bergmann, 1900-12.

8 pts. ([40] p., 5 plates; [28] p., 5 plates; [24] p., 5 plates; [24] p., 5 plates; [20] p., 5 plates; [24] p., 5 plates; [20] p., 5 plates; [22] p., 5 plates): ill.; 40 cm.

Forty plates illustrating the more rare ophthalmic diseases, provided as a supplement to the *Atlas der Ophthalmoskopie* (278). As in the earlier atlas, the plates were all lithographed after Oeller's own oil sketches. Text in German and English; each part has an added title-page in English. English translation by Thomas Snowball.

280 Oertel, Johann Gottfried, proponent.

De trachomate, praeside . . . Christiano Vater. . . . Wittenberg: Io. Gothofr. Meyer, 1704.

24 p.; 20 cm. (4to)

A dissertation on trachoma by a student of Christian Vater (1651-1732), professor of medicine at Wittenberg.

Oetinger, Ferdinand Christoph, 1719-1772, praeses.

"De lapsu palpebrae superioris."

In Dissertationes medicae selectae Tubingenses (112) 3:229-277.

281 Ohlemann, Friedrich Wilhelm Max.

Ocular therapeutics for physicians and students. . . . Translated and edited by Charles A. Oliver. Philadelphia: P. Blakiston's Son & Co., 1899.

xv, [1], [9]-274 p.; 21 cm.

Translation of Ohlemann's *Augenärztliche Therapie für Ärzte und Studierende* (Wiesbaden, 1896). This book was the first on ocular therapeutics to be published since Carl Ferdinand Graefe's *Repertorium augenärztlicher Heilmittel* in 1817. Leaving aside all claim to have written a textbook of ophthalmology, Ohlemann limits himself strictly to the treatment of eye diseases.

Oliver, Charles Augustus, 1853-1911, ed.

See Donders (116), Juler (214), Ohlemann (281), *System of diseases of the eye* (367).

O'Malley, Charles Donald.

See Fuchs (145) and Geminus (151).

Ostade, Adrian van, 1610-1685, engr.

See Print 14.

281.1 Pagenstecher, Hermann, 1844-1932.

Atlas der pathologischen Anatomie des Augapfels. Herausgegeben von Dr. Herm[ann] Pagenstecher und Dr. Carl Genth. Atlas of the pathological anatomy of the eyeball . . . translated into English by W. R. Gowers. Wiesbaden: C. W. Kreidel, 1875.

viii, [112] p., XXXVIII plates; 34 cm.

A German-English bilingual "atlas of the pathological anatomy of the eyeball. [Its] copper-plates are descriptive of the pathological changes in the anterior segment of the eyeball, and the pathological changes of the choroid, retina, and intra-ocular end of the optic nerve" (BOA I:158).

A student of Albrecht von Graefe in Berlin, Hermann Pagenstecher continued his studies abroad and became an assistant to his brother, Alexander Pagenstecher, at the eye clinic of Wiesbaden in 1875. Four years later he was promoted to director of the clinic, and in 1890 was appointed professor of ophthalmology. In addition to the above work and several articles, he published a monograph on cataract surgery [*Die Operation des grauen Stars in geschlossener Kapsel* (Wiesbaden, 1877)], which further developed his brother's new method of extraction of the lens in the closed capsule through a scleral incision (1866); cf. Garrison, p. 611.

BOA I:158; Fischer II:1164 (imprint dated: 1873-75); G-M 5910 (imprint dated: 1873-75); NUC 437:452; Pagel, col. 1249.

282 Pallucci, Natalis Giuseppe, 1719-1797.

Description d'un nouvel instrument propre à abaisser la cataracte avec tout le succès possible. Paris: Son of d'Houry, 1750.

22 p., [1] plate; 16 cm. (12mo)
Bound with (283, 284, 285).

This collection of four treatises on cataract represents the author's principal ophthalmologic writings. "Never a convert to the extraction method of dealing with cataract, he invented a very original instrument with which to perform the depression operation. It consisted of a trocar-cannula. When the trocar was in place, the device was used to perforate the sclera. As soon, however, as the proper opening had been made, the trocar was withdrawn well back into the tube, leaving in the scleral perforation a blunt-ended cannula with which the operation was completed without the slightest fear of injury to the iris or ciliary body" (AmEncOph XII:9215).

AmEncOph XII:9215; BOA II:78; Hirschberg §401; Waller 7072.

283 Pallucci, Natalis Giuseppe, 1719-1797.

Histoire de l'opération de la cataracte, faite à six soldats invalides. Paris: Son of d'Houry, 1750.

56 p.; 16 cm. (12mo)
Bound with (282, 284, 285).

AmEncOph XII:9215; BOA II:78; Hirschberg §401; Waller 7073.

284 Pallucci, Natalis Giuseppe, 1719-1797.

Lettre à Monsieur le Marquis de ***, sur les opérations de la cataracte. Paris: s.n., 1751.

39 p.; 16 cm. (12mo)
Bound with (282, 283, 285).

AmEncOph XII:9215; Hirschberg §401.

285 Pallucci, Natalis Giuseppe, 1719-1797.

Methode d'abbattre la cataracte. Paris: d'Houry, 1752.

[4], iv, xvi, 204 p., 2 plates; 16 cm. (12mo)
Bound with (282, 283, 284).

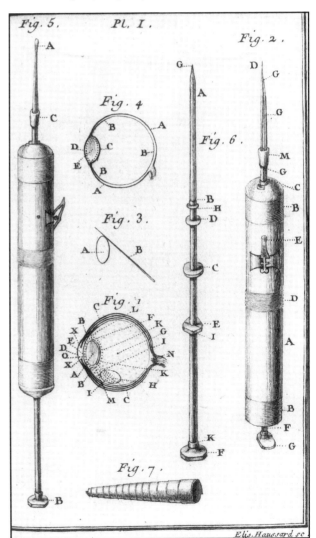

(285) Pallucci, Natalis Giuseppe. *Methode d'abbattre la cataracte*, 1752. Plate I. (10 x 16 cm.)

Hirschberg §401; Waller 7074.

286 Pallucci, Natalis Giuseppe, 1719-1797.

Methodus curandae fistulae lacrymalis. Vienna: J. T. Trattner, 1762.

117, [5] p., 3 plates; 20 cm. (8vo)

After discussing the different methods generally employed in the treatment of lachrymal fistula, the author proposes a new method which consisted of inserting a cannula into the lachrymal duct, passing a fine gold thread from the sac towards the nasal fossa through the nasal duct, and introducing a simple corrosive to clear the obstruction. The treatise is illustrated with a set of copperplate engravings.

AmEncOph XII:9215; Hirschberg §401.

287 Panas, Photinos, 1832-1903.

Leçons sur les maladies inflammatoires des membranes internes de l'oeil comprenant l'iritis, les choroïdites et le glaucome. . . . Rédigées et publiées par E. Kirmisson. Paris: V. Adrien Delahaye & Co., 1878.

[4], 246 p.; 21 cm.

An important work on the inflammatory diseases of the eye. Born on the island of Cephalonia, Panas took his medical degree at Paris in 1860, where he remained for the rest of his life. One of the leading lights in the establishment of the new French school of ophthalmology, he became the first professor of ophthalmology on the Faculté de Médecine; wrote the best French text-book on eye diseases (1894); and was one of the founders of the *Archives d'Ophtalmologie*.

Hirsch IV:487; Hirschberg §1274.

Pansier, Pierre, 1864-1939.

See Collectio ophthalmologica veterum auctorum (82).

288 Panum, Peter Ludwig, 1820-1885.

Physiologische Untersuchungen über das Sehen mit zwei Augen. Kiel: Schwers, 1858.

[4], 94, [2] p., [2] plates: ill.; 28 cm.

One of the foremost Danish physiologists of the nineteenth century, Panum is especially noted for his work in physiological chemistry, collaborating at different times with such figures as Virchow, Koelliker and Cl. Bernard (46). His publications on the physiology of vision are not numerous, being limited to the present work and a number of articles in von Graefe's *Archiv für Ophthalmologie*.

Hirsch IV:493; Waller 7098.

288.1 Pappenheim, Samuel Moritz, 1811-1882.

Die specielle Gewebelehre des Auges mit Rücksicht auf Entwicklungsgeschichte und Augenpraxis. Breslau: G. P. Aderholz, 1842.

vi, 286 p., [4] plates; 23 cm.

Considered by many to be the first work on the histology of the eye including aspects of pathological and comparative anatomy. The volume is illustrated with four plates lithographed after Pappenheim's original drawings. In his introduction Pappenheim claims to have discovered the corneal nerves, but in fact it was Friedrich Schlemm who first described these nerves in 1830. "Pappenheim followed them further into the corneal stroma and described them more precisely" (Hirschberg §1007). Pappenheim published several other noteworthy physiological studies, and in 1847 he received the Grand Prix of the Académie des Sciences for *The reproductive organs of the five classes of vertebrates*.

BM 179:622; Callisen XXXI:142; Hirsch IV:496; Hirschberg §1007; NUC 440:524.

Paré, Ambroise, 1510-1590.

See Guillemeau (168).

289 Parfait-Landrau, Jean François, b. 1797.

Mémoire sur un nouveau procédé à introduire dans l'opération de la cataracte par extraction, au moyen duquel les malades sont mis a l'abri des cataractes membraneuses secondaires. Paris: A. Boucher for Duplessis & Ponthieu, 1827.

vi, [7]-62 p., [1] plate: port.; 22 cm.

A modification of the extraction operation for cataract is proposed by the author, which he claims would diminish the chances of secondary cataracts occurring. Hirschberg credits Parfait-Landrau with discovering the condition now termed *synchisis scintillans*.

Hirschberg §606-607.

290 Pasch, Georg, 1661-1707.

De novis inventis, quorum accuratiori cultui facem praetulit antiquitas, tractatus, secundum ductum disciplinarum, facultatum atque artium in gratiam curiosi lectoris concinnatus. Editio secunda, priori quarta parte auctior. . . . Leipzig: Heirs of Joh. Gross, 1700.

[20], 456, 475-812, [126] p.; 22 cm. (4to)

"Cet ouvrage savant, mais un peu indigeste, est recherché. L'auteur se propose de prouver que la plupart des opinions regardées comme nouvelles étaient deja connues des anciens, et qu'on retrouve dans leurs écrits le germe de toutes les idées de philosophie, de morale et de politique des modernes; il s'attache ensuite à faire voir que toutes les découvertes dans les arts et les sciences ne sont que le résultat et le développement des connaissances qui ont été transmises par l'antiquité . . . " (BioUni XXXII:213).

In no way is the tone of this volume deprecatory to the moderns, however. It is a detailed and still useful history of developments in seventeenth century science and technology, and is much quoted by Thorndike. In Chapter XXIX of the section "De inventis medicis" Pasch discusses theories of vision and the treatment of various disorders of the eye. The "De inventis physico-mathematico-mechanicis" includes sections on optics and various kinds of optical instruments. The first edition was published at Kiloni in 1695 under the title *Schediasma de curiosis hujus seculi inventis.*

291 Pauli, Friedrich, 1804-1868.

Ueber den grauen Staar und die Verkrümmungen, und eine neue Heilart dieser Krankheiten. Stuttgart: Hallberger, 1838.

439 p., [1] plate; 19 cm.

A work on cataract by a noted German surgeon, one of whose specialties was this operation. Pauli was also the first to perform the operation for strabismus on a living person. This copy is from the library of Ernst August, King of Hanover (1771-1851).

Hirsch IV:530; Hirschberg §533.

Paulus Aegineta, 625?-690?
See Aetius, of Amida (5).

291.1 Pauly, Jean Baptiste.

De visu, dissertatio physiologica, quam in Augustissimo Ludoviceo Medico Monspeliensi, Deo duce, & auspice Dei-parâ, tueri conabitur, auctor Joannes-Baptista Pauly, ex oppido Sancti Eparchii, in Comitatu Fuxensi, Artium Liberalium Magister, & jamdudùm medicinæ alumnus, die .mensis Februarii, anni 1777; pro Baccalaureatus gradu obtinendo. Montpellier: J. Martel, 1777.

24 p.; 24 cm. (4to)

Peckham, John, Archbishop of Canterbury, ca. 1230-1292.
See Lacepiera (222).

291.2 Peckham, John, Archbishop of Canterbury, ca. 1230-1292.

Ioannis Archiepiscopi Cantuariensis, perspectivae communis libri tres. Iam postremò correcti ac figuris illustrati. Cologne: A. Mylius for Birckmann, 1592.

[1], 47, [1] leaves: ill.; 21 cm. (4to)

A sixteenth century edition of John Peckham's thirteenth century treatise on optics, "which was the generally accepted medieval handbook on the subject, and was used in the universities until Kepler's day. Peckham was a Franciscan monk who died as Archbishop of Canterbury in 1292. His work is largely based on the Arabic writers, chiefly Ibn al-Haitham [Alhazen] (8). Peckham's most original contribution to optics is his description of concave refracting surfaces, the first time that such glasses were mentioned" (BOA II:80).

Perspectiva communis is divided into three parts: 1. about the properties of light; 2. about reflection; 3. about refraction. The printed versions contain several remarkable woodcut illustrations, among those a diagram of the eye, which Sarton considers "probably the earliest to appear in print" (Sarton II:1028). The first edition of the *Perspectiva* was published in Milan, 1482. Some notable editions: Leipzig, 1504; Venice 1504; Cologne, 1508; Nuremberg, 1542; Cologne, 1542, 1627.

Bird, p. 174 (1504, 1542 eds.; 1593 Italian ed.); BM 182:676; BOA II:80 (1504 ed.); Durling 3579-3581 (1504, 1542 eds.); James, p. 39 (1482 ed.); NUC 447:117; Sarton II:1028-1030 (1482, 1504, 1505?, 1508, 1542, 1627 eds.).

Pellier de Quengsy, George.
See Pellier de Quengsy (292).

292 Pellier de Quengsy, Guillaume, 1751-1835.

Recueil de mémoires et d'observations, tant sur les maladies qui attaquent l'oeil & les parties qui l'environment, que sur les moyens de les guérir, dans lequel l'auteur, après, avoir donné un précis de la structure de cet organe, expose un nouveau procédé pour extraire la cataracte, avec un instrument de son invention, & réfute l'efficacité prétendue de l'abaissement. Montpellier: J. Martel, 1783.

xv, [1], 549, [7] p., [1] plate; 21 cm. (8vo)

Truc and Pansier, historians of the Montpellier school of ophthalmology, describe Pellier de Quengsy as a teacher of the first rank, an innovator with original ideas, and one of the most clever and brilliant practitioners of the eighteenth century. The present collection of memoirs includes his earlier publication on cataract extraction, together with extracts from the writings of Guerin, Daviel, Bordenave, Thomassin, Gouan, his father, brother, and others on this subject. Pellier popularized Daviel's cataract extraction operation (2) in Montpellier and simplified it with an instrument of his own invention, the 'ophthalmotome'. To discourage unauthorized reprintings of this work the dedicatory epistle is numbered (no. 446) and initialed by the author.

Hirschberg §380-381.

293   Pellier de Quengsy, Guillaume, 1751-1835.

Précis ou cours d'opérations sur la chirurgie des yeux, puisé dans le sein de la pratique, & enrichi de figures en taille-douce, qui réprésentent les instrumens qui leur sont propres, avec des observations de pratique trèsintéressantes. Paris: Didot, the younger & Mequignon. Montpellier: Rigaut, Roullet, 1789-1790.

2 v. (xxxiv, [2], 437, [9] p., 26 plates; xiii, [3], 152, 143-404 p., 8 plates): port.; 21 cm. (8vo)

Comprehensive and fully illustrated, this is the first monograph in the world's literature devoted exclusively to the surgery of the eye. It is especially noteworthy for its description of the earliest attempt to treat scarred corneas surgically. Pellier de Quengsy's method consisted of making an artificial cornea out of glass and substituting it for the scarred cornea of the patient. The crystal was supported by a silver ring and then sewn by direct suturing onto the patient's eye (1:94-104 & plate 4). All attempts failed. Only at the beginning of the nineteenth century did autotransplants and homotransplants begin to meet with varying degrees of success through the work of Reisinger, Stilling, Koenigshoefer, Markus, and others.

Hirschberg §380-381.

Pellier de Quengsy, Jean Henri.
See Pellier de Quengsy (292).

Peter of Limoges, d. 1306.
See Lacepiera (222).

294   Peters, Eli Otto, b. 1810.
De blepharoplastice. Leipzig: Staritz, 1836.

43 p., [l] plate; 22 cm.

This Leipzig thesis on blepharoplasty consists of an historical section followed by several accounts of surgical cases. Von Ammon noted [*Monatsschrift für Medicine, Augenheilkunde und Chirurgie* 2:493-495 (1839)] that many figures used by Carron du Villards (71) to illustrate blepharoplastic operations were taken from this dissertation.

Hirschberg §568.

Philosophical Society of Edinburgh.
Medical essays and observations.
See Demours (97).

Philumenus.
See Aetius, of Amida (5).

Phipps, Jonathan Wathen.
See Wathen (406).

295   Piazza, Pietro.
Specimen physico-mathematicum publice datum super opticae theorias ad oculum hominis applicatas. Florence: Bonducci, 1779.

55 p., [l] plate; 27 cm. (4to)

While emphasizing the anatomy of the human eye, vision and optics, the book also deals with optical mirrors and lenses, microscopes and telescopes (particularly Galileo's telescope). The copperplate includes an anatomical representation of the eye. This dissertation is dedicated to the Grand Duke Peter Leopold of Tuscany.

296   Pilz, Josef, 1818-1866.
Compendium der operativen Augenheilkunde. Nach seinem Lehrbuch der Augenheilkunde. Prague:

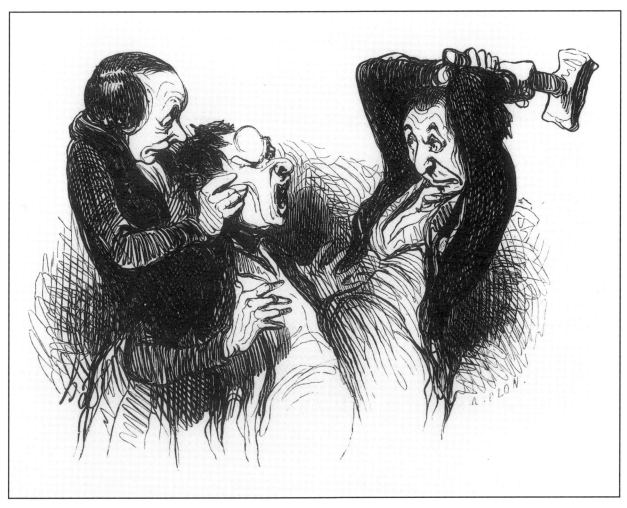

(129) Fabre, Antoine François Hippolyte. *Némésis médicale illustrée...*, 1840. Vol. I, p. 217; illustration by Honoré Daumier. (11 x 8 cm.)

Karl André, 1860.

[8], 202 p., 5 plates; 22 cm.

Written at the request of his students, Pilz's *Compendium* was largely based on his much esteemed *Lehrbuch der Augenheilkunde*, published at Prague the year before.

Hirsch IV:607; Hirschberg §1217.

297 Platter, Felix, II, 1605-1671.

[Theoria . . . cataracta]: ex monumentis Felicis Platerii . . . proponit Felix Platerus. Basel: J. Schroterus, 1626.

[20] p.; 20 cm. (4to)

In 1583, Felix Platter published an anatomical treatise which proposed the revolutionary concept that the retina, rather than the crystalline lens, is the true visual receptor of the eye. The treatise was largely ignored until Platter's nephew and namesake republished it in 1626, resulting in recognition of the novel proposal concerning the retina.

298 Plemp, Vopiscus Fortunatus, 1601-1671.

Ophthalmographia sive tractatio de oculo. Editio altera. Cui praeter alia accessere affectionum ocularium curationes. Louvain: H. Nemp, 1648.

[16], 240 p.; 34 cm. (fol.)

Plemp was professor of medicine at Louvain and one of the foremost physicians of his period. He is perhaps best remembered for his belated though vigorous advocacy of Harvey's discovery of the circulation of the blood. While there is little in the way of novel researches in this work, it is interesting to note that Plemp was the first to espouse the optical theories of Kepler (216.1), originally announced some twenty years previously. He speculated that clouding of the lens might be the cause of cataract but he proceeded no further with this idea. It was not until the beginning of the next century with the work of Maître-Jan (243, 244), Brisseau (63), and Heister (182) that a true understanding of the nature of cataract began to emerge.

BOA I:167; Hirschberg §315.

299 Plenck, Joseph Jacob, Ritter von, 1738-1807.

Doctrina de morbis oculorum. Vienna: R. Graeffer, 1777.

219, [5] p.; 21 cm. (8vo)

Plenck is credited with giving the first course of lectures on

eye diseases in Hungary. His *Doctrina de morbis oculorum* was "perhaps the first useful compendium which contains the achievements of the renaissance of ophthalmology in the eighteenth century and presents them to the student and physician in an easily accessible and understandable way" (Hirschberg §480).

Plenck's work was reissued twice in Latin, translated into Italian, German, and Portuguese [see Santa Anna (323)] and pirated by William Rowley in an English translation in 1790. Rowley's plagiarism went undetected for forty years until Mackenzie alluded to it in a footnote in his textbook (241). However, it was not until 1910 that Hirschberg fully exposed Rowley's plagiarism in his "Über ein abgeschriebenes Lehrbuch der Augenheilkunde," *Centralblatt für Praktische Augenheilkunde* 34:2-14 (1910). See also Charles Snyder, "Why, William Rowley?" *Archives of Ophthalmology* 75:102-105 (1966).

Hirsch IV:632; Hirschberg §480.

300 Plenck, Joseph Jacob, Ritter von, 1738-1807.

[Ganka shin-sho]. Osaka: Gungyokudo; Kyoto: Kobundo, 1815-16.

6 v.: ill.; 26 cm.

For nearly two centuries before Perry's expedition to Edo (Tokyo), the Dutch enjoyed exclusive access to Japan, and were the source of a subtle western influence on Japanese intellectual life. During the last seventy-five years of this period, the term *rangaku* was applied to the study of the Dutch language, as well as to Dutch (i.e. western) medicine, science, mathematics, etc.

The present work, entitled *A new work on ophthalmology*, is a translation of Plenck's *Verhandeling over de oogziekten* (Rotterdam, 1787), the Dutch version of his *Doctrina de morbis oculorum* (299). Western ophthalmology was first introduced to Japan with the translation and publication of this work. The first five volumes contain the translation of Plenk's text by Sugita Rikkyô (Shān-Tián, Lì-qīng). The sixth volume is a pathological and therapeutic supplement written by Sugita's student Matsuda Kinsai (Sōng-Tián, Qín-zhái). The set is written in Chinese characters with Japanese reading marks, and is printed from woodblocks on rice paper. The first volume and the supplement are illustrated with woodcuts, many of which are hand-colored.

Huard, p. 158.

Plenck, Joseph Jacob, Ritter von, 1738-1807. *Yan kē xīn shū.*

See his Ganka shin-sho (300).

301 Porta, Giovanni Battista della, 1535?-1615.

Magiae naturalis libri viginti, in quibus scientiarum naturalium divitiae, & deliciae demonstrantur. Jam de novo, ab omnibus mendis repurgati in lucem prodierunt. Hanover: D. & D. Aubry & C. Schleich for Wechel, 1619.

[32], 622 p.; 18 cm. (8vo)

Porta's immensely popular work on natural magic, first published in 1558 in four books but later enlarged to the present twenty books, was reissued in numerous editions and translations. Of particular interest to this collection are Porta's experiments in optics (Book 17). He was one of the principal inventors of the opera glass and was the first to suggest the combination of lenses to form a telescope or microscope. Partington [*History of chemistry* (London, 1961) 2:15-25] provides a detailed account of the author and this, his most celebrated work.

Hirschberg §307; Wellcome I:5188.

302 Porterfield, William, 1695-1771.

A treatise on the eye, the manner and phaenomena of vision. Edinburgh: A. Miller (London) & G. Hamilton and J. Balfour, 1759.

2 v. ([2], xxxi, [3], 450, [2] p., 5 plates; xxxv, [1], 435 p., 3 plates); 20 cm. (8vo)

"Porterfield was professor of the institutes and practice of medicine at Edinburgh from 1724-26. His book included many original observations. It was the first important British work on the anatomy and physiology of the eye" (G-M 1484.2). Cf. Burton Chance, "William Porterfield, M.D.: an almost forgotten opticophysiologist," *Archives of Ophthalmology* 16:197-207 (1936).

BOA II:86; G-M 1484.2; Hirschberg §457.

Portius, Simon, 1496-1554.

See Porzio (303).

303 Porzio, Simone, 1496-1554.

De coloribus oculorum. Florence: L. Torrentino, 1550.

57 p.; 22 cm. (4to)

One of the earliest monographs on ophthalmology in which the author attempts to explain the cause of the variety of colors of eyes. The position of the eyes and the opinions of Aristotle and Galen on the structure of the eye are also discussed. The author lectured on medicine at Pisa from 1546 to 1552 and was also known as a scientist and philosopher.

BOA I:169; Durling 3742; Wellcome I:5218.

Possevino, Antonio, 1533 or 4-1611.

See Possevino (304).

304 Possevino, Antonio, d. ca. 1637.

Theoricae morborum libri quinque. Addita methodus studiorum medicinae ex Bibliotheca selecta ejus patrui. Mantua: F. Osanna, 1600.

256 p.; 15 cm. (8vo)

The *Theoricae morborum* is a poem in Latin hexameters which includes a section of lll lines (p. 24-28) on ophthalmology. Among the marginal references are: *Morbi oculorum; Convulsio; Visus iners; Glaucoma; Suffusio; Cornea rupta; Epiphora.*

Possevino, a Mantuan physician, was a nephew of the well-known Italian Jesuit writer Antonio Possevino (1533 or 4-1611). Pages 160-256 contain an extract from the latter's great work *Bibliotheca selecta* (Rome, 1593) dealing with the study of medicine and the methods of the great physicians.

Durling 3748.

305 Post, Alfred Charles, 1806-1886.

Observations on the cure of strabismus, with engravings. . . . With an appendix on the new operation for the cure of stammering. New York: C. S. Francis, 1841.

viii, [9]-67 p., 7 plates; 16 cm.

The operation for the cure of strabismus was first successfully performed by Dieffenbach (110) on October 26, 1839. Post, a New York surgeon, was probably the first American to operate for strabismus. A set of tinted lithographs by Nathaniel Currier (1813-1888) illustrate the anatomy of the muscles involved, the instruments used, and the methods of operation. This is one of the few scientific works illustrated by Currier who in 1850 formed the famous partnership with J. Merritt Ives.

Hirschberg §749.

305.1   Pott, Percivall, 1714-1788.

Observations on that disorder of the corner of the eye, commonly called fistula lachrymalis. London: C. Hitch and L. Hawes, 1758.

vii, [1], 84 p.; 20 cm. (8vo)

The first edition of Pott's observations on lacrimal fistula, which was long considered to be definitive on the subject. The *Observations* went through numerous English editions, and was translated into German in 1771. It describes the anatomy of the parts, and "with regard to the treatment of lachrymal obstruction lays down three varieties of the disease: (1) Simple dilatation of the sacculus and obstruction of the nasal duct . . . ; (2) Inflammation, abscess, or ulceration of the same parts . . . ; (3) Obliteration of the natural duct, attended sometimes with caries of the bone" (James, p. 113).

Percivall Pott "was one of the busiest and most famous surgeons in England during the middle of the eighteenth century" (Heirs 928). He was a general surgeon at St. Bartholomew's Hospital from 1744 for almost a half century, and was described by many as a surgical genius. His oeuvre consists of several epoch-making masterpieces, such as his treatises on hernia, head injuries, spinal caries ("Pott's disease"), and hydrocele. On the other hand—according to Hirschberg—Pott "had a deleterious influence on the development of ophthalmology, because he defended couching against the cataract extraction" (§393).

AmEncOph XIII:10329; Blake, p. 360; Hirsch IV:664; Hirschberg §393; James, p. 113; NUC 467:530; Ovio I:1265 (1763 ed.); Pybus 1620 (1769 ed.).

305.2   Pott, Percivall, 1714-1788.

Observations on that disorder of the corner of the eye, commonly called fistula lachrymalis. The fourth edition, improved. London: Hawes, Clarke and Collins, 1772.

[4], vii, [1], 67 p.; 22 cm. (8vo)

The fourth improved edition of Pott's famous treatise on lacrimal fistula [cf. (305.1)].

Blake, p. 360; James, p. 113 (1758 ed.); NUC 467:530.

306   Powell, James W., fl. 1847.

The eye: its imperfections and their prevention; comprising a familiar description of the anatomy and phisiology, of the organ of vision: rules for the preservation, improvement, and restoration of sight, with remarks on near sight and aged sight; on optics, and the use and abuse of spectacles, with directions for their selection. New York: The author, 1847.

[2], xiv, [15]-139, [7] p., [1] plate; 21 cm.

The purpose of this small volume was to advertise Dr. Powell's practice rather than to contribute to ophthalmic knowledge. Acclaimed by the popular press, the work was properly ignored by reviewers in the professional journals. Powell dedicated this commercial publication to Arthur Jacob, M.D., professor of anatomy and physiology in Dublin, whose lectures he attended from 1828 to 1833.

Hirschberg §1035.

307   Power, Henry, 1829-1911.

Illustrations of some of the principal diseases of the eye, with a brief account of their symptoms, pathology, and treatment. London: John Churchill and Sons, 1867.

vii, [1], 631 p., XII plates: ill.; 23 cm.

"A good example of the Victorian era" is how Power's obituary in the *British Medical Journal* begins. He was a man of prodigious energy; hardly anyone could have held more offices; occupied more hospital posts; translated, edited or written more publications—and still have been one of London's leading ophthalmic surgeons for half a century. The present work is Power's major contribution to ophthalmic literature. The twelve lithographic plates are after Power's own watercolors, painted from life.

BOA I:170; Hirsch IV:668; Hirschberg §660.

308   Priestley, Joseph, 1733-1804.

The history and present state of discoveries relating to vision, light, and colours. London: J. Johnson, 1772.

2 v. (v, [9], xvi, 422 p., 14 plates, 1 table; [2], 423-812, [12] p., 9 plates); 26 cm. (4to)

Undertaken as the first volume of a proposed history of all branches of experimental science, this work presents one of the earliest historical accounts of theories of vision, light, and color. Its value lies chiefly in its distillation and narration of the works of others. Priestley, a supporter of the corpuscular theory of light, sought to provide direct experimental proof for this hypothesis in opposition to the wave theory. Priestley's knowledge of mathematics was inadequate for the task which he had set; the book was a financial failure; and he abandoned his scheme to write a multivolume theory of science.

BOA I:171; Crook S479; Hirschberg §88.

(169) Guillié, Sébastien. *Essai sur l'instruction des aveugles, ou exposé analytique des procédés employés pour les instruire*, 1817. Frontispiece. (11.5 x 20 cm.)

309 **Puget, Louis de, 1629-1709.**

Observations sur la structure des yeux de divers insectes, et sur la trompe des papillons, contenuës en deux lettres au R. P. Lamy . . . & dans un memoire qui explique les figures de quelque objets qu'on découvre par le secours du microscope. Lyons: L. Plaignard, 1706.

[8], 157, [3] p., 3 plates; 17 cm. (8vo)

These two letters addressed to the Reverend Père Lamy, a Benedictine father, contain early microscopical observations on the structure of the eyes of such insects as flies, grasshoppers, and crayfish and on the butterfly's proboscis. The first letter was originally published in the *Journal des Sçavans* (January 31, 1704).

BOA II:87.

309.1 **Ramón y Cajal, Santiago, 1852-1934.**

Die Structur des Chiasma Opticum, nebst einer allgemeinen Theorie der Kreuzung der Nervenbahnen. Aus dem Spanischen übersetzt von Dr. J. Bresler, mit einem Vorwort von Dr. P. Flechsig. Leipzig: J. A. Barth, 1899.

vi, [2] , 66 p.: ill.; 25 cm.

A four part treatise on the optic chiasm, on the general theory of the decussation of the sensory and motor tracts, as well as on the corpus callosum and the association fibers.

Santiago Ramón y Cajal was an eminent Spanish neurohistologist, who found his way to medicine through his love of drawing and anatomy. After serving as a regimental surgeon in Cuba, he returned to Spain and became professor of anatomy at the University of Zaragoza in 1877. Later he was on the medical faculties at the Universities of Valencia, Barcelona, and Madrid, where he specialized in histologic studies. He received recognition through a demonstration of silver-impregnated brain sections in 1889, was awarded honorary degrees from Oxford and Cambridge, and gave a series of lectures at Clark University (Worcester, Massachusetts) in the 1890s. In 1906 Ramón y Cajal was the Nobel Prize recipient jointly with Camillo Golgi for their work on the structure of the nervous system. In addition to well over 250 articles on histology, Ramón y Cajal published a number of monographs including one on the retina (cf. Founders, p. 74-77; Garrison, p. 681-682).

NUC 480:295.

309.2 **Rampinelli, Ramiro, 1697-1759.**

Lectiones opticæ. Brescia: J. B. Bossini, 1760.

xxxii, 242, [2] p., [1], XXXII, [1] plates: [1] port.; 26 cm. (4to)

Fifteen "lessons" on optics by the Italian mathematician Ludovico Rampinelli. An Olivetan Benedictine monk, Rampinelli took the first name Ramiro and taught in the monasteries of his order in Bologna and Milano. He was the teacher of Maria Gaetana Agnesi, who—although a woman—was appointed professor at the University of Bologna in 1748. Rampinelli became professor of mathematics at the University of Pavia a year earlier. His other known work, *Istituzioni di meccanica* is an unpublished manuscript.

Lectiones was edited after the author's death by Caesareus Sommariva. It is a richly illustrated volume with thirty-two folding plates with diagrams, a frontispiece portrait of the author, decorative ornamental initials, borders, vignettes, some woodcuts, and some copper engravings.

NUC 480:378; Poggendorff II:565-566.

310 **Ramsay, Andrew Maitland, 1859-1946.**

Atlas of external diseases of the eye. Glasgow: James MacLehose and Sons; New York: The Macmillan Co., 1898.

xvi, 195 p., XLVIII plates; 29 cm.

Ramsay was a prominent Glasgow ophthalmic surgeon of the first quarter of this century, whose fame justly rests on this atlas, one of the finest productions of its kind. With thirty chromolithographs and eighteen photogravures, the atlas illustrates cases Ramsay dealt with at the Glasgow Eye Infirmary. The chromolithographs were produced by Maclagan & Cumming after photographs taken and colored by A. H. Geyer. The eighteen photogravures were prepared by the well-known Glasgow firm of T. & R. Annan.

BOA I:172.

Rawson, Sir William, 1783-1827.

See Adams (4, 4.1).

311 **Redi, Francesco, 1626-1698.**

Lettera intorno all'invenzione degli occhiali. Florence: F. Onofri, 1678.

14 p., [1] plate; 24 cm. (4to)

An important document in the history of eyeglasses in which Redi relates the discovery of a reference to their invention in a manuscript dated 1299 which he regarded as the earliest reference to the use of spectacles. Redi ascribed the invention of eyeglasses, or at least their perfection, to the Dominican friar Allessandro della Spina (d. 1313). The evidence on this subject is fragmentary; however, it would seem that eyeglasses developed from a type of reading glass which probably took the form of a plano-convex lens laid directly on a page to enlarge the letters.

BOA II:88; Hirschberg §297.

311.1 Reghellini, Giovanni Maria, 1710-1772.

Osservazioni sopra alcuni casi rari medici, e chirurgici. Venice: P. Bassaglia for the author, 1764.

[4], cxxxii p., [1] plate: ill. ; 25 cm. (4to)

Provenance: A. Rossi (inscription); —Ferdinando Palasciano (bookstamp); —Umberto Calamida (bookplate).

Six treatises on some unusual medical and surgical cases by the Venetian physician and surgeon, Giovanni Reghellini. The second and sixth treatises describe cataract operations. "Reghellini reports a patient in whom after the couching, the lens reappeared in the anterior chamber. He pushed it back into the interior of the eye while the patient was lying down. Reghellini criticizes [Jacques] Daviel's extraction method [p. xxix-xxx], because it leads to numerous failures" (Hirschberg §404).

Blake, p. 375; BM 200:176; Haller Chir II:329; Hirschberg §404; NUC 485:553; Waller 7809.

Reichenbach, Johann Friedrich.

"Cautelae et observationes circa extricationem cataractae novam methodum synizesin operandi sistentes."

In Dissertationes medicae selectae Tubingenses (112) 3:278-323.

Rembrandt, Hermanszoon van Rijn, 1607-1669.

See Print 16.

311.2 Reuss, August, Ritter von, 1841-1924.

Ophthalmometrische Studien von Dr. Aug. Reuss, Assistenten an der Augenklinik der Wiener Universität; und Dr. M. Woinow aus Moskau. Vienna: Wilhelm Braumüller, 1869.

[4], 59 p.: diagrs., 5 woodcut ills. ; 24 cm.

Ophthalmometric studies by August Reuss and M. Woinow (422.2) containing "examinations on corneal astigmatism after the cataract extraction, about the angle alpha and a new apparatus by Woinow to measure the intraocular pressure" (Hirschberg §901).

"Reuss was born November 9, 1841 in Bilin, Boehemia, and studied in Prague and Vienna. Between 1866-1870 he was assistant at Arlt's eye clinic; in 1870 he became assistant, in 1885 associate professor. In 1904 he was appointed full professor. When the Allgemeine Poliklinik was established in Vienna, Reuss became the director of the eye department and remained in this position for decades" (Hirschberg §1235). Complementing his academic and clinical career, Reuss published numerous significant works on the causes of blindness, the transillumination of ocular coats, color blindness, inflammatory eye diseases, trachoma, corneal erosion, and keratitis.

(311) Redi, Francesco. *Lettera intorno all'invenzione degli occhiali*, 1678. Title page. (17 x 24 cm.)

BM 201:339; Fischer II:1287; Hirsch V:978; Hirschberg §901, 1235; NUC 490:29; NYAM 33:106; Pagel, col. 1369.

Reuss, Christian Friedrich, 1745-1813, ed.

See Dissertationes medicae selectae Tubingenses (112).

312 Reveillé-Parise, Joseph Henri, 1782-1852.

Hygiène oculaire, ou avis aux personnes dont les yeux sont foibles et d'une trop grande sensibilité; avec de nouvelles considérations sur les causes de la myopie ou vue basse, sur l'action des verres concaves et convexes ouvrage particulièrement destiné aux gens de lettres, aux hommes d'état, et à toutes les personnes qui se livrent aux travaux du cabinet. Paris: Cellot for Méquignon-Marvis, 1816.

[4], 193, [l] p.; 19 cm. (12mo)

A popular work on the hygiene of the eyes which went through many editions and translations. Early in his career the author was attached as a physician to Napoleon's armies in Austria, Spain, Holland, and at Waterloo but his reputation grew out of his later work as a writer and medical journalist rather than as a practitioner. Dealing mainly with diseases of the eye affecting students, men of letters, and those whose work involves much reading, this book enters into the field of occupational diseases.

Hirschberg §470.

Rhazes (Abū Bakr Muḥammad ibn Zakarīyā Abrazi), 865?-925?

"Treatise on the smallpox and measles."
See Mead (254).

Rheterius, Joannes, trans.

See Fabricius von Hilden (133).

A rich storehouse or tresurie for the diseased.

See T., A. (368).

313 Richter, August Gottlieb, 1742-1812.

A treatise on the extraction of the cataract. Translated from the German. With a plate; and notes by the translator. London: J. Murray, 1791.

xv, [1], 214 p., [l] plate; 23 cm. (8vo)

Richter, considered the "Reformer of German Surgery," was editor of the first surgical journal, *Chirurgische Bibliothek*, 1771-1796. He is credited with removing the extraction operation for cataract from the hands of itinerant oculists and placing it in those of the 'regular-bred' surgeons. This English translation was taken from the first edition of the author's *Abhandlung von der Ausziehung des grauen Staares* (Göttingen, 1773).

Hirschberg §423-424.

Riester, F. J., trans.

See Weller (412).

Riolan, Jean, 1538-1605.

See Bailey (30.1).

Risner, Friedrich, d. 1580, ed.

See Alhazen (8).

Romano, Fra Teofilo, trans.

See Lacepiera (222).

Roosa, Daniel Bennett St. John, 1838-1908, ed. & trans.

See Stellwag von Carion (354) and (355).

313.1 Rosas, Anton, Edler von, 1791-1855.

Lehre von den Augenkrankheiten. Zum Gebrauche für practische Aerzte und Wundärzte, wie auch zur Benutzung als Leitfaden beim klinischen Unterrichte. Vienna: J. B. Wallishausser, 1834.

xiv, 599, [1] p.; 20 cm.

Note: In the Becker Library's copy signature 9 is misbound, causing an error in the sequence of pagination.

A systematic textbook on ophthalmology in two main parts: 1. pathology and therapy of eye diseases; 2. organic defects of the eye.

A Viennese of Hungarian origin, Anton Rosas was one of the leading ophthalmic surgeons practicing in the first half of the nineteenth century. At first, he was assistant to G. J. Beer (37-40) at the Vienna Eye Clinic, then later he became professor of ophthalmology in Padua, where he established an ambulatory eye institute. Having returned to Vienna in 1821 he succeeded Beer at the eye clinic and became professor of ophthalmology at the University of Vienna. Through the simplification of some methods of treatment and the invention of suitable instruments for eye surgery, he greatly contributed to the advancement of ophthalmology. He was a prolific medical author who wrote with equal facility in both German and Italian.

AmEncOph XV:11467; BM 207:53; Callisen XXXII:2; Hirsch IV:876; NUC 508:685; Waller 8166a.

314 Rosenmüller, Johann Christian, 1771-1820.

Partium externarum oculi humani imprimis organorum lachrymalium descriptio anatomica iconibus illustrata. Leipzig: S. Linck, 1797.

xlvi, [5]-72 p., 5 plates; 24 cm. (4to)

Bound with Haase (173).

Rosenmüller's treatise on the external parts of the human eye and particularly the lachrymal glands is introduced by an extensive annotated bibliography of more than 175 works on this subject. The author, professor of anatomy and surgery at Leipzig, was an able artist and the copperplate engravings illustrating this book are from his own drawings.

Hirschberg §532; Waller 8225.

315 Rowley, William, 1743-1806.

An essay on the ophthalmia or inflammation of the eyes, and the diseases of the transparent cornea; with improvements in the methods of cure. London: F. Newbery, 1771.

[2], ii, 47 p.; 19 cm. (8vo)

The first of several ophthalmic works by one of the more curious figures in eighteenth century British ophthalmology, a man once described as having "the appearance of quackery and reliability at the same time." The greater part of the work is given to the treatment of ophthalmia; the last seven pages to leukoma.

Blake, p. 390; Hirsch IV:904; Hirschberg §396.

316 Rowley, William, 1743-1806.

A treatise on the principal diseases of the eyes; containing a critical and candid examination of the antient and modern methods of cure, of the present defective modes of practice, with an account of new, mild, and successful methods for the cure of diseases of this organ. London: F. Newbery, 1773.

[4], iv, 12, xiii, [14]-159 p.; 21 cm. (8vo)

In 1771 the author established the St. John's Hospital for Diseases of the Eyes, Legs, and Breast in London, considered by some to have been the first special eye hospital in England. The institution was defunct by 1773 but its name reveals three of Rowley's primary medical interests. He published three ophthalmological works in his lifetime; the first, a treatise on ophthalmia, appeared in 1771 and the last, a direct plagiarism of Plenk's textbook (299) was issued in 1790. The present work deals primarily with the medical treatment of eye diseases, though the author asserts that he is perhaps the first author of an ophthalmological work to possess a thorough knowledge of both medicine and surgery. The book was favorably, though not enthusiastically, received by the profession. It is unknown why after the publication of this creditable work Rowley resorted to such bold plagiarism seventeen years later. Cf. Charles Snyder, "Why, William Rowley?" *Archives of Ophthalmology* 75:102-105 (1966).

BOA I:183; Hirschberg §392.

317 Ruete, Christian Georg Theodor, 1810-1867.

Die Scrophelkrankheit, insbesondere die scrophulöse Augenentzündung. Göttingen: Dieterich, 1838.

xii, 222 p., VIII plates; 22 cm.

"Er gehört zu den Gründen der Reform der Augenheilkunde. Von ihm rührt die Augenspiegelung im ungekehrten Bilde und die Erfindung eines neuen Ophthalmotrops her. Er brauchte zuerst das Wort *Uebersichtigheit*" (Hirsch). This work on phlyctenular conjunctivitis was the first of Ruete's many monographs, written while he was *Privat-Docent* at Göttingen. Plates III thru VIII are hand-colored, but without much care or attention to chromatic accuracy.

Hirsch IV:918; Hirschberg §483.

318 Ruete, Christian Georg Theodor, 1810-1867.

Lehrbuch der Ophthalmologie für Aerzte und Studirende. Brunswick: F. Vieweg & Son, 1845.

xvi, 820 p.: ill.; 21 cm.

The last systematic textbook of ophthalmology published in German before the introduction of the ophthalmoscope. Ruete, Karl Himly's (191) protegé, included a description of hypermetropia in the second edition of this work (1853) which marked a real advance in the understanding of the condition. He is also remembered for having introduced ophthalmoscopy by means of the inverted image.

(217) Kircher, Athanasius. *Ars magna lucis et umbrae in decem libros digesta*, 1646. Frontispiece.
(19 x 26.5 cm.)

Hirschberg §483.

319 Ruete, Christian Georg Theodor, 1810-1867.

Bildliche Darstellung der Krankheiten des menschlichen Auges. Leipzig: B.G. Teubner, 1854-60.

9 pts. in 6 v.: ill.; 39 cm.
I-II (1854): viii, 63 p., plates I-VIII.
III (1855): iv, [2], 40 p., plates IX-XII, Supplementtafel I.
IV (1855): [4], 20 p., plates XIII-XVI.
V-VI (1856): iv, 34 p., plates XVII-XXIV.
VII-VIII (1858): viii, 65 p., plates XXV-XXXIII.
IX (1860): [4], 17 p., plate XXXIV, Supplementtafeln II-V.

An important work on eye diseases, therapeutics and ocular surgery. The nine sections of this work are illustrated with thirty-nine engraved plates, most of which are superbly hand-colored. It is interesting that Ruete should have preferred this older, more time-consuming and expensive method to chromolithography. The detail and intensity of colors in these plates are superior to anything that chromolithography was capable of at this period. Plates II-VIII provide ophthalmoscopic views of the fundus; the remaining plates illustrate the external diseases of the eye.

Hirsch IV:918; Hirschberg §483.

Rufus, of Ephesus, fl. late 1st cent. B.C. -mid- 1st cent. A.D.?
See Aetius, of Amida (5).

320 Rungius, Johannes, 16th cent.

De praecipuis visus symptomatis eorumque causis physica & medica contemplatio. Basel: L. Osten, 1578.

[46] p.; 19 cm. (4to)

Rungius, the younger son of a family of noted Protestant theologians from the Pomeranian town of Greifswald, studied medicine at Basel and in 1578 presented this thesis on sight and the defects of vision. It deals primarily with physiological optics and theories of vision from a humanistic rather than a medical viewpoint, but it appears to be the earliest published ophthalmological thesis. Huldrych M. Koelbing provides an account of the author and an analysis of the significance of this work in the early history of ophthalmology in *Renaissance der Augenheilkunde: 1540-1630* (Bern & Stuttgart: Hans Huber, 1967).

Hirschberg §953.

321 Russel, J., Physician and Oculist.

His elixirated spirit of scurvy-grass, both plain and purging. With his pectoral lozenges and worm-powder. And also his pills of scurvy-grass. London?: s.n., ca. 1690.

1 leaf; 235 x 171 mm.

Provenance: A. E. Russell (bookplate); —Society of Apothecaries, London (bookplate).

This broadsheet is a remarkable and possibly unique advertisement of a seventeenth century London physician, oculist, and apothecary. Fifteen crude woodcuts surround the text of the first page, two of which illustrate eye surgery. The Bodleian Library holds a similar broadside by J. Russel (Wing R2340) with similar cuts but a quite different text. A second Russel broadside from the British Museum is reproduced by L. A. G. Strong in *Dr. Quicksilver 1660-1742: the life and times of Thomas Dover, M.D.* (London: A. Melrose, 1955). Accompanying the broadside are a single sheet of letterhead stationary from the Society of Apothecaries of London which contains references to scurvy grass (cochlearia) in books in the Society's library and a letter (1953) from the Bodleian Library describing its copy of a Russel broadside.

Saemisch, Theodor, 1833-1909, ed.
See Handbuch der gesammten Augenheilkunde (176).

322 Saint-Yves, Charles de, 1667-1733.

Nouveau traité des maladies des yeux, les remedes qui y conviennent, & les operations de chirurgie que leurs guérisons éxigent. Avec de nouvelles decouvertes sur la structure de l'oeil, qui prouvent l'organe immédiat de la vûë. Paris: P. A. Le Mercier, 1722.

[30], 373, [33] p.; 17 cm. (12mo)

"Records the removal of a cataract 'en masse' from a living subject" (G-M 5827). Saint-Yves extracted a cataractous lens which had been dislodged and forced into the anterior chamber by an unsuccessful attempt at depression. While this was the author's only published work, it assured him a permanent place in the history of ophthalmology. Shastid (AmEncOph XV:11496-11498) cites seven innovations and observations first announced in this treatise, including the first extensive use of silver nitrate in treating eye diseases, the earliest use of silver nitrate in cases of ophthalmia neonatorum, and the first exact description of gonorrheal ophthalmia. The dedication is signed by the author and the *Avis* (p. [19]) states that only copies so signed are genuine.

G-M 5827; Hirschberg §359; Waller 8406.

Salamon, Christian.

"Observations on some points of the anatomy of the eye."

See Travers (379) p. [381]-389.

323 Santa Anna, Joaquim José de.

Elementos de cirurgia ocular. Lisbon: S. T. Ferreira, 1793.

viii, 279 p., [3] plates; 21 cm. (4to)

Often described as the first Portuguese textbook of ophthalmology, this treatise was not an original work but rather an acknowledged translation of two standard works on the eye. In the foreword Santa Anna states that the sections on the anatomy and physiology of the eye were taken from Deshais-Gendron's treatise (101) and those on pathology and therapy from Plenk's text (299). This translation of Plenk's work and the less honorable plagiarism of it by William Rowley [cf. (316)] were first fully recognized by Julius Hirschberg and detailed in "Über ein abgeschriebenes Lehrbuch der Augenheilkunde," *Centralblatt für praktische Augenheilkunde* 34:2-14 (1910).

Hirschberg §971.

324 Santerelli, Giovanni Battista Geremè, b. ca. 1770.

Delle cateratte. . . . Forli: Dalla stamperia dipartimentale, 1810.

128 p., III plates; 22 cm. (8vo)

Santerelli's second monograph on cataract received scant attention from his contemporaries, doubtless because it was written in Italian. From the beginning of his medical studies Santerelli's interests were focused on the treatment of cataract. A student of both Angelo Nannoni (270) and his son Lorenzo (271), Santerelli had numerous opportunities to witness the operation of depression preferred by the former, and the extraction performed by the latter. Later, during his tour of the principal universities of Europe, Santerelli continued to pay particular attention to techniques of cataract surgery employed by the most eminent ophthalmic surgeons. The present work is a digest of his observations. In the first seven chapters the author describes both depression and extraction before declaring his preference for extraction in the eighth and final chapter. The text is illustrated with three very detailed folding copperplate engravings, printed on especially heavy paper.

Callisen VII:168, XXVIII:192; Hirschberg §1114.

325 Santi, Felice.

Il discorso . . . sull'uso, ed officio del punto scoperto da Soemering nel fondo dell'occhio umano. Perugia: F. Baduel, 1816.

23 p.; 24 cm. (4to)

Francesco Buzzi in 1782 was the first to notice the yellow spot in the human retina. His observation attracted no attention, however, and it was Samuel Thomas Soemmerring who in 1795 "re-discovered" and described the macula lutea, making its existence generally known. Soemmerring imagined this *macula flava* to be an actual perforation in the retina, which he made responsible for the "blind-spot" of Mariotte in the field of vision.

In the present discourse the author, professor of medicine at Perugia, discusses the function of this *macchia giallognola* (yellow spot), or *il punto di Soemering*, which he describes as functioning as a second pupil, absorbing the visual rays or images of objects received by the retina, and directing them through its aperture to the optic nerve.

Sarrasin, Jean Antoine, 1547-1598, ed.

See Fabricius von Hilden (133).

325.1 Sarti, Cristofano.

L'ottica della natura e dell'educazione indirizzata a risolvere il famoso problema di Molineux. Lucca: F. Bonsignori, 1792.

xvi, 227 p.: ill.; 20 cm. (8vo)

An Italian scientist's answer to a famous question attributed first to William Molineux (*Dioptrica nova*, 1692), that is, whether or not a person born blind but suddenly having gained vision (e.g., by cataract operation) would be able to recognize different shapes of objects by sight without touching the objects. "The question was examined by many philosophers [Locke, Leibniz, Diderot, G. Berkeley, etc.] of the eighteenth century, but also practically by ophthalmologists who had gained personal experience in that field. A whole literature exists on this topic" (Hirschberg §455).

NUC 521:202.

Sarwey, Theophil Andreas, respondent.

"De paracentesi oculi in hydrophthalmia, et amblyopia senum."

In Dissertationes medicae selectae Tubingenses (112) 1:341-370.

326   Saunders, John Cunningham, 1773-1810.

A treatise on some practical points relating to the diseases of the eye. . . . To which is added, a short account of the author's life, and his method of curing the congenital cataract, by his friend and colleague, J. R. Farre. London: J. McCreery for Longmans, 1811.

xliii, [l], 216 p., 9 plates: port.; 25 cm. (8vo)

In 1805 Saunders founded the first ophthalmological hospital in London, the Royal London Ophthalmic Hospital, now "Moorfields," known then as the London Dispensary for Curing Diseases of the Eye and Ear. This work was published posthumously at the expense of the Governors of the Hospital and by subscription to aid the author's widow. In this treatise Saunders first introduced belladona in the treatment of eye disease.

(325.1) Sarti, Cristofano. *L'ottica della natura e dell'educazione indirizzata a risolvere il famoso problema di Molineux*, 1792. Frontispiece. (6 x 7.8 cm.)

BOA I:185; Hirschberg §634.

Sauvages de la Croix, François Boissier de, 1706-1767, praeses.

See Guillemard (167).

327   Scarpa, Antonio, 1752-1832.

Saggio di osservazioni e d'esperienze sulle principali malattie degli occhi. Pavia: B. Comino, 1801.

[4], xi, [1], 278, [2] p., 4 plates: port.; 31 cm. (fol.)

"This beautifully illustrated work was the first text-book on the subject to be published in the Italian language. Its author has been called 'the father of Italian ophthalmology' " (G-M 5835). In this work Scarpa first described the operation of iridodialysis. The chapters on diseases of the vessels in the eye, on cataract, and on staphyloma are particularly noteworthy. Scarpa's books were all superbly illustrated with his own drawings and the plates in this work, engraved by Faustino Anderloni, bear witness to Scarpa's artistic talent. Duke-Elder considered this the greatest work on ophthalmic pathology that had appeared up to its time (7:476-477).

G-M 5835; Hirschberg §449.

328   Scarpa, Antonio, 1752-1832.

Practical observations on the principal diseases of the eyes: illustrated with cases. Translated from the Italian of Antonio Scarpa . . . with notes, by James Briggs. London: T. Bensley for T. Cadell and W. Davies, 1806.

xx, [4], 536, [16] p., 3 plates; 23 cm. (8vo)

First English edition of Scarpa's classic textbook which marked "the highest culmination of the Galenic tradition of ophthalmic pathology" and in which "all inflammations of the eye were merely 'ophthalmias' without specific differentiation" (Duke-Elder 7:476-477).

Duke-Elder 7:476-477; Hirschberg §449.

Scarpa, Antonio, 1752-1832.

See also Weiss (140.2).

329   Schaeffer, Johann Gottlieb, 1720-1795.

Geschichte des grauen Staares und der neuen Operation solchen durch Herausnehmung der

Crystalllinse zu heylen nebst einigen daraus gefolgerten und erörterten Fragen. Regensburg: J. L. Montag, 1765.

[4], 26 p., [1] plate; 20 cm. (4to)

Because of the untimely death of his father, Schaeffer was forced to become an apprentice to an apothecary until his older brother, a noted naturalist and theologian, made it possible for him to take up his education. He took his medical degree at Altdorf in 1745 and practiced for the remainder of his life in Regensburg where he was the first to introduce inoculation. This is the first edition of a noted work on the radical treatment of cataract in which the author essentially follows Daviel's method (2).

Hirschberg §420; Waller 8560.

Schedel, Hartmann, 1440-1514.
See Print 18.

330 Scheffler, Hermann, 1820-1903.

The theory of ocular defects and of spectacles. Translated from the German . . . by Robert Brudenell Carter. . . . With prefatory notes and a chapter of practical instructions. London: Longmans, Green, and Co., 1869.

xxii, 240 p.; 30 cm.

This translation of Scheffler's *Die Theorie der Augenfehler und der Brille* (Wien, 1868) includes seventy-three printed pages of material which did not appear in the German original. This matter, giving practical instructions on the examination of the eye and the selection of lenses, was specifically requested from the author by Carter for inclusion in his English translation. Carter felt that this book successfully approached problems left unresolved in Donders's work on defects of accommodation and refraction (115).

BOA I:186.

331 Scheiner, Christoph, 1575-1650.

Oculus hoc est: fundamentum opticum, in quo ex accurata oculi anatome, abstrusarum experientiarum sedula pervestigatione, ex invisis specierum visibilium tam everso quam erecto situ spectaculis, necnon solidis rationum momentis radius visualis eruitur; sua visioni in oculo sedes decernitur; anguli visorii ingenium aperitur. . . . Innsbruck: D. Agricola, 1619.

[14], 254 p.: ill.; 20 cm. (4to)

"Scheiner, a Jesuit astronomer, was a pioneer in physiological optics. He demonstrated how images fall on the human retina, noting the changes in curvature of the lens during accommodation, and devised the pin-hole test ('Scheiner's test') to illustrate accommodation and refraction" (G-M 1480). The schematic diagram of the eye offered by the author was the first scientifically accurate representation of the human eye and as such marked a dramatic advance over the centuries-old Galenic conception of this organ.

BOA II:94; G-M 1480; Hirschberg §310; Waller 8585.

332 Scheiner, Christoph, 1575-1650.

Pantographice, seu ars delineandi res quaslibet per parallelogrammum lineare seu cavum, mechanicum, mobile; libellis duobus explicata, & demonstrationibus geometricis illustrata: quorum prior epipedographicen, sive planorum, posterior stereographicen, seu solidorum aspectabilium viuam imitationem atque projectionem edocet. Rome: L. Grignani, 1631.

[12], 108 p.: ill.; 25 cm. (4to)

An interesting but lesser-known work of Scheiner's, in which his interests in optics and mechanics are combined. The pantograph or tracer is an instrument which he invented for making copies on a predetermined scale of any given plane design.

Hirschberg §310.

Scheligius, Albertus, fl. 1583, ed.
See Mercuriale (256).

333 Schenck von Grafenberg, Johannes, 1530-1598.

Obseruationes medicae de capite humano: hoc est, exempla capitis morborum, causarum, signorum, eue[n]tuum, curationum, vt singularia, sic abdita & monstrosa. Ex clariss. medicorum, ueterum simul & recentiorum scriptis. . .collecta. Basel: Officina Frobeniana, 1584.

[48], 448, [20] p.; 16 cm. (8vo)

One of the most distinguished physicians of his time, Schenk's *magnum opus* was his *Observationum medicarum rariorum libri VII*, originally published at Basel (1584-97) and reprinted in numerous editions throughout the seventeenth century. The work is a massive compilation of descriptions of pathological states of all the parts of the human body, drawn from the whole of medical literature, from the writings of Hippocrates to those of Schenck's own contemporaries. The present small octavo volume is an abridgement of the first of these seven books, treating the diseases affecting the various parts of the head. The diseases of the eyes are discussed on pages 296-334.

Durling 4107; Osler 3932; Waller 8593; Wellcome I:5824.

Schlagintweit, Wilhelm August Joseph, 1792-1854.

See Neue Bibliothek (272.1).

334 Schmidt, Johann Adam, 1759-1809.

Über Nachstaar und Iritis nach Staaroperationen. Vienna: A. Camesina, 1801.

[2], 84 p.; 28 cm. (4to)

"Inflammation of the iris was named iritis by Schmidt. In 1801, with Himly, he founded the first journal devoted to ophthalmology, the *Ophthalmologische Bibliothek*" (G-M 5836). This is the first book form edition of this work which originally appeared in *Abhandlung Roemisch-Kaiserlich-Königlich Josephinische Medicinische-Chirurgische Academie*, Vienna, 2:209-292 (1801).

Hirschberg §471.

334.1 Schoen, Johann Matthias Albrecht, 1800-1870.

Handbuch der pathologischen Anatomie des menschlichen Auges. Hamburg: Hoffmann und Campe, 1828.

xiv, [2], 233, [1] p.; 21 cm.

A textbook on the pathological anatomy of the human eye, considered the second monograph on the subject—James Wardrop's *Essays on the morbid anatomy of the human eye*, 1808 (400) being the first. Johann Matthias Schoen practiced as an internist all his life, but he specialized in ophthalmology and published numerous works in this field. He is noted for the first exact description of the gonorrheal eye inflammation (1834) and for the explanation of arcus senilis (1831); cf. Gorin, p.120.

AmEncOph XV:11573; BM 215:728; Gorin, p. 120; Hirsch V:118; NUC 528:695.

335 Schoen, Johann Matthias Albrecht, 1800-1870.

Nosologisch-therapeutische Darstellung der go-

norrhoïschen Augenentzündung. Hamburg: Aug. Campe, 1834.

xii, 131, [3] p.; 19 cm.

One of the earliest monographs on gonorrheal ophthalmia.

Hirsch V:118; Hirschberg §359, 515.

Schreger, Bernhard Nathanael Gottlob, 1766-1825, trans.

See Soemmerring (349).

336 Schuster, Julius, 1886-1949.

Nachwort zu Goethe, Beyträge zur Optik und historische Skizze zur "Grossen Tafel." Hildesheim: G. Olms, 1964 (Berlin, 1928).

xxxvi p.; 17 cm.

Issued with Goethe (156).

Schwalbe, Gustav Albert, 1844-1916.

See Wecker (408.1).

Schweinitz, George Edmund de.

See De Schweinitz (100.1).

Schweling, Henricus, respondent.

"De oculo."

See Coper (87).

337 Scultetus, Johannes, 1595-1645.

ΧΕΙΡΟΠΛΟΘΗΚΗ, seu . . . Armamentarium chirurgicum XLIII. tabulis aeri elegantissimè incisis, nec ante hac visis, exornatum. Opus posthumum . . . in quo tot, tam veterum ac recentiorum instrumenta ab authore correcta, quàm noviter ab ipso inventa, quot ferè hodiè ad usitatas operationes manuales feliciter peragendas requiruntur, depicta reperiuntur, cum annexa brevi tabularum descriptione, & sequentibus cautionibus ac curationibus chirurgico-medicis per omnes ferè corporis humani partes externas observatis. . . . The Hague: A. Vlacq, 1656.

[24], 180 (i.e. 160), 159-328, [14] p.: ill.; 19 cm. (8vo)

Bound with G. Bidloo's Exercitationum anatomico-chirurgicarum decas (49).

The third edition of a copiously illustrated manual of surgical technique and instruments that went through at least fourteen Latin editions after its first publication at Ulm in 1653. It was translated into German, Dutch, English and French as well. Tabulae XXXIII and XXXVI illustrate procedures for various operations on the eye, which are described in the accompanying text (p. 115-119, 127-132). Among the one hundred surgical observations appended to the plates and text, *observationes* XX, XXI, XXXIV and XXXVI deal with ocular disorders.

Includes an extra engraved title-page dated 1657.

Manchester 2238.

338 Seiler, Burkhard Wilhelm, 1779-1843.

Beobachtungen urspruenglicher Bildungs-fehler und gaenzlichen Mangels der Augen. Dresden: E. Blochmann for Walther, 1833.

[8], 64, [2] p., 1 plate: ill.; 47cm.

In 1833 J. A. W. Hedenus (1760-1833) celebrated fifty years of service to the Medico-Chirurgical Academy of Dresden at which time F. A. von Ammon (12, 13, 14, 15), Ludwig Choulant, August Wilhelm Hedenus, and Seiler published memorial essays to mark the occasion. Seiler's contribution, a treatise on congenital defects and malformations of the eyes, was the first monograph on this subject. The work was described by von Ammon as a classic which greatly enriched the literature of ophthalmology.

Hirschberg §518.

Seiz, Georg Friedrich, respondent.

"De empyesi oculi s[ive] pure in secunda oculi camera stagnante."

In Dissertationes medicae selectae Tubingenses (112) 2:175-195.

338.1 Selected monographs: [Adolf] Kussmaul [*sic*] and [Adolf] Tenner on epileptiform convulsions from hæmorrhage; [Albrecht] Wagner on the resection of bones and joints; [Albrecht von] Graefe's three memoirs on iridectomy in iritis, choroiditis, and glaucoma. London: The New Sydenham Society, 1859.

viii, [2], 380 p.: ill.; 22 cm.

Series: New Sydenham Society; v. 5.

The third monograph in this volume is a collection of essays on iridectomy by Albrecht von Graefe. Realizing their significance, Thomas Windsor (1811-1910) obtained the author's permission to translate these three essays, originally published as articles in von Graefe's *Archiv für Ophthalmologie* between 1855 and 1858. They are: "On iridectomy as a means of treatment in chronic iritis and irido-choroiditis" (Bd. II, Abt. II:202-257); "On iridectomy in glaucoma, and on the glaucomatous process" (Bd. III, Abt. II:[456]-560); and "Additional clinical remarks on glaucoma, glaucomatous diseases, and their treatment by iridectomy" (Bd. IV, Abt. II:127-61).

In the first essay on *coremorphosis*, or the construction of an artificial pupil, von Graefe explains his adaption of iridectomy for the treatment of iritis and irido-choroiditis. The year following the publication of this article, in June of 1856, von Graefe performed his first iridectomy for the treatment of glaucoma. The results were published in 1857 in the second article of this collection. Von Graefe's perfection of the operation of iridectomy revolutionized the treatment of acute congestive glaucoma. Hirschberg likened its impact on ocular therapeutics to Daviel's description of the operation for cataract extraction (2) more than a century earlier.

BM 142:1423-1424; NUC 413:410; Reynolds 2958.

338.2 Selva, Lorenzo, ca. 1716-1800.

Sei dialoghi ottici teorico-pratici, dedicati all' eccellentissimo Senato da Lorenzo Selva, Ottico Publico Stipendiato. Venice: S. Occhi, 1787.

XII, 184 p., IV folding plates; 28 cm. (fol.)

Provenance: Nec versa retorquent G. P. C. (bookplate); — Fratelli Salimbeni (book label).

"A series of six dialogues giving instruction on the defects of the eyes and the means of correcting them, [as well as about] optical instruments . . . and theories of light, particularly those of Newton. The first dialogue deals with the construction of the camera obscura, the second and third with models of the telescope, the fourth with the achromatic telescope, the fifth with microscopes, and the sixth with burning mirrors . . ." (BOA II:98). The volume is decorated with head- and tail-pieces and woodcut initials; the four copperplates at the end depict optical instruments in remarkably clear design.

Lorenzo Selva "was an optician established at Venice who submitted various microscopes of his invention to the Royal Academy of Science at Paris. The Academy approved of one of these models, as it was 'purely catoptric and was easier to construct, clearer and more simple than a dioptric one' " (ibid.).

BOA II:98; Dawson, p. 500; NUC 537:672; Poggendorff II:901.

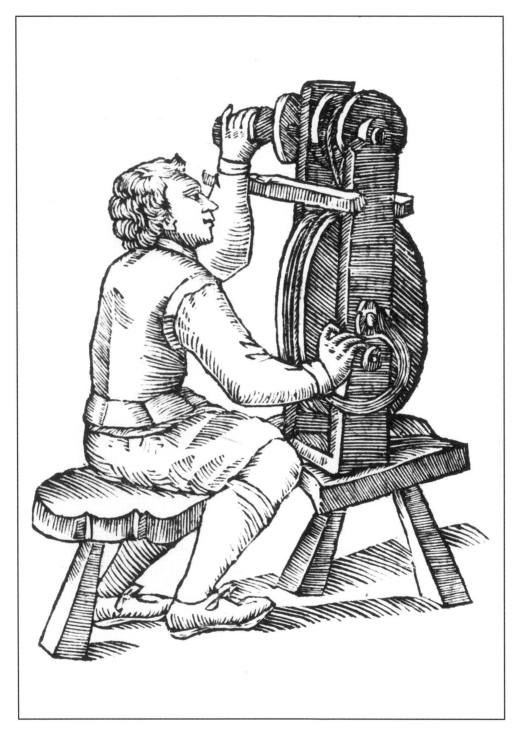

(245) Manzini, Carlo Antonio. *L'occhiale all'occhio dioptrica pratica...*, 1660. Woodcut
illustration on p. 158. (9 x 11 cm.)

339   Serre, Henri Auguste, 1802-1870.

Essai sur les phosphènes ou anneaux lumineux de la rétine considérés dans leur rapports avec la physiologie et la pathologie de la vision. Paris: Victor Masson, 1853.

xx, 472 p.: diagrs.; 22 cm.

Julius Pagel remarked about this work in Hirsch's *Biographisches Lexikon*, "Auch haben seine gründlichen Untersuchungen über die 'Phosphene', deren Bedeutung allerdings durch die Erfindung des Augenspiegels hinfällig geworden ist, ein gewisses historisches Interesse und zeigen immerhin seine ingeniöse Methode zur Untersuchung der Retina." The term *phosphene* originates with Serre (d'Uzes), who combined the Greek το φως, light, with φαινομαι, to appear.

Hirsch V:234; Hirschberg §619.

Shān-Tián, Lì-qīng, 1786-1846, trans.
See Plenck (300).

340   Sichel, Jules, 1802-1868.

Traité de l'ophthalmie, la cataracte et l'amaurose, pour servir de supplément au Traité des maladies des yeux de Weller. Paris: G. Baillière,. . .et al., 1837.

xi, [1], 750, [2] p., 4 plates; 22 cm.

"Le besoin d'un bon traité d'ophthalmologie est vivement senti en France. . . . La traduction de l'ouvrage de Weller et le manuel de M. Stoeber sont les seuls ouvrages que nous ayons pu recommander jusqu'ici à ceux qui voulaient acquérir des connaisances spéciales sur cette branche de pathologie" (Préf., p. [vii]). Thus Sichel presents his reasons for offering the present work, which he hoped would at least in part remedy this deficiency. It remains, along with his *Mémoire sur le glaûcome* (Brussels, 1842) and the *Iconographie ophthalmologique* (Paris, 1852-59) one of Sichel's three most important contributions to ophthalmic literature. German born and educated, Sichel migrated to Paris in 1829, where he remained the rest of his life, earning the appellation "der Apostel des deutschen Augenheilkunde in Frankreich."

BOA I:192; Heirs 914; Hirschberg §559, 560.

340.1   Sichel, Jules, 1802-1868.

Nouveau recueil de pierres sigillaires d'oculistes romains, pour la plupart inédites, extrait d'une monographie inédite de ces monuments épigraphiques. Paris: V. Masson & Son, 1866.

119 p.; 24 cm.

Provenance: Inscribed by the author to Monsr. Chéron; —Ex libris Ed. Bonnet, D.M.P. (bookplate).

Jules Sichel was a polymath whose interests included the history of medicine, ancient and oriental languages, archaeology, and entomology. He also assembled valuable collections of books, butterflies, and ancient Roman inscription stones. These stones are in fact small rectangular stamps made of serpentine, nephrite, or slate and inscribed in Latin with names of ophthalmologists, description of medications, and their mode of application. *Nouveau recueil* is Sichel's second publication on the subject, *Cinq cachets inédits de médecins oculistes romains* (Paris, 1845) being the first (cf. Hirschberg §194, 559).

Hirschberg §559; NUC 545:171.

341   Signorotti, Francesco.

Informazione fatta dal chirurgo Francesco Signorotti . . . contro M. Domenico Anel, qual pretese esser egli l'unico inventore, ed il primo trovatore di stromento atto alla guariggione delle fistole lacrimali. Geneva & Torino: P. M. Dutto, 1713.

12 p.; 19 cm. (4to)
Bound with Anel (16, 17, 18).

Hirschberg §361.

Signorotti, Francesco.
See Melli (255).

Sigwart, Georg Friedrich, 1711-1795, praeses.
"Novum problema chirurgicum de extractione cataractae ultra perficienda."
In Dissertationes medicae selectae Tubingenses (112) 3:134-228.

Sigwart, Georg Friedrich, 1711-1795.
"Specimen ophthalmiologiae de sanatione ophthalmiae sive ophthalmicis externis, ut singulari specie solidae praxeos medicae."
In Dissertationes medicae selectae Tubingenses (112) 3:324-415.

342 Sloane, Sir Hans, 1660-1753.

An account of a most efficacious medicine for soreness, weakness, and several other distempers of the eyes. London: D. Browne, 1745.

[4], 17 p.; 20 cm. (8vo)

Sloane was an eminent London physician and naturalist, first assistant to Sydenham, Newton's successor as President of the Royal Society, and an inveterate collector. His library of more than 50,000 books and 3,500 manuscripts was purchased on his death by the British government and formed the nucleus of the British Museum. This pamphlet, the only separate medical work published by Sloane, is indicative of the dismal state of ophthalmic medicine in the mid-eighteenth century. The 'efficacious medicine' which Sloane recommends here for all cases of ophthalmia was a once-secret liniment compounded of viper fat, aloes, and hematite. The principal ingredient, tutty of crude zinc oxide obtained from the flues of smelting furnaces, was known and used by the earliest Arabic ophthalmologists. The liniment closely resembles several given more than a century before by the anonymous A. T. in the home-remedy book, *A rich storehouse* (368). Burton Chance published an account of this "wretched" work in 1938, "Sir Hans Sloane's account of an efficacious medicine for soreness of the eyes," *Archives of Ophthalmology* 19: [912]-925.

Hirschberg §392.

343 Smee, Alfred, 1818-1877.

The eye in health and disease; with an account of the optometer, for the adaption of glasses, for impaired, aged, or defective sight; being the substance of lectures delivered at the Central London Ophthalmic Hospital. . . . Second edition: to which is appended, a paper on the stereoscope and binocular perspective. London: Longman and Co., 1854.

[4], [iii]-iv, [vii]-viii, 99 p., IV plates: ill.; 23 cm.

The second edition of a work originally published in 1847 under the title *Vision in health and disease*. A surgeon with an interest in the diseases of the eye, Smee is better known for his considerable achievements in the field of electro-metallurgy.

Hirsch V:306; Hirschberg §663.

344 Smith, Priestly, b. 1845.

Glaucoma: its causes, symptoms, pathology, and treatment. London: J. & A. Churchill, 1879.

xv, [l], 281 p., [l4] plates; 22 cm.

An eminent British ophthalmologist, Priestly Smith was ophthalmic surgeon at Queens Hospital, Birmingham, and professor of ophthalmology at the University from the founding of that chair in 1897 until 1912. He also wrote the section on glaucoma in Norris and Oliver's *System of diseases of the eye* (367).

345 Smith, Robert, 1689-1768.

A compleat system of opticks in four books, viz, a popular, a mathematical, a mechanical, and a philosophical treatise. To which are added remarks upon the whole. Cambridge: The author and C. Crownfield; London: S. Austen and R. Dodsley, 1738.

2 v. ([6], vi, [8], 280 p., 45 plates; [2], [281]-455, [l], 171, [13] p., 18 plates); 26 cm. (4to)

A comprehensive textbook on light and one of the most noted works of the eighteenth century written by the Master of Trinity College and founder of what are still known as 'Smith's Prizes' in mathematics at Cambridge. Appended to Smith's text is James Jurin's "Essay upon distinct and indistinct vision." Jurin (1684-1759) was a London physician interested in physiological optics.

BOA I:194; Hirschberg §344.

346 Smith, Robert, 1689-1768.

Volkomen samenstel der optica of gezigtkunde, behelzende eene gemeenzaame, eene wiskonstige, eene werktuiglyke en eene natuurkundige verhandeling: verrkyt met veele aanmerkingen van den schryver, als mede met eene verhandeling van Dr. Jurin over het duidelyk en onduidelyk zien. Alles met zeer veele plaaten opgehelderd. In 't Engelsch beschreeven door den heere Robert Smith. Amsterdam: I. Tirion, 1753.

2v. ([22], 488 p., 61 plates; [2], 489-778, [22] p., 23 plates; 26 cm. (4to)

A Dutch translation of the standard eighteenth century text on the physics of light, grinding and polishing lenses, the construction of optical instruments, and the history of telescopic discoveries. Smith's *System* was also translated into German and French.

Hirschberg §344.

347 Soemmerring, Detmar Wilhelm, 1793-1871.

An extract of Detmar Wilhelm Soemmerring's thesis:

a comment on the horizontal section of eyes in man and animals. Edited by S. Ry Andersen and Ole Munk. Translated by H. D. Schepelern. Copenhagen: s.n., 1971.

76, [4] p.: ill.; 25 cm.

Translation and facsimile of portions of the author's doctoral dissertation, one of the first systematic studies of the comparative anatomy of the vertebrate eye. The first edition of this dissertation (1818) is in the Becker Library's General Rare Book Collection. The author was the son of the distinguished anatomist and ophthalmologist S. T. von Soemmerring (348, 349). "This volume is also published as Supplementum No. ll0 of Acta ophthalmologica (Kbh.)" (colophon).

Hirschberg §539.

Soemmerring, Samuel Thomas, 1755-1830, praeses.

See Noethig (273.2).

348   Soemmerring, Samuel Thomas, 1755-1830.

Abbildungen des menschlichen Auges. Frankfurt am Main: Varrentrapp & Wenner, 1801.

x, 110 p., 16 plates; 40 cm. (fol.)

"Soemmerring is best remembered for his fine anatomical illustrations, of which those devoted to the human eye are a good example" (G-M 1489). Ludwig Choulant declared this book "Soemmerring's most perfect work" which with Zinn's monograph (426) formed the basis for all modern research on the structure of the eye.

G-M 1489; Hirschberg §464.

349   Soemmerring, Samuel Thomas, 1755-1830.

Icones oculi humani. Frankfurt am Main: Varrentrapp & Wenner, 1804.

viii, 94 p., 16 plates; 40 cm. (fol.)

The Latin edition of Soemmerring's great anatomical atlas was translated by Bernhard Nathanael Gottlob Schreger (1766-1825). The plates for this edition were taken from the copperplate engravings based on Koeck's drawings which appeared in the original German edition of 1801 (348). "In preparing the drawings Soemmerring was less concerned with correct

perspective than with the architectonically correct representation of the material" (DicSciBio 12:510). The work was faulted by contemporary English reviewers only for its great expense.

DicSciBio 12:510; Hirschberg §464; Waller 9046.

Soemmerring, Samuel Thomas, 1755-1830.

See Demours, A. P. (96).

Sommariva, Cæsareus, ed.

See Rampinelli (309.2).

Sōng-Tián, Qín-zhāi.

See Plenck (300).

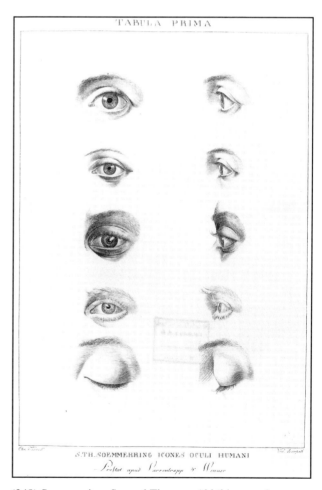

(348) Soemmering, Samuel Thomas. *Abbildungen des menschlichen Auges*, 1801. Plate I. (25 x 34 cm.)

Soranus, of Ephesus, fl. 2nd cent.

See Aetius, of Amida (5).

350 Sous, Gustave, b. 1832.

Traité d'optique considérée dans ses rapports avec l'examen de l'oeil. . . . Deuxième édition revue et augmentée. Paris: Octave Doin, 1881.

xvi, 512 p.: ill.; 23 cm.

A fundamental treatise on optics and ophthalmoscopic examination. First edition, Paris, 1879.

BOA I:198.

Spalding, James Alfred, b. 1846, trans.

See Mauthner (252).

351 Spindler, Johann, 1777-1840.

Ueber Entzündungen des Auges und ihre Behandlung. Würzburg: J. Stahel, 1807.

[4], 158 p.; 20 cm. (8vo)

On the management of various inflammations of the eyes by a well-known German medical historian and ophthalmologist.

Hirschberg §530.

352 Stellwag von Carion, Karl, 1823-1904.

Lehrbuch der praktischen Augenheilkunde. Vienna: Wilhelm Braumüller, 1861.

xiii, 737 p., [3] plates: ill.; 23 cm.

Stellwag von Carion has never received adequate recognition among English-speaking historians for his importance to nineteenth century ophthalmology. His three-line obituary in the *Ophthalmoscope*, for instance, describes him simply as "a name more familiar to an older generation of ophthalmic surgeons." He was not a great surgeon, but he was an outstanding teacher and researcher, and one of the most important figures in the great Viennese school of ophthalmology in the nineteenth century. His most widely successful work was the *Lehrbuch*. It was an extremely important textbook which was more reflective of the major developments in the two decades following the invention of the ophthalmoscope than any equivalent work of the period. This first edition was followed by four other German editions, and was translated in English, Italian and Hungarian.

Hirschberg §1249.

353 Stellwag von Carion, Karl, 1823-1904.

Der intraoculare Druck und die Innervations-Verhältnisse der Iris vom augenärztlichen Standpunkte aus betrachtet. Vienna: Wilhelm Braumüller, 1868.

vii, [1], 100 p.; 24 cm.

Hirsch V:413; Hirschberg §1249.

354 Stellwag von Carion, Karl, 1823-1904.

Treatise on the diseases of the eye, including the anatomy of the organ. . . . Translated from the third German edition and edited by Charles E. Hackley . . . and D. B. St. John Roosa. . . . With an appendix by the editors. New York: William Wood & Co., 1868.

xiv, [2], 774 p., [3] plates: ill.; 23 cm.

The first American edition of Stellwag's *Lehrbuch der praktischen Augenheilkunde*, translated from the third German edition. Successive editions of Stellwag's textbook were not mere reprints of the preceding edition. Stellwag conscientiously included in each new edition the most recent developments in ophthalmology (excepting the 5th German edition, which was a simple reprint of the 4th). This edition, for instance, includes 150 pages of material not in the second German edition and substantial changes in almost every part of the work.

Hirsch V:413; Hirschberg §1249, 1250.

355 Stellwag von Carion, Karl, 1823-1904.

Treatise on the diseases of the eye, including the anatomy of the organ. . . . Translated from the fourth German edition and edited by D. B. St. John Roosa . . . Charles S. Bull . . . and Charles E. Hackley. . . . Fourth revised and enlarged edition. New York: William Wood & Co., 1873.

[2], xvii, [3], 915 p., [4] plates: ill.; 24 cm.

It is possible that Stellwag's textbook found more readers in England, the United States, Italy, and Hungary than in Austria and Germany, so wide was its appeal. This edition is based on the fourth and best German edition of 1870.

BOA I:200; Hirsch V:413.

356 Stellwag von Carion, Karl, 1823-1904.

Abhandlungen aus dem Gebiete der praktischen Augenheilkunde. Ergänzungen zum Lehrbuche. . . . Unter mitwirkung der Herren Prof. Dr. C. Wedl und Dr. E. Hampel. Vienna: Wilhelm

Braumüller, 1882.

xii, 387 p.; 23 cm.

The fifth and final edition of Stellwag's *Lehrbuch* was published in 1882. Rather than entirely re-edit the work, Stellwag chose to complement it with a volume of eight essays on various topics. The second essay in this collection, "Zur pathologischen Anatomie des Glaukoms," was written by Carl Wedl. A second series, *Neue Abhandlungen* (357), was issued in 1886.

Hirsch V:413; Hirschberg §1249, 1250.

357 Stellwag von Carion, Karl, 1823-1904.

Neue Abhandlungen aus dem Gebiete der praktischen Augenheilkunde. Ergänzungen zum Lehrbuche. . . . Unter Mitwirkung der Herren . . . Dr. Emil Bock und Dr. Ludwig Herz. Vienna: Wilhelm Braumüller, 1886.

viii, 297 p.: ill.; 23 cm.

The second series of essays published by Stellwag to complement his *Lehrbuch der praktischen Augenheilkunde*, the final edition of which was published in 1882. This volume is divided into two parts: the first on entropium and ektropium; the second on the surgical treatment of cataract. The first series of *Abhandlungen* (356) was published in 1882.

Hirsch V:414; Hirschberg §1249, 1250.

Stellwag von Carion, Karl, 1823-1904.

See also Wedl (409).

358 Steno, Nicolaus, 1638-1686.

De solido intra solidum naturaliter contento dissertationis prodromus. Leyden: J. Moukee, 1679.

115, [4] p., 2 plates (wanting); 14 cm. (12mo)
Bound with (359).

The second edition of Steno's famous work on the principles of geology written as the prelude to a larger work which was never published.

Osler 4023.

359 Steno, Nicolaus, 1638-1686.

Observationes anatomicae, quibus varia oris, oculorum, & narium vasa describuntur, novique salivae, lacrymarum & muci fontes deteguntur. Et

novum nobilissimi Bilsii de lymphae motu & usu commentum examinatur & rejicitur. Leyden: P. de Graaf, 1680.

[12], 108 p., [3] plates; 14 cm. (12mo)
Bound with (358).

Niels Stensen or Steensen, known by the Latin form Steno which he adopted, was a seventeenth century Danish anatomist, geologist, and theologian. Steno studied medicine in Copenhagen under Bartholinus, in Leyden with Sylvius, and later with Balsius in Amsterdam. His earliest researches focused on the glandular and lymphatic systems, and his work in this period laid the anatomical foundation for an understanding of the entire lacrimal system. He discovered the ducts of the lacrimal gland in a sheep's head and deduced that the 'innominated gland' secreted tears. He "determined the purpose of the lachrymal fluid—to facilitate the movement and cleansing of the eyelids on the same principle that applied to the saliva and the mucous membrane of the intestinal canals. He grouped the afferent and efferent lachrymal ducts around the tear gland proper and what was then called *glandula lacrimalis*, in the inner eye corner" (DicSciBio13:31-32).

Hirschberg §305; Waller 9227.

360 Stephenson, Sidney, 1862-1923.

Ophthalmic nursing. London: The Scientific Press, 1894.

xiii, [3], 188 p.: ill.; 19 cm.

Stephenson was well known in Britain at the turn of the century both as an ocular surgeon and for his public health work in epidemic ophthalmia and trachoma. He is probably best known, however, as the founder and editor of *The Ophthalmoscope* (1903-16), which merged in 1917 with the *Royal London Ophthalmic Hospital Reports* and the *Ophthalmic Review* to form the *British Journal of Ophthalmology*. Stephenson was editor of this new publication for its first seven volumes. *Ophthalmic nursing* is Stephenson's most important book. A second edition was published in 1902 and a third in 1912.

361 Stephenson, Sidney, 1862-1923.

Contagious ophthalmia: acute and chronic. London: Baillière, Tindall and Cox, 1900.

vi, [7]-84 p., [1] plate: ill.; 19 cm.

BOA I:200; Fischer II:1503.

362   Stevenson, John, 1778-1846.

On the morbid sensibility of the eye, commonly called weakness of sight. London: J. Gillet for S. Highley, 1811.

[4], 108 p.; 22 cm. (8vo)

Just as the title of this book contains little more than an indication of a symptom of disease, the work itself offers little beyond random observations on weakness of sight. Stevenson presents a history of some diseases, chiefly inflammation of the posterior chamber, where this "morbid sensibility of the eye" is merely a symptom, as it is in the great proportion of diseases of the eye. The author rightly opposed the common and unsuccessful treatment of ocular affections by tonic medicines and employed an opposite mode of treatment, by bleeding, purgatives, and an antiphlogistic regimen.

Hirschberg §632a.

363   Stevenson, John, 1778-1846.

A practical treatise on cataract. London: W. Thorne for Highley & Son & Longmans, 1813.

[8], 123, [1] p., [1] plate; 24 cm. (8vo)

Stevenson studied with Saunders (326) and in 1830 established the Royal Infirmary for Cataract. His career was sufficiently distinguished to win him a place as oculist and aurist to William IV and later to Leopold I, King of the Belgians. "Stevenson undertook to operate upon cases of cataract at an earlier period than was thought advisable by other surgeons, and his infirmary was founded with the express design of carrying out his mode of treatment" (DicNatBio 18:1125).

Hirschberg §632a.

364   Stilling, Benedict, 1810-1879.

Die künstliche Pupillenbildung in der Sclerotica. Nebst einem Anhange über die Verpflanzung der Hornhaut, Keratoplastik. Marburg: N. G. Elwert, 1833.

xvi, 143, [1] p., [1] plate; 21 cm.

Stilling took his medical degree at Marburg in 1833 with a dissertation entitled *De pupilla artificiali in sclerotica conformanda*. The present work is a greatly expanded, largely rewritten German edition of this highly original dissertation. It is illustrated with a single hand-colored copperplate engraving. Shastid in the *American Encyclopedia of Ophthalmology* (XVI:12260) gives the following description of the original Latin edition: "In this dissertation Stilling describes the first (his own) successful attempt at the transplantation of corneal tissue into an opening in the sclera. Dieffenbach had, in 1830, made the same attempt, but without success. Stilling performed his experiment on the rabbit. The transplanted cornea not only grew tight to its position, but remained transparent."

Waller 9256.

365   Stratford, Samuel John.

A manual of the anatomy, physiology, & diseases of the eye and its appendages. London: T. Wood for Longmans, 1828.

xiv, [2], 199, [1] p., [1] plate; 22 cm.

"Mr. Stratford's book is evidently the production of a practical man, who writes from what he has seen; hence the descriptions of the various diseases are accurate, and the plans of treatment recommended highly appropriate. The student will find it highly useful. We are sorry that we cannot extend our praise to the plates; without the text, it would be difficult to say what they were intended to represent. The author will do well also, in the next edition (which we believe will soon be called for) to correct the numerous typographical errors which exist" (*The Lancet*, October 18, 1828, p. 87). A second edition was apparently never called for.

BOA II:103.

366   Stromayr, Caspar, 16th cent.

Die Handschrift des Schnitt-und Augenarztes Caspar Stromayr in Lindau im Bodensee. In der Lindauer Handschrift (P.I.46) vom 4. Juli 1559. Mit einer historischen Einführung und Wertung von Walter von Brunn. Berlin: Idra-Verlagsanstalt, 1925.

xxvii, [1], 194 p., [195]-364 leaves; 24 cm.

Little is known of the life of the author beyond the fact that he specialized as a cutter of hernia and a coucher of cataract. Written in 1559, the manuscript escaped notice for 350 years in the city library of Lindau until it was resurrected in 1909 and published in this facsimile edition through the efforts of Walter von Brunn, the noted surgical historian. Primarily a surgical work dealing with hernia, the manuscript includes a section on the anatomy and surgery of the eye.

Hirsch V:458.

Sturm, Johann Christoph, 1635-1703, praeses.

Iridis admiranda.

See Volckamer (393).

(321) Russel, J. *His elixirated spirit of scurvy-grass, both plain and purging*, ca. 1690. Broadsheet. (23.5 x 17.1 cm.)

Sugita, Rikkyô, 1786-1846, trans.
See Plenck (300).

Sutton, Samuel, fl. 1743.
See Mead (254).

367   System of diseases of the eye.

By American, British, Dutch, French, German, and Spanish authors. Edited by William F. Norris . . . and Charles A. Oliver. Philadelphia and London: J. B. Lippincott Company, 1900 (c1896-99).

4 v. (xvii, [2], [7]-672 p., [22] plates; [2] , ix, [1] , [11]-556 p., [12] plates; xii, 962 p., [44] plates; xii, 949 p., [38] plates): ill.; 25 cm.

The first "system" of the diseases of the eye in the English language. The editors' intention was to compile a work that would occupy a place in English ophthalmic literature equivalent to that held in German by the *Handbuch der gesammten Augenheilkunde* of Graefe and Saemisch, and in French by the *Traité complet d'ophtalmologie* of Wecker and Landolt (408.1).

Chance, p. 183-84; Hirschberg §767.

368   T., A.

A rich storehouse or treasurie for the diseased. Wherein are many approved medicines for divers and sundry diseases, which have beene long hidden and not come to light before this time. First set foorth for the benefit and comfort of the poorer sort of people, that are not of ability to goe to the phisitions. By G. W. And now sixtly augmented and inlarged by A. T. London: R. Blower, 1616.

[14], 68, 99-176 leaves; 18 cm. (4to)

The initials of the original author (A. T.) and the 'augmentor' (G. W.) were interchanged in both the fifth (1612) and sixth editions. The identity of A. T., a practitioner of "physicke and chirurgerie" and G. W. remains a mystery, though Charles Singer has suggested that the latter was the well-known poet George Whetstone. The book is a compendium of popular medicine which contains remedies and advice to "the poorer sort of people" for all the commoner diseases. Readers are cautioned against "things very hurtful for the sight" such as "garlicke, onyons and leekes . . . much weeping, and over much watching" and encouraged "to look upon any greene or pleasant coulours."

STC 23609.

369   Tagliacozzi, Gaspare, 1545-1599.

De curtorum chirurgia per insitionem, libri duo. In quibus ea omnia, quae ad huius chirurgiae, narium scilicet, aurium, ac labiorum per insitionem restaurandorum cum theoricen, tum practicen pertinere videbantur, clarissima methodo cumulatissimè declarantur. Additis cutis traducis instrumentorum omnium, atque deligationum iconibus, & tabulis. . . . Venice: G. Bindon, jr., 1597.

[28], 94, [2], 95, [1], 47, [33] p.: ill.; 32 cm.

The greatest classic in the history of plastic surgery, known especially for its description of rhinoplasty. Described are Tagliacozzi's methods of correcting facial deformities by skin grafting, illustrated with twenty-two full-page woodcuts depicting each stage of the operation for the restoration of the nose, ears and lips.

This is the state without the license on the verso of the title-page. Neither woodcut XII nor the explanatory text for wood-cut XVI are printed, though the leaves are present with the appropriate printing on their opposite sides. Page 51 of "Liber secundus" is misnumbered page 53. Page 52 is correctly numbered, though in another state page 52 is misnumbered page 54. Extra engraved title-page.

Cushing T16; Durling 4310; G-M 5734; Gnudi; Harvard II:488; Heirs 236; Manchester 2390; Pybus 2088; Waller 9451; Wellcome I:6210.

370   Taylor, John, 1703-1772.

An account of the mechanism of the eye. Wherein its power of refracting the rays of light, and causing them to converge at the retina, is consider'd: with an endeavor to ascertain the true place of a cataract, and to shew the good or ill consequences of a judicious or injudicious removal of it. Norwich: H. Cross-grove, 1727.

ix, l0-74 p., [1] plate: port.; 19 cm. (8vo)

John Taylor, commonly known as the 'Chevalier,' was the most famous eighteenth century itinerant oculist and one of the most striking medical personalities of that century. This was Taylor's first published work and it is notable for its freedom from the extravagant and pretentious claims which mark his later works. Taylor offers a brief account of the anatomy of the eye, the true nature of cataract, and a description of a common couching operation, noting the usual attending complications. The bibliography of Taylor and Tayloriana is tortuous, immense, and still largely uncharted. The best account of his life and perhaps the fullest bibliography is George Coats's "The Chevalier Taylor," *Royal London Ophthalmic Hospital Reports* 20:1-

92 (1915), reprinted in R. R. James's *Studies in the history of ophthalmology in England prior to the year 1800* (Cambridge: University Press for the *British Journal of Ophthalmology*, 1933).

Hirschberg §366A, 437, 840.

Taylor, John, 1703-1772.

See also The English impostor . . . (123).

371 Taylor, John, 1703-1772.

Le mechanisme ou le nouveau traité de l'anatomie du globe de l'oeil, avec l'usage de ses différentes parties, & de celles qui lui sont contiguës. Paris: M. E. David, 1738.

[8], vii, [1], 413, [3] p., 6 plates: port.; 20 cm. (8vo)

Notwithstanding Samuel Johnson's claim that Taylor was the most ignorant man he had ever known, he did produce this complete treatise on the anatomy, physiology, and pathology of the eye. Taylor also discussed optics and refraction as they related to the phenomenon of vision making this, according to Hirschberg, one of the earliest ophthalmological works to include such subjects. Of great interest to the historian and bibliographer is the catalogue of authors (p. 371-387) which includes forty-four references to works on the anatomy of the eye, and sixty-six to its diseases.

Hirschberg §366A, 437, 840; Waller 9502.

372 Taylor, John, 1703-1772.

Tractat von Augenkrankheiten, nebst einem Briefe des Herrn von L*** über die Kunst das Gesicht in gutem Zustand zu erhalten, wie auch die Schwachheiten desselben zu vermeiden. . . . Frankfurt und Leipzig: s.n., 1750.

9, 8-70 p.; 17 cm. (8vo)

The pretentious but well-connected Chevalier Taylor made his first trip to Germany in 1750, during which time this small tract was published.

Blake, p. 446.

372.1 Taylor, John, 1703-1772.

Saggio sopra la vera sede della visione con una critica de'sentimenti degli antichi, e moderni del Cavaliere di Taylor . . . inventore del nuovo modo di ristabilire la vista perduta per varj vizj nell'asse

dell'occhio, et autore di molte opere, scritte in varie lingue. Rome: s.n., 1755.

[4], 5-55, [1] p.; 17 cm. (8vo)

Partial contents: XLV domande (p. 41-51).

Tenner, Adolf.

See Selected monographs (338.1).

373 Tenon, Jacques Rene, 1724-1816.

Mémoîres et observations sur l'anatomie, la pathologie, et la chirurgie. Paris: Widow of Nyon, 1806.

xxiv, 496 p., 7 plates; 20 cm. (8vo)

A collection of twenty-five memoirs by a celebrated Parisian anatomist, surgeon, and ophthalmologist. The first eleven essays deal with ophthalmological subjects and include his "Observations anatomiques sur quelques parties de l'oeil et des paupieres" (p. [193]-207) which presents his famous description of the fibrous capsule and the interfascial space of the orbit. Known to anatomists since Galen as the 'tunica adnata,' details of the fascia surrounding the eyeball were first discovered and adequately described by Tenon in this work. His investigations were largely forgotten until the strabismus operation, introduced by Dieffenbach (110) and Bonnet (54) and Dalrymple (90), revived anatomical investigations of the orbit. Tenon's observations and descriptions are eponymously recognized in "Tenon's capsule" and "Tenon's space." It is interesting to note that Tenon was an octogenarian when his major ophthalmological writings were published.

Hirschberg §365; Waller 9515.

Textor, Benoît, fl. 1530-1556.

"Of the nature and divers kinds of cancers or cankers."
See Banister (32).

Thomassin, Jean François, 1750-1828.

See Pellier de Quengsy (292).

374 Thomin, Marc Mitouflet, 1707-1752.

Instruction sur l'usage des lunettes ou conserves, pour toutes sortes de vues. Marques auxquelles on peut connoître si les vues longues ordinaires ont besoin de conserves ou lunettes, des verres convexes qui leur conviennent, & des verres concaves qui sont propres aux vues courtes. Methode pour se conserver la vue; avec une dissertation sur ce que les personnes âgées la recouvrent quelquefois dans un âge avancé. Paris: C. Lamesle, 1746.

130, [2] p.; 17 cm. (12mo)

Written for the general public by an optician and mirror-maker, this treatise discusses the preservation of vision and the use of spectacles for the correction of imperfect sight. The corrective properties of various convex and concave lenses are described. A hand-colored engraving by Larmessin (Print 4) depicts the costume and wares of such an eighteenth century craftsman.

BOA I:210; Waller 9558.

374.1   Thomin, Marc Mitouflet, 1707-1752.

Traité d'optique mechanique, dans lequel on donne les régles & les proportions qu'il faut observer pour faire toutes sortes de lunettes d'approche, microscopes simples & composés, & autres ouvrages qui dépendent de l'art. Avec une instruction sur l'usage des lunettes ou conserves pour toutes sortes de vûes. Paris: J. B. Coignard; A. Boudet, 1749.

xii, 372, [4] p., 4 folding plates; 20 cm. (8vo)
Provenance: G. L. Chanaud (bookstamp).

"An eighteenth century treatise [in two parts] on mechanical optics, containing rules and proportions for making all kinds of spectacles [and] microscopes . . . [followed by instructions] for the use of glasses for the different kinds of defects" (BOA I:210).

The volume is a decorative example of eighteenth century book art with its fine copperplates, engraved title vignette, woodcut initials, and head- and tail-pieces. The original marbled endpapers and full leather binding with gold-tooling on the spine complement the typographical beauty of the book.

BM 161:578; BOA I:210; NUC 388:209; Poggendorff II:1097.

375   Thomson, Spencer, fl. 1848-1883.

The structure and functions of the eye, illustrative of the power, wisdom and goodness of God. London: Groombridge and Sons, 1857.

xv, [16]-272 p.: ill.; 19 cm.

A popular work on the anatomy of the eye and the physiology of vision. The illustrations were newly engraved after originals in the works of Zinn, Bowman, Carpenter, Müller and others. Thomson was the author of several other popular works

on medicine and botany.

BOA I:211.

376   Thorington, James, 1858-1944.

Retinoscopy (or shadow test) in the determination of refraction at one meter distance, with the plane mirror. . . . Second edition, revised and enlarged. Philadelphia: P. Blakiston, Son & Co., 1898.

xv, [1], 9-72 p.: ill.; 21 cm.

This small volume was one of the first books in which the "shadow test" was clearly explained. Its usefulness to the profession is attested by the fact that it went through nine printings of six editions between 1897 and 1913.

Hirschberg §1031.

377   Thurneisser zum Thurn, Leonhard, 1531-1596.

Βεβαιωσις αγωνισμου das ist Confirmatio concertationis oder ein Bestettigung desz jenigen so streittig, häderig, oder zenckisch ist, wie dann ausz Unverstandt die neuwe und vor unerhörte Erfindung der aller nützlichesten und menschlichem Geschlecht der notturftigesten Kunst desz Harnnprobirens ein Zeitlang gewest ist . . . in dreyzehen kurtzer Büecher an Tag geben. Berlin: Grauwen Closter, 1576.

[6], 107 leaves, 2 plates: ill.; 31 cm. (fol.)

(374.1) Thomin, Marc Mitouflet. *Traité d'optique mechanique*, 1749. Title page illustration. (7.5 x 5.5 cm.)

Chemist, adventurer and follower of Paracelsus, Thurneisser zum Thurn started out as a goldsmith's apprentice. After unsuccessfully passing bricks of tin coated with gold as gold bars, he began a life of wide travels and successive adventures. He became inspector of mines in the Tyrol, and after curing the wife of the Elector of Brandenburg of a desperate illness, became his personal physician in 1578. In Berlin he made his fortune in usury, astrology, pretended alchemical miracles and secret medicaments, only to end his life in a convent in Cologne, alone and in poverty.

This work on a variety of medical topics is interestingly illustrated with many woodcuts, several of which reveal interior and exterior views of the body through overlapping woodcut flaps.

Durling 4352; Grässe 6:154.

Tiedemann, Friedrich, 1781-1861, praeses.

See Muck (265.1).

Tomasini, Jacopo Filippo, 1597-1654.

"Hieronymi Fabricii ab Aquapendente vita."

See Fabricius ab Aquapendente (132).

377.1   Tournier, J. Th. Alexandre.

Coup-d'oeil sur les spécialités morbides et thérapeutiques; thése présentée et soutenue à la Faculté de Médecine de Paris, le 11 août 1827; par J.-Th.-Alexandre Tournier, d'Oizon, Département du Cher; docteur en médecine; bachelier ès-lettres; Élève de l'École pratique; ancien Élève des hôpitaux militaires. Paris: Didot le jeune, 1827.

40 p.; 28 cm. (4to)

Provenance: Inscribed by the author to Rigondet.

BM 240:511.

378   Traber, Zacharias, 1611-1679.

Nervus opticus sive tractatus theoricus, in tres libros opticam catoptricam dioptricam distributus. In quibus radiorum â lumine, vel objecto per medium diaphanum processus, natura, proprietates, & effectus, selectis, & rarioribus experientiis, figuris, demonstrationibusque exhibentur. Vienna: J. C. Cosmerovin, 1675.

[24], 225, [1] p., 33 plates; 33 cm. (fol.)

Published in the same year that Isaac Newton (273) was making his great advances in the study of light, this encyclopedic and lavishly illustrated book is a classic on optics, combining both physical and physiological optics. The anatomy and physiology of the eye and the physical properties of light are dealt with extensively. There is a great deal of historical information about the development of the science from Aristotle to the work of such contemporaries as Kepler (216.1), Kircher (217), Aguilon (6) and Scheiner (331, 332). Traber's analysis is particularly advanced in the areas of refraction of light and the theory of color vision. The author was professor of mathematics at Vienna and later rector of the Jesuit seminary there. His scientific work is described in *Scriptores provinciae Austriacae Societatis Jesu . . . Tomus primus* (Vienna, 1855). The book itself is an extremely fine example of the press of Johann Christoph Cosmerovin.

Countway 9:794.

Tractatus de egritudinibus oculorum ex dictis sapientium veterum compillatis. Ejusdem tractatus de quibusdam dubiis circa dicta oculorum concurrentibus. (Fragmentum). Publiés pour la première fois et précédés d'un aperçu sur la pratique de l'oculistique au moyen âge.

In Collectio ophthalmologica veterum auctorum (82), fasc. 6.

379   Travers, Benjamin, 1783-1858.

A synopsis of the diseases of the eye, and their treatment: to which are prefixed, a short anatomical description and a sketch of the physiology of that organ. London: G. Woodfall for Longmans, 1820.

xix, [1], 425 p., 6 plates; 22 cm. (8vo)

"The earliest systematic treatise in English on diseases of the eye. The book became the authority in Europe and America. Travers, a pupil of Sir Astley Cooper, became surgeon to St. Thomas's Hospital" (G-M 5843). Travers succeeded Saunders (326) as surgeon to the London Infirmary for Diseases of the Eye and was the first hospital surgeon in England to dedicate himself entirely to the study of the eye. The present work was the result of his observations at the Eye Infirmary. Travers's *Synopsis* quickly went through three English editions, an Italian translation by Dr. Apolloni, and an American edition edited by Dr. Delafield. An appendix (p. [381]-389) contains an essay by Christian Salamon entitled "Observations on some points of the anatomy of the eye."

BOA I:214; G-M 5843; Hirschberg §448, 636; Waller 9661.

380 Treviranus, Gottfried Reinhold, 1776-1837.

Beiträge zur Anatomie und Physiologie der Sinneswerkzeuge des Menschen und der Thiere. Erstes Heft. Beitrage zur Lehre von den Ge-sichtswerkzeugen und dem Sehen des Menschen und der Thiere. Bremen: J. G. Heyse, 1828.

91, [1] p., 4 plates; 40 cm.

Although planned as a thorough work on the anatomy and physiology of the sense organs, only the present volume was ever published. It deals with the mechanism of eyesight in humans and animals and includes tables on the dimensions of the eye and illustrations of different parts of the eye after the author's own drawings. Treviranus was the first to describe the retinal layers, but he inverted them and showed the optic nerve fibers on the outside facing the choroid.

Hirschberg §1017.

381 Trnka von Kržowitz, Wenzel, 1739-1791.

Historia amauroseos omnis aevi observata medica continens. Vienna: R. Graeffer, 1781.

[8], 705, [30] p.; 21 cm. (8vo)

An elaborate historical account of blindness from various causes. This work is characteristic of the author's meticulous and laborious approach to such studies. This is but one of a number of historical compilations on aspects of medicine written by this Bohemian anatomist and surgeon.

Hirschberg §480.

382 Trnka von Kržowitz, Wenzel, 1739-1791.

Historia ophthalmiae omnis aevi observata medica continens. Vienna: Widow of C. Landerer for R. Graeffer, 1783.

[16], 592, [16] p.; 18 cm. (8vo)

Trnka's principal ophthalmological writing, valuable for its numerous references to authors now little known. An index to the authors and subjects cited is provided, thereby increasing the usefulness of this work.

Hirschberg §480.

382.1 Troja, Michele, 1747-1827.

Lezioni intorno alle malattie degli occhi ad uso della nuova Università eretta da RE N.S. nel Regio Spedale degl' Incurabili. Naples: Stamperia Simoniana, 1780.

xii, 463 p., 2 plates; 19 cm. (8vo)

A collection of lectures originally delivered by Michele Troja in 1779 at the Hospital for Incurables in Naples. Troja was chief-surgeon and lecturer on ophthalmology in this hospital until 1781 when he became surgeon to the royal court. In 1799 he followed the royal family to Sicily, but soon returned to Naples, where he worked as chief-surgeon in two hospitals and was among the founders of the Institution for the Education of the Blind.

The first part of the *Lezioni* deals with the structure of the eye, as well as the principles of optics and vision. The second part discusses the diseases of the adnexa oculi, and the third, the diseases of the eyeball. According to Hirschberg, the book was hard to obtain in Germany at the time, and it was quite rare even in Italy (cf. §407).

AmEncOph XVII:13094; Blake, p. 459; NUC 602:83; Hirsch V:642; Hirschberg §407.

Tscherning, Marius Hans Erik, 1854-1939, ed. & trans.

See Young (423.2).

383 Tyrrell Frederick, 1797-1843.

A practical work on the diseases of the eye, and their treatment, medically, topically, and by operation. London: Metcalf for J. Churchill, 1840.

2 v. ([2], lviii, 533, [1] p., [5] plates; [2], xii, 566 p., [4] plates); 23 cm.

The author was nephew and pupil of Sir Astley Cooper, and for the last twenty years of his life, surgeon at the London Infirmary for Diseases of the Eye. A peculiar feature of this work is the almost total absence of any reference to the work of others. Saunders (326) and Farre (ibid.) receive passing notice, but the work of the author's immediate predecessors at the Eye Infirmary, Travers (379) and Lawrence (231.1-233.1), goes completely unrecognized. This absence of historical material provided the focus for the criticisms of the work which appeared in the *London Medical Gazette* [27:245-248 (1840)] and *The Lancet* [2:449-457 (1839-1840)]. *The Lancet* reviewer concluded, "Had we, ourselves, proceeded on the principle pursued by Mr. Tyrrell, we should not have reviewed his writings at all."

BOA I:217; Hirschberg §638.

Udall, Nicholas, 1505-1556, trans.

See Geminus (151).

(323) Santa Anna, Joaquim José de. *Elementos de cirurgia ocular*, 1793. Plate [1]. (15 x 19 cm.)

383.1   Ueber Augen, Augenübel, Kurzsichtig- und Weitsichtigkeit, Brillen und Fern- gläser.

Oder: Kurze Anweisung, ein gutes Gesicht zu erhalten und ein mangelhaftes zu verbessern. Aus den Schriften bewährter Augenärzte und Optiker gezogen. Eichstädt: J. M. Beyer; Leipzig: J. A. Barth, 1824.

vi, [2], 94 p., [1] color plate; 20 cm.

Inscription and provenance: *O selig, wer so die Kultur in ihrem Festgewande sehen und empfinden kann.* J. Georgios Goettlich, parochus" (verso of front cover).

NUC 606:543.

384   Vallez, Prosper Josephus, fl. 1841-1866.

Traité théorique et pratique de médecine oculaire, comprenant l'historique de l'ophthalmologie, l'anatomie descriptive, la physiologie, la physique, l'hygiène, l'ophthalmoscopie, la pathologie, et la thérapie des parties constituantes de l'oeil. Brussels: Janssens-Deffosse, 1853.

[4], v, [1], [5]-592 p.; 23 cm.

A general treatise on the eye and its diseases by an obscure Belgian ophthalmologist. Vallez makes no mention of Helmholtz's ophthalmoscope. The word *l'ophthalmoscopie* on the title-page refers simply to the examination of the eye, not ophthalmoscopy. In the preface the author states that ocular surgery is not included in this volume because of the number of treatises already available on the subject. Nonetheless Vallez published a surgical sequel to this volume in 1858 (385).

Hirschberg §801.

385   Vallez, Prosper Josephus, fl. 1841-1866.

Traité théorique et pratique de la chirurgie de l'oeil et de ses dépendances. Brussels: Les principaux libraires, 1858.

xviii, 642 p.; 22 cm.

The surgical complement to Vallez's earlier treatise on ophthalmology (384). The work is divided into three sections: the first on surgical instruments; the second on the surgery of the globe; and the last on the surgery of the palpebrae, lacrymal apparatus and orbit. Remedying the defect of his earlier work, mention is made here of the ophthalmoscope (in the second chapter). In general Vallez's works are nondescript productions which have left their author in deserved obscurity.

Hirschberg §801.

Van Mons, Charles Jacques, 1800-1836, jt. author.

See Vleminckx (392).

Vater, Christian, 1651-1732, praeses.

See Oertel (280).

386   Veasey, Clarence Archibald, 1869-1957.

Ophthalmic operations as practiced on animals' eyes. Philadelphia: The Edwards & Docker Co., 1896.

viii, [9]-99 p.: ill.; 19 cm.

"A concise account of operations performed on animals' eyes to enable students of ophthalmology to become acquainted with the technique of the various operative procedures" (BOA I:218).

BOA I:218.

386.1   Verdet, Émile, 1824-1866.

Leçons d'optique physique . . . publiées par M. A. Levistal. Paris: Imprimerie impériale, 1869-70.

2 v. ([4], iii, [1], 584; [4], 648 p.): ill., diagrs.; 24 cm.

Series: Oeuvres de É. Verdet publiées par les soins de ses éléves; v. V-VI.

"Lessons in physical optics dealing with reflection, refraction, interference, the polarization of light and a résumé of geometrical optics" (BOA I:218).

Émile Verdet was a lecturer at a teachers' training college and also professor at the École Polytechnique in Paris. He published several works on physics and chemistry in the 1860s.

BOA I:218; NUC 633:121; Poggendorff III:1387 (vol. 2: 1872).

387   Vesalius, Andreas, 1514-1564.

De humani corporis fabrica libri septem. [Facsimile reprint] Brussels: Culture et Civilisation, 1964 (Basel: J. Oporinus, 1543).

[4], [12], 661, 658-659, [37] p., 2 tables: ill., port.; 42 cm.

"By this epoch-making work Vesalius, the 'Father of Modern Anatomy,' prepared the way for the rebirth of physiology by Harvey. More important still, he undermined the widespread reverence for authority in science and prepared the way for independent observation in anatomy and clinical medicine. The publication of this book was the greatest event in medical history since the work of Galen" (G-M 375). There was, in fact, little on the visual system in Vesalius's *magnum opus* that was not mentioned by Galen. However, he did show the crystalline lens was not the seat of vision and that when removed, the lens produced an apparent enlargement of objects when looked at through it, much like a convex lens of glass. This copy is number 1887.

Hirschberg §305.

Vesalius, Andreas, 1514-1564.

See Geminus (151).

388 Vespa, Giuseppe, 1727-1804.

Lettera . . . scritta ad un amico, in occasione d'un nuovo strumento inventato per tagliare la cornea lucide nel fare l'operazione della cateratta per estrazione. Florence: Moucke, 1769.

xxviii p., [l] plate; 21 cm. (8vo)

This uncommon tract is in the form of a letter addressed to a friend of the author's, apparently an English surgeon, who had claimed that Vespa's instrument was copied from one owned by him. Vespa, better known for his work in obstetrics, had spent several years in Paris as a student of Levret, where presumably he developed this new instrument for extracting cataract. References are made in the letter to Daviel (2), Morand (2), Wincel (probably Wenzel), and to the instrument maker, Cheret. A fine copperplate, tinted in blue, illustrates different views of the instrument and its surgical application.

388.1 Vetch, John, 1783-1835.

An account of the ophthalmia which has appeared in England since the return of the British Army from Egypt. London: C. Stower for Longman, Hurst, Rees and Orme, 1807.

viii, 141, [3] p., [1] color plate; 23 cm.

Publishers' advertisement on the last two pages.

An early work by John Vetch containing the first description of Egyptian ophthalmia, subsequently named trachoma by the Danish physician Bendz. The book describes the symptoms, treatment, and prevention of the disease. Appendices include exact accounts on the "time of attack and duration of pain" in certain cases (Appendix I); recipes for a lotion, a cream, and a wash for ulcerous sores (Appendix II); and a "diet-table of regimental hospitals" (Appendix III). A German translation by H. S. Michaelis was published in 1817.

"Vetch was born in East Lothian (Scotland) and studied in Edinburgh; he graduated as a doctor of medicine in 1804 and then served for a long time in the army; he dedicated his activities to caring for soldiers affected with the so-called *Egyptian ophthalmia* (in the Ophthalmic Detachments and in the general hospital for the ophthalmic cases in the army)" (Hirschberg §629).

AmEncOph XVIII:13548; Callisen XX:111-112; Dawson 6893; G-M 5839; Hirsch V:741; Hirschberg §629; NUC 635:326.

389 Vetch, John, 1783-1835.

Observations relative to the treatment by Sir William Adams, of the ophthalmic cases of the army. London: J. Davy for J. Callow, 1818.

26 p.; 22 cm. (8vo)

John Vetch and Sir William Adams (4, 4.1) were the principals in a bitter controversy which arose in 1817 and 1818 over the nature and treatment of Egyptian ophthalmia. The controversy was touched off by Adams whose prolix and confused *Letter to the Right Honourable and Honourable the Directors of Grenwich Hospital* (1817) not only advocated a violent and unsound treatment of ophthalmia with strong emetics but also falsely claimed priority for his treatment of the third stage of this disease, and sought for his services some gesture of national gratitude. In this brief reply Vetch delivered a concise and convincing statement of the facts which all but destroyed Adams's pretensions and claims for both priority of discovery and a Parliamentary grant.

Hirschberg §629.

390 Vetch, John, 1783-1835.

A practical treatise on the diseases of the eye. London: Cox and Baylis for the author and Burgess & Hill, 1820.

x, [2], 267, [1] p., 3 plates; 23 cm. (8vo)

In the present work Vetch presents a systematic treatise on the prognosis and treatment of ocular affections, particularly ophthalmic inflammations and ophthalmia. The second part of the work contains a full history of the Egyptian ophthalmia which was so devastating to the British and French armies during the Napoleonic campaigns.

BOA I:218; Hirschberg §629.

Vitelo (Vitellio, Vitellius), 13th cent.

See Witelo (422.1).

391   Vittori, Leonello, d. 1520.

Practica medicinalis . . . liber de medendis morbis membrorum omnium totius corporis humani, nunquam antea in lucem aeditus. Hoc opus novum et ante hac nullibi excusum Joannes Kufnerus Trochoreus . . . brevibus scholiis illustravit. Qui & Leonellum ipsum, ne vota studiosorum diutius remoraretur, in salutem male habentium orbi communicavit. Ingolstadt: A. Weissenhorn, 1545.

[8], 187, [1], 107, [1] leaves; 20 cm. (4to)

Vittori, a native of Faenza in the Romagne, studied medicine at Bologna where he later became professor of logic, philosophy, and medicine. His writings are thoroughly in the Arabic tradition and in this work he draws heavily on Avicenna's *Canon.* Several chapters (fol. 47-57) deal with vision and diseases of the eye.

Durling 4672.

392   Vleminckx, Jean François, 1800-1876.

Essai sur l'ophthalmie de l'armée des Pays-Bas. Brussels: C. J. Demat's Son; H. Remy, 1825.

[4], vi, 119, [1] p., [1] table; 21 cm.

Both Hirschberg and Hirsch mention the sensation caused by the present book which marks the beginning of Belgian ophthalmology. It deals with the outbreak of "military ophthalmia" which had struck the Belgian army since 1815. The authors maintain that the disease is independent of the Egyptian ophthalmy which had been introduced by the soldiers returning from Napoleon's Egyptian campaign. Vleminckx became a prominent physician at Brussels and was instrumental in the foundation of the Ophthalmological Institute of Brabant in 1848.

Hirschberg §790.

393   Volckamer, Christopher Theophilus, fl. 1700, respondent.

Θαυμαντιαδος θαυμασια sive iridis admiranda sub rationis accuratius examen revocata eruditorumq[ue] ventilationi publicae in Alma Altdorffina Universitate exposita sub praesido M. Joh. Christophori Sturmii. Nürnberg: W. M. Endter, 1699.

[2], 185 p., [4] plates; 23 cm. (4to)

Volder, Burchardus de, 1643-1709, ed.

See Huygens (199).

394   Voltaire, François Marie Arouet de, 1694-1778.

Eléméns de la philosophie de Neuton. Mis à portée de tout le monde. Amsterdam: J. Desbordes, 1738.

2, [2], 399, [1] p., [7] plates: ill., port.; 18 cm. (8vo)

More than any other eighteenth century work, Voltaire's *Eléméns* made popular the ideas and spirit of Newtonian science among the educated populace of Europe. Though devoted principally to optics, Voltaire also discusses Newton's theory of gravity and his cosmology. The volume is illustrated with seven engraved plates, numerous illustrations in the text, and beautifully engraved head- and tail-pieces wholly in the spirit of the best book decoration of the period. This copy bears the bookplate of Lytton Strachey, with notes in the hand of his friend Roger Senhouse, including the comment, "Seldom have science and literature been joined in so beautiful a book."

Lacking frontis. portrait. *See also* Newton (273), Algarotti (7), and Banières (31).

Wallis 155.1.

Wagner, Albrecht, 1827-1871.

See Selected monographs (338.1).

Walaeus, Johannes, 1604-1649.

"Epistolae duae. De motu chyli, et sanguinis ad Thomam Bartholinum."

In Bartholin (33).

Waldeyer-Hartz, Wilhelm, von, 1836-1921.

See Wecker (408.1).

395   Walker, John, 1803?-1847.

The principles of ophthalmic surgery; being an introduction to a knowledge of the structure, functions, and diseases of the eye: embracing new views of the physiology of the organ of vision. London: S. Bentley for J. Taylor, 1834.

xii, 195 p.; 18 cm.

A slender but concise and comprehensive volume which was well received by the reviewers in the leading medical journals and by the profession. An appendix provides an excellent glossary of all the terms generally employed in ophthalmic surgery, with their etymology, and German and French synonyms.

Hirschberg §678.

396 Wallace, William Clay, fl. 1836-1850.

Wonders of vision, a treatise on the eye; containing discoveries of the causes of near and far sightedness, and of the affections of the retina, with remarks on the use of medicines as substitutes for spectacles. . . . Third edition. New York: H. A. Chapin & Co., 1841.

90 p.: ill.; 19 cm.

"An early American surgeon, of considerable importance in ophthalmology because of his skill and because of his writings on the comparative anatomy of the eye" (AmEncOph XVIII:13686). The first edition of this work was published at New York in 1836 under the title *The structure of the eye*. A second edition with the title *A treatise on the eye* was published at New York in 1839. Another edition, also designated the third, was published under the same title as the second at New York in 1841.

AmEncOph XVIII:13686; Hirschberg §750; NUC 646:411.

397 Wallroth, C. Friedrich Wilhelm.

Syntagma de ophthalmologia veterum. Specimen medico-philologicum. Halle: C. A. Kummel, 1818.

xx, 254, [2] p.; 21 cm. (8vo)

An historical treatise on the ophthalmological knowledge of the ancients, this was the first scholarly effort in this branch of medical history which later became the special province of such German historians as Andreae, Hirsch, Magnus, and Hirschberg.

Hirschberg §32.

398 Walther, Philipp Franz von, 1782-1849.

Abhandlungen aus dem Gebiete der practischen Medicin besonders der Chirurgie und Augenheilkunde. . . . Erster Band. Landshut: Philipp Krüll, 1810.

x, [2], 504 p., 3 plates; 22 cm. (8vo)

An early collection of essays on surgery and ophthalmology by the foremost German surgeon of his time. Two of these four essays are on ophthalmic topics, the first, "Über die Krankheiten der Crystallinse und die Bildung des Staares" (p.

1-90); and the last, "Über die Augenentzündung, ihr Wesen und ihre Formen" (p. [357]-504). Both essays are discussed in detail by Hirschberg (Bd. XIV, Abt. 2, p. 211-16). Of the first he writes, "Dies ist die Abhandlung W.'s, die bei seinen Zeitgenossen bedeutende (allerdings dem Vf. noch nicht genügende) Anerkennung gefunden hat." A second volume was never published.

Callisen XX:372; Hirsch V:840; Hirschberg §506.

399 Walther, Philipp Franz von, 1782-1849.

Die Lehre vom schwarzen Staar und seiner Heilart. Aus v. Graefe's und v. Walther's Journal der Chirurgie und Augenheilkunde Band XXX. besonders abgedruckt. Berlin: G. Reimer, 1841.

[2], iv, 217 p.; 21 cm.

A treatise on amaurosis reprinted from the journal established and edited by von Graefe and von Walther, two of Germany's most celebrated surgeons. "Amaurosis" as an expression of blindness formerly indicated a clinical entity and constituted a diagnosis with pathological specificity.

Hirschberg §505.

399.1 Walton, Henry Haynes, 1816-1889.

A practical treatise on the diseases of the eye. Third edition. London: J. & A. Churchill, 1875.

[2], xxxii, 1188, [4] p., 8 plates: ill.; 23 cm.

"[A] . . . treatise giving ample details on the use of ophthalmic instruments, the pathology of diseases of the eye, examination with the ophthalmoscope, the treatment of strabismus, anomalies of accommodation and of refraction of the eye" (BOA I:222). The volume includes an *Anatomical introduction* by A. T. Norton, and a chapter (XIV) entitled *The ophthalmoscope* by T. C. Allbutt. The book went through three editions: the first and second editions were published under the titles *A treatise on operative ophthalmic surgery* (London, 1853) and *A treatise on the surgical diseases of the eye* (London, 1861). An American edition appeared in 1875.

Henry Haynes Walton studied medicine in London and later in Paris. He became surgeon at the Central London Ophthalmic Hospital in 1843, and then at the ophthalmic division of St. Mary's Hospital, where he also worked as an instructor of anatomy, operative surgery, and ophthalmology.

AmEncOph XVIII:13689; BM 252:630; BOA I:222; Hirsch V:842; Hirschberg §662; NUC 647:406.

400 Wardrop, James, 1782-1869.

Essays on the morbid anatomy of the human eye. Edinburgh: G. Ramsay and Co. for A. Constable

(328) Scarpa, Antonio. *Practical observations on the principal diseases of the eyes*, 1806. Frontispiece.
(19 x 27 cm.)

and Co. . . . and John Murray . . . (London), 1808-18.

2 v. (xxxi, [1], 159 p., 7 plates; x, 274 p., 8 plates); 25 cm.

"Wardrop was the first to classify the various inflammations of the eye according to the structure attacked" (Chance, p. 72). Inspired by the pathological anatomy of Bichat, Wardrop's topographical description of ocular disease earned him the title "the first modern ophthalmologist" from Duke-Elder. The most important of his many publications in surgery and ophthalmology, Wardrop uses here for the first time the term *keratitis*, and provides the first accurate description of retinoblastoma. The two volumes are illustrated with fifteen remarkable plates, most of them prepared by Patrick Syme of Edinburgh. A second edition was published in 1834.

BOA I:222; Chance, p. 72; G-M 5840; Hirsch V:845; Hirschberg §628.

401 Ware, James, 1756-1815.

Remarks on the ophthalmy, psorophthalmy, and purulent eye. With methods of cure, considerably different from those commonly used; and cases annexed, in proof of their utility: also, the case of a gutta serena cured by electricity. The second edition, with additions. London: C. Dilly, 1787.

vii, [1], 156 p.; 21 cm. (8vo)

Ware studied under Jonathan Wathen (405, 406) and from 1777 to 1791 shared his London practice which specialized in the treatment of diseases of the eye. This book, the second and enlarged edition of Ware's first published work, includes many cases which were attended by both the author and Wathen. Ware was the first "bare oculist" to be elected Fellow of the Royal Society of London, a distinction that greatly contributed to the recognition of ophthalmic surgery as a scientific endeavor.

Hirschberg §398.

401.1 Ware, James, 1756-1815.

Chirurgical observations relative to the epiphora, or watery eye, the scrophulous and intermittent ophthalmy, the extraction of the cataract, and the introduction of the male catheter. London: C. Dilly 1792.

vi, [2], 78 p., [1] folding plate; 21 cm. (8vo)

This work of Ware was republished in 1805 in his collected *Chirurgical observations relative to the eye* (2 v.), as the second part of volume 1. The whole collection was translated into German by Johann Runde and appeared in Göttingen in 1809 with an introduction and comments by Karl Himly (191).

Blake, p. 481; BM 253:62; Hirschberg §398; NUC 648:493.

402 Ware, James, 1756-1815.

An enquiry into the causes which have most commonly prevented success in the operation of extracting the cataract; with an account of the means by which they may either be avoided or rectified. To which are added, observations on the dissipation of the cataract, and on the cure of the gutta serena. Also, additional remarks on the epiphora; or, watery eye. The whole illustrated with a variety of cases. London: H. Murray and J. Walter for C. Dilly, 1795.

[2], vii, [1], 172 p.; 21 cm. (8vo)

"In the various departments of surgery . . . as well as in those of common life, it is of no small importance to be acquainted with the mistakes of others" (Pref., p. iii). With this in mind, Ware presents here a collection of observations on the reasons for the failure of cataract operations. These he attributes to six factors: from too small a corneal incision; from wounding the iris; from allowing a portion of the vitreous humor to escape; from incomplete extraction of the lens, leaving a part in the eye; from undue pressure after the operation; and from prematurely exposing the eye to too strong light. The three treatises on dissipation of cataract, gutta serena and epiphora had all been published by the author prior to their appearing here.

Blake, p. 481; Hirsch V:847; Hirschberg §398; James, p. 105.

403 Ware, James, 1756-1815.

Remarks on the fistula lachrymalis; with the description of an operation considerably different from that commonly used; and cases annexed in proof of its utility; to which are added, observations on haemorrhoids; and additional remarks on the ophthalmy. London: Murray and Highley . . . and J. Walter for C. Dilly, 1798.

[4], 86, [2], 30, [2], 33, [3] p., 2 plates; 21 cm. (8vo)

In order to simplify the opening of lacrimal obstructions, Ware proposed a new operation involving the introduction of a tube or style into the nasal duct. The treatment formerly employed, following the recommendations of Percivall Pott (305.1, 305.2) and Joseph Warner (404, p. 15-25), had been to open the cyst and dilate it with a sponge, passing a bougie or piece of catgut through the nasal duct, or even to create an artificial duct by puncturing the os unguis. In the final tract Ware defends the use of *tinctura thebaica* in the treatment of "ophthalmy."

Blake, p. 481; Hirsch V:847; Hirschberg §398.

Ware, Lyman, 1841-1916, trans.

See Arlt (24).

404   Warner, Joseph, 1717-1801.

A description of the human eye, and its adjacent parts; together with their principal diseases, and the methods proposed for relieving them. London: L. Davis, 1773.

xiv, [2], 109 p., 2 plates; 21 cm. (8vo)

This was perhaps the first useful textbook based on practical knowledge composed by an English writer. It was highly regarded by such contemporaries as Beer (37-40) and Richter (313), despite its rather small anatomical content.

Hirschberg §394.

405   Wathen, Jonathan, 1729-1808.

A dissertation on the theory and cure of the cataract: in which the practice of extraction is supported; and that operation, in its present improved state, is particularly described. London: T. Cadell and C. Dilly, 1785.

[8], 166 p.; 23 cm. (8vo)

"Wathen describes the symptoms and signs and insists on the impossibility of curing cataract by medical means. He lays down excellent rules for the diagnosis of the condition, and as to whether the case is ready for operation. He deprecates the practice of operating in cases of uni-ocular cataract. He describes the old operation of couching and then that of extraction . . ." (James, p. 114).

Hirschberg §397; James, p. 114.

406   Wathen, Jonathan, 1729-1808.

A new and easy method of curing the fistula lacrymalis: the second edition, with considerable improvements. To which is added, a dissertation on the epiphora vera; or, true watery eye: and the zeropthalmia; or, dry eye. Also, an appendix on the treatment of patients after the operation for the cataract: in which are shewn the evils attendant on long confinement and continued bandages: and an opposite practice recommended. Illustrated with cases. London: Phipps. C. Dilly, 1792.

[4], xi, [1], 104 p., [1] plate; 21 cm. (8vo)

The author's "new method," announced in the first edition of this work published in 1781, consisted of "inserting a tube, and leaving it in the natural passage." This method was advanced as an alternative to Heister's practice of perforating the os lacrimale. The work is dedicated to John Hunter.

Hirschberg §397.

407   Watson, Alexander, 1799-1879.

Anatomical description of the human eye. Edinburgh: A. Balfour & Co. for Maclachlan and Stewart, 1828.

[2], 16 p., [1] plate; 24 cm.

The author, a distinguished Scottish ophthalmologist and authority on legal medicine, known later as Watson-Wemyss after inheriting an estate in Fife, was the author of the first compendium of ophthalmology in the English language, published in 1822. This brief work was probably written to serve as a guide to students in obtaining an understanding of the relative position of the constituent parts of the eye. The diagram of the vertical section of the eye and the accompanying description are from Soemmerring's atlas (348, 349).

Hirschberg §699.

Watson, Sir William, 1715-1787.

See Mead (254).

Weber, Christoph Theophil, respondent.

"De palpebrarum tumoribus cysticis casuque speciali magni tumoris steatomatico-scirrhosi e palpebra superiore et orbita feliciter nuperrime extirpati."

In Dissertationes medicae selectae Tubingenses (112) 1:283-312.

Webster, Warren, 1835-1896, trans.

See Mauthner (252).

408   Wecker, Louis de, 1832-1906.

Thérapeutique oculaire. . . . Leçons recueillies et rédigées par le Dr. Masselon. Paris: Octave Doin, 1878-79.

2 v. ([4], 388; [4], [389]-803 p.): ill.; 24 cm.

Wecker made several monumental contributions to ophthalmic

literature—among them this work—which alone would have secured his reputation as one of the great ophthalmologists of the second half of the nineteenth century. His writings are noted as masterpieces of both scientific accuracy and literary style.

Wecker's medical studies took him to Würzburg (M.D., 1855), Vienna, Berlin and Paris (2nd M.D., 1861), where he studied under such figures as Arlt (20-24), Jaeger (202-207), von Graefe (160, 161), Sichel and Desmarres (102, 103). Like Meyer (258) and Sichel (340, 340.1), Wecker was one of those Germans who elected to live and work in Paris. He made many contributions to the progress of ophthalmology, among them his introduction of the ophthalmoscope into France. Wecker invented several ingenious surgical instruments and operative techniques, such as sclerotomy as a cure for glaucoma and his method of tatooing the cornea (vol. 1, p. 207).

Fischer II: 1650; Hirschberg §1264.

408.1   Wecker, Louis de, 1832-1906.

Traité complet d'ophthalmologie par L. de Wecker et E. Landolt. Anatomie microscopique par les professeurs J. Arnold, A. Iwanoff, G. Schwalbe et W. Waldeyer. Paris: V. A. Delahaye & Co.; A. Delahaye & É. Lecrosnier; Lecrosnier & Babé, 1880-89.

4 v.: ill.; 24 cm.

Library's copy lacks volume 4.

Provenance: Lane Medical Library, Stanford University (bookplate, stamps).

A monumental treatise by Wecker and E. Landolt (228) regarded—along with the *Graefe-Saemisch Handbuch*—as one of the best ophthalmologic handbooks of the nineteenth century. "Cet ouvrage remplacé la troisième édition du Traité de Wecker (prix Châteauvillard)" (title page). The first edition—yet without Landolt's part—was published under the title *Études ophthalmologiques* (Paris, 1863-66), while the second had the title: *Traité théoretique et pratique des maladies des yeux* (Paris, 1867-68).

BM 254:446 (imprint dates: 1878-89); Fischer II:1650 (imprint dates: 1878-89); G-M 5919; Gorin p. 189, 190; Hirschberg §1264 (imprint dates: 1878-89); NUC 652:692.

409   Wedl, Carl, 1815-1891.

Atlas der pathologischen Histologie des Auges. Unter Mitwirkung des Herrn Prof. Dr. C. Stellwag von Carion herausgegeben von Prof. Dr. C. Wedl. Leipzig: Georg Wigand, 1860-61.

4 pts. (xiv p., V plates; V plates; V plates; IX plates); 33 cm.

"Das Werk ist Rokitansky gewidmet und sollte die

hervorstechendsten Merkmale der pathologischen Processe des Auges in Bild und Wort vorführen. Die in lateinischer Sprache gegebenen Diagnosen sind von Stellwag berichtigt worden. Der Atlas ist zum Studium insbesondere für Augenärzte bestimmt. Viele Objekte wurden in Lupen-Vergrosserung gezeichnet, zur Aufbewahrung Weingeist bevorzugt, zu Schnitten auch ein Mikrotom und Eintauchen der Objekte in Leim-Lösung angewendet, die Zeichnung von Dr. C[arl] Heitzmann [1836-1894] ausgeführt" (Hirschberg §1180).

Stellwag von Carion in his *Lehrbuch* (352) called this atlas "a rich mine of unadorned facts, which has often been widely used by others, but which is apt to be seldom cited." Each plate is accompanied by a leaf of descriptive letterpress.

Hirsch V:877; Hirschberg §1180.

Wedl, Carl, 1815-1891.
See also Stellwag von Carion (356).

410   Weigel, Carolus Heinricus Bernhard, defendant.

Dissertatio inauguralis sistens experimenta chemica et instrumenta chirurgica emendata . . . praeside Christ. Ehrenfried Weigel. Greifswald: A. F. Rose, 1785.

[6], 50 p., 1 plate; 19 cm. (4to)

Defended at the University of Greifswald, this dissertation is divided into two parts. Of interest here is the second part, describing surgical instruments devised or improved by the author, nearly all of them for use in operations of the eye. Several of these are illustrated on the folding copperplate engraving, cut after the author's own drawings.

410.1   Weinhold, Carl August, 1782-1829.

Anleitung den verdunkelten Krystallkörper im Auge des Menschen, sammt seiner Kapsel umzulegen. Ein ophthalmiatrischer Versuch zur Vervollkommung der Depressions des grauen Staares und der künstlichen Pupillenbildung. Zweite mit Zusätzen vermehrte Ausgabe. . . . Meissen: F. W. Goedsche, 1812.

xxxiv, 111, [1] p., [2] plates; 18 cm. (8vo)

A treatise on an improved method of cataract operation with the aid of a new instrument invented by Weinhold. The instrument, a combination of a pair of scissors and a cataract needle, was used as a cutting device "in order to form a new pupil, to

(378) Traber, Zacharias. *Nervus opticus sive tractatus theoricus, in tres libros opticam catoptricam dioptricam distributus*, 1675. Frontispiece. (15.5 x 25.5 cm.)

separate the lens capsule from the uvea and from the scars of an aftercataract" (Hirschberg §499). The book (first published in 1809) contains two copper plates delineating the device; the second plate is hand-colored.

An accomplished physiologist and surgeon, Weinhold first practiced in Meissen and then was director of the clinic in Tartu, Estonia. In 1814 he became professor of pharmacology at the Medical-Surgical College of Dresden and in 1817, the director of the surgical and ophthalmological clinic in Halle. In cataract operation, Weinhold originally performed extraction exclusively, later he practiced extraction and couching with equally good results. Ultimately, he claimed that couching could completely replace extraction (cf. Hirschberg §499).

Hirschberg §499; NUC 654:121.

410.2 Weiss, Ludwig Samuel, 1804-1838?

Die Augenheilkunde und die Lehre der wichtigsten Augenoperationen: nach den Erfahrungen Jüngken's, Beer's, Himly's, Scarpa's und anderer berühmten Augenärzte, sowie nach eigenen Beobachtungen in gedrängter Kürze dargestellt. Zweite Auflage. Quedlinburg; Leipzig: Gottfr. Basse, 1844.

vi, [2], 251, [1] p.; 20 cm.

NUC 654:444.

Welbank, Richard, ed.
See Frick (142).

411 Weller, Carl Heinrich, 1794-1854.

Die Krankheiten des menschlichen Auges, ein Handbuch für angehende Aerzte. Nach den besten in- und ausländischen Werken, mit besonderer Berücksichtigung der Beer'schen Erfahrungen, bearbeitet und durch eigene Beobachtungen vermehrt. Zweite verbesserte und vermehrte Auflage. Berlin: J. F. Starcke for Schüppel, 1822.

x, 413, [1] p., 5 plates; 22 cm.

The second edition of a useful and popular handbook of ophthalmology which was frequently re-issued and was translated into Russian and French. Weller's work was the standard text in the period between Scarpa (327, 328) and Mackenzie (241).

Hirschberg §524.

412 Weller, Carl Heinrich, 1794-1854.

Traité théorique et pratique des maladies des yeux . . . traduit de l'allemand sur la dernière édition, par F. J. Riester; augmenté de notes, par L. Jallat. Paris: Germer-Baillière, 1832.

2 v. ([4], vii, [1], 396 p.; [4], iii, [1], 320 p., 6 plates); 22 cm.

The second French edition of this authoritative handbook, translated from the third German edition (1826), is introduced by a full bibliography extending to thirty-four pages. Weller played an important part in the developing understanding of glaucoma and the attending increase in intraocular pressure. In 1826 he wrote of the hardness of the eye, not only in the established condition but also in the developing condition, combining the descriptions of Beer and Demours.

Hirschberg §524.

413 Wells, John Soelberg, 1834-1879.

A treatise on the diseases of the eye. . . . Fourth American from the third English edition, with copious additions. By Charles Stedman Bull. Philadelphia: Henry C. Lea's Son & Co., 1883.

xix, [1], [33]-846 p., VI plates: ill.; 24 cm.

The fourth and final American edition of what is often regarded as the best work on the diseases of the eye then extant in the English language. "The want has often been expressed," Wells wrote in the preface to the first London edition of 1869, "of an English treatise on the diseases of the eye, which should embrace the modern doctrines and practice of the British and foreign schools of ophthalmology." The present work more than fulfilled that need, inaugurating a new era in English ophthalmic literature. Copiously illustrated with 257 wood-engravings and six chromolithographs after Liebreich, it has been called by Hirschberg "vielleicht der beste Lehrbuch der Reform-Zeit bis zu Tagen der Encyklopädie von Graefe-Saemisch" (§650).

Hirsch V:894, Hirschberg §650.

414 Wells, William Charles, 1757-1817.

Two essays: one upon single vision with two eyes; the other on dew. A letter to the Right Hon. Lloyd, Lord Kenyon and an account of a female of the white race of mankind, part of whose skin resembles that of a negro; with some observations on the causes of the differences in colour and form between the white and negro races of men. . . . With a memoir of [the author's] life, written by himself. London: T. Davison for A. Constable & Co. (Edinburgh) and Longmans (London), 1818.

lxxiv, [2], 439, [1] p.; 22 cm. (8vo)

In his "Essay upon single vision with two eyes" originally published in 1792, Wells presents a new theory of binocular vision based on the concept of visible direction and experimental evidence on the duration of impressions on the retina. Wells's theory of visible direction had a great influence on the science of spectacle making in the early part of the nineteenth century. An analysis of this essay by R. R. James appeared in the *British Journal of Ophthalmology* 12:[561]-569 (1928). The author's other works reprinted in this first and only collected edition are of significance in the fields of meteorology, ventilation, and evolution.

Hirschberg §746; Osler 4210.

415   Wenzel, Jakob, d. 1810.

Traité de la cataracte, avec des observations qui prouvent la nécessité d'inciser la cornée transparente & la capsule du crystallin, d'une manière diverse, selon les differentes espèces de cataractes. Paris: Lottin for P. J. Duplain, 1786.

xii, 224, [2] p., [1] plate; 20 cm. (8vo)

A treatise on cataract by the son of Baron Michael de Wenzel, one of the most famous ophthalmic surgeons of the late eighteenth century. In the present work the younger Wenzel describes his father's methods of operating for cataract and for creating an artificial pupil. Numerous case histories provide a glimpse of the elder Wenzel's practice.

Hirschberg §355.

416   Wenzel, Jakob, d. 1810.

Manuel de l'oculiste, ou dictionnaire ophthalmologique, contenant une description anatomique de l'oeil; une définition des maladies qui l'affectent; des observations particulières sur les médicamens et les opérations qui peuvent les guérir; enfin une notice des auteurs qu'il convient de consulter; ouvrage utile aux personnes du monde et à celles qui se livrent à l'étude de cette branche de la médecine. Paris: Lavater, 1808.

2 v. (xii, [2], 522, [2] p.; [4], 287, [1], 32 p., 23 plates); 20 cm. (8vo)

A compendium of eighteenth century ophthalmic knowledge

and practice illustrated by a number of engravings showing the instruments and operative procedures of the leading practitioners. The dictionary arrangement and full index enhance the usefulness of this work.

Hirschberg §355.

417   Weylandt d'Hettanges, N.

Notice sur la question de savoir s'il serait possible de rétablir les sensations de vision au moyen d'un oeil artificiel qui transmettrait a la rétine les rayons de lumière convenablement réfractés. Orange: Raphel, 1846.

32 p., 3 plates; 23 cm.

The author, an oculist and former army surgeon, believed that it might be possible to restore vision by an artificial eye which would transmit light rays to the retina in an appropriate refraction. The pamphlet is dedicated to the Queen of Spain because of the prevalence of eye disease in that country.

Wier, Johann, 1515-1588.

"A discourse of the scorby."

See Banister (32).

417.1   Williams, Henry Willard, 1821-1895.

A practical guide to the study of the diseases of the eye: their medical and surgical treatment. Boston: Ticknor and Fields; New York: Sheldon & Co. and W. Wood; Philadelphia: J. B. Lippincott & Co. and Lindsay & Blakiston, 1862.

xii, 317, [1] p.; 20 cm.

A prominent American ophthalmologist, Williams spent three years in Europe pursuing his specialty with Sichel (340, 340.1) and Desmarres (102, 103) in Paris, Jaeger (202-207) and Rosas (313.1) in Vienna, and Dalrymple (90, 91) and Lawrence (231.1-233) in London. Professor of ophthalmology at Harvard, Williams was the first in the United States to deliver a complete course of lectures on the diseases of the eye (apart from general medicine and surgery), and one of the first in this country to specialize exclusively in ophthalmology.

"Williams was one of the earliest to use etherization in cataract operations and pioneered a new method of suturing the flap after cataract extraction. He advanced the treatment of iritis without mercury and translated one of [Julius] Sichel's lesser works into English" (Heirs 1889). The present work comprises methods for eye examination and systematic discussions of eye diseases and their treatment. The book went through six editions and some more reprintings between 1862 and 1880.

AmEncOph XVIII:14031; Heirs 1889; Hirsch V:945; Hirschberg §756; NUC 665:69.

418   Williams, Henry Willard, 1821-1895.

The diagnosis and treatment of the diseases of the eye. Boston: Houghton, Mifflin and Company. Cambridge: The Riverside Press, 1882 (c1881).

xii, [2], 464 p., [5] plates: ill.; 22 cm.

419   Williams, John, fl. 1815.

Traité des maladies des yeux, avec des observations pratiques constatant les succès obtenus, tant à Paris quà Londres, par l'usage d'un topique inventé par J. Williams. Paris: Maugeret, 1814.

151, [1] p.; 20 cm. (8vo)

Bound with Beer (38) and Williams (420, 421).

An Anglo-French quack whose career closely rivaled Taylor's for pretension and effrontery. Williams, who described himself as the proprietor of a dispensary at High Holborn and honorary oculist to Louis XVIII, began to practice in Paris about 1814. He did not operate for cataract but sold a remedy for 500 francs which he claimed prepared the patient for the operation. With the July Revolution of 1830 his license to practice in France was finally revoked. The author's claim to membership in the Legion of Honour has twice been carefully obliterated from the text of this copy, as it was in the copy described by Hirschberg.

BOA I:229; Hirschberg §555.

420   Williams, John, fl. 1815.

Compte rendu des cures faites sur des maladies des yeux réputées incurables, avec un topique inventé par Jn. Williams. Paris: Royer; London: The author, 1815.

[2], 60 p.; 20 cm. (8vo)

Bound with Beer (38) and Williams (419, 421).

Hirschberg §555.

421   Williams, John, fl. 1815.

Observations nouvelles sur les maladies des yeux et des oreilles. Paris: J. L. Chanson, 1816?

44, 16 p.; 20 cm (8vo)

Bound with Beer (38) and Williams (419, 420).

Hirschberg §555.

422   Wilson, George, 1818-1859.

Researches on colour-blindness. With a supplement on the danger attending the present system of railway and marine coloured signals. Edinburgh: Sutherland & Knox; London: Simpkin, Marshall and Co., 1855.

[4], xx, [5]-180 p.: ill.; 23 cm.

The first book on color-blindness, and the most important monograph on the subject until the publication of Holmgren's work in 1877 (194.1). It first began to appear in the November 1853 issue of the *Edinburgh Monthly Journal of Medical Science*, and was continued in the *Transactions of the Royal Scottish Society of the Arts*, before being published in book form. Wilson was the first in Britain publicly to point out the potential hazards of color-blindness in railwaymen and seamen. This copy is inscribed by the author to Dr. James Stark, who was colorblind, and whose case (Dr. K.) is described on pages 22-24. A pencil note on the front free-endpaper states "This copy was lent to [Frithiof] Holmgren [1831-1897] by S. [Stark] when

(8) Witelo. *Opticae libri decem*, 1572. (In Alhazen, *Opticae thesaurus*.) Title page illustration. (14 x 15.5 cm.)

H. intended to publish his work on colour-blindness." Book-plate of William Stirling (1851-1932).

BOA I:229; Sherman, p. 144-147; Waller 10343.

Windsor, Thomas, 1811-1910, trans.
See Selected monographs (338.1).

422.1 Witelo, 13th cent.

Vitellionis mathematici doctissimi Περι οπτικης, id est de natura, ratione, & proiectione radiorum uisus, luminum, colorum atq[ue] formarum, quam uulgo Perspectiuam uocant, libri X. . . . Nunc primum opera mathematicor[um] praestantiss. dd. Georgij Tanstetter & Petri Apiani in lucem aedita. Nürnberg: I. Petreius, 1535.

[4], 297 leaves: ill. (diagrs.); 33 cm. (fol.).

Provenance: Sergio Bettini (bookstamp).

A textbook on optics composed between 1270 and 1278 by Witelo (Vitelo, Vitellius, Vitellio), a Polish physicist and philosopher. The text is largely derived from the *Optics* of Alhazen (8) and served for several centuries as an important link between the Greco-Arabic science and the Latin world. "Witelo employs the experimental as well as the mathematical method and instruments as well as theorems" (Thorndike II:456). His theories on magnifying glasses, refraction, the rainbow, and burning mirrors are hardly superior to those of his predecessors', but his philosophical (and sometimes psychological) approach is quite original. He discusses "ordinary perception (*aspectus simplex*) and attentive perception, spontaneous and unconscious reasoning which affects our vision, perception of the third dimension of space, etc." (Sarton II:1027).

Witelo was born in Silesia and was educated in Paris, Padua, and Viterbo. Besides his *Perspectiva*, he wrote two theological treatises. He died, probably in the Premonstratensian monastery of Witow, Poland, at an unknown date.

Bird 2422; BM 249:790; Durling 4757; Gorin p. 28; Hirsch V:971; NUC 669:643; Sarton II:1027-1028; Thorndike II:454-456.

Witelo, 13th century.
See Alhazen (8).

Woinow, M., d. 1875, jt. author.
See Reuss (311.2).

422.2 Woinow, M., d. 1875.

Ophthalmometrie. Vienna: A. Holzhausen for W. Braumüller, 1871.

vi, 130 p.: ill.; 24 cm.

The first monograph on ophthalmometry, discussing the methods and possible findings of examinations with the aid of a new instrument, the ophthalmometer or keratometer. The device was invented by Hermann Helmholtz (134.1, 185) who was Woinow's teacher in Heidelberg, and to whom Woinow dedicated his book.

Woinow studied in Russia, Germany, and Austria, practiced in Moscow and founded a private eye hospital there. A successful ophthalmologist, reputable teacher, and prolific author, he died very young in 1875. His three monographs discuss ophthalmometry, and his numerous articles include subjects such as ametropia, the blind spot, binocular vision, color vision, accommodation, ocular motions, etc.

Hirschberg §901; Hirsch V:978; NUC 670:554.

Wolf, Caspar, 1532-1601, ed.
See Houllier (195).

Wood, Casey Albert, 1856-1942, trans.
See ᶜAlī ibn ᶜĪsā (9) and Grassus (162).

423 Woolhouse, John Thomas, 1650?-1734.

Dissertationes ophthalmicae de cataracta et glaucomate, contra systema sic dictum novum dnn. Brissaei, Antonii, Heisteri & aliorum, e gallica in Latinam linguam translatae a Christophoro Le Cerf, filio. Frankfurt am Main: W. C. Multz, 1719.

[14], 350, [30] p.; 16 cm. (8vo)

A skillful English ophthalmic surgeon and oculist to King James II, with whom he went into exile in 1688, Woolhouse is noted as having approached perilously close to charlatanism by his writings and practice. He is said to have proposed iridectomy in 1711, more than a decade before Cheselden. The present work, in the second edition, translated into Latin from the 1717 edition, is a collection of dissertations and letters attacking the publication by Brisseau (63), Maître-Jan (243, 244) and Heister (182) on the nature of cataract. Woolhouse steadfastly maintained that cataract consisted of a thickened humor or membrane in a space between the pupil and the lens. A poem on Hovius's discovery of the circulation of blood through the eye (196) accompanied by 104 historical notes is included (p. 247-275).

Hirschberg §329.

(424) Zahn, Johann. *Oculus artificialis...*, 1685-86, fund. I, p. 203. Figure 23.
(16.5 x 27.5 cm.)

423.1 Young, Thomas, 1773-1829.

A course of lectures on natural philosophy and the mechanical arts. London: W. Savage for Joseph Johnson, 1807.

2 v. (xxiv, [2], 796 [i.e. 776] p., XLIII plates (2 col.); xii, [2], 738 p., 15 plates): ill.; 28 cm. (4to)

"A series of lectures Young delivered in 1802-1803 as Professor of Natural History at the Royal Institution, revised for publication in 1807" (Norman 2277). The lectures and appended reprints of earlier writings collected in this two volume set concern a variety of fields in physics and mathematics as well as physical and physiological optics. Topics include: the novel doctrine of interference which—exploiting Huygens's ideas (198, 199)—established the wave theory of light; the proposition of the electromagnetic theory of light; and color blindness. The section "Observations on vision" (II:523-531) provides detailed description of the eye and was considered by many the best of its time. Volume II, pages 87-520 contain "A catalogue of works relating to natural philosophy and the mechanical arts" offering a systematic classification of scientific disciplines, followed by the catalog of titles arranged in that classification scheme. Among Young's several contributions to ophthalmology were: hypotheses on the mechanism of accommodation (1792, 1801), the first description of ocular astigmatism (1801), and the trichromatic theory of color sensation (1802; further developed by Helmholtz and Maxwell). In Hirschberg's words: "Thomas Young perfected the theory of vision as it was possible around the turn of the eighteenth to the nineteenth century" (§459).

Biographical sources include: *Memoir of the life of Thomas Young* by Hudson Gurney (London, 1831); *Life of Thomas Young* by George Peacock (London, 1855); *Eulogy on Thomas Young* by François Arago (Smithsonian Institution, Annual report, 1869); *Thomas Young, natural philosopher, 1773-1829* by Alexander Wood (Cambridge [Eng.], 1954); *Thomas Young: forgotten genius* by Daniel Kline (Cincinnati, c1993).

AmEncOph XVIII:14101; BM 262:550; Dawson 7281; Hirsch V:1017; Hirschberg §459; Norman 2277; Osler 7783; Poggendorff II:1384; Sherman, p. 14.

423.2 Young, Thomas, 1773-1829.

Oeuvres ophthalmologiques de Thomas Young: traduites et annotées par M. Tscherning. Copenhagen: A. F. Höst & Son, 1894.

[8], 248 p., [1], III color plates: ill., port.; 24 cm.

BOA I:233; Hirschberg §459; NUC 679:548.

Zacharias.

Tractatus de passionibus oculorum qui vocatur sisilacera, id est secreta secretorum. Compilatus circa annos 1143-1180.

In Collectio ophthalmologica veterum auctorium (82), fasc. 5.

424 Zahn, Johann, 1641-1707.

Oculus artificialis teledioptricus sive telescopium, ex abditis rerum naturalium & artificialium principiis protractum nova methodo, eaque solida explicatum ac comprimis e triplici fundamento physico seu naturali mathematico dioptrico et mechanico, seu practico stabilitum. Opus curiosum practico-theoricum magna rerum varietate adnoratum, multorum votis diu expetitum, omnibus artium novarum studiosis perquam utile quo philosophiae atque mathesi praesertim mixtae, nec non universo pene hominum statui amplissimis adjumentis consulitur; nova plurima abstrusa curiosa technasmata recluduntur, ipsaque ars telescopiaria facillime addiscenda, ac sumptibus non adeo magnis in praxim adducenda proponitur, adeoque telescopium ex tenebris in lucem asseritur. Würzburg: Q. Heyl, 1685-86.

3 pts. in 1 v. ([22], 190 (i.e. 218) p., 1 table; [2], 271 p., 2 plates, 5 tables; [10], 281 p., 28 plates, 2 tables): ill.; 31 cm. (fol.)

"Includes the first complete history of early microscopes" (G-M 263). The author, a German philosopher who belonged to the Premonstratensian order at Herbipolis (Würzburg), displayed a detailed knowledge of vision, the properties of light, and the structure of the eye. Copiously illustrated throughout with folding plates and smaller woodcuts, many of which are after the works of Scheiner (331, 332), Chérubin d'Orléans (75.1), and Kircher (217). The final section deals with the grinding and polishing of lenses and the construction of microscopes, telescopes, the camera obscura, and other optical instruments.

BOA I:235; G-M 263.

425 Zeis, Eduard, 1807-1868.

Abhandlungen aus dem Gebiet der Chirurgie. Leipzig: Gebauer, 1845.

iv, 100 p., 4 plates; 21 cm.

The first of these three surgical essays, published originally a decade earlier in Ammon's *Zeitschrift für Ophthalmologie*, deals with diseases of the eye lids, and particularly with the physiology and pathology of the conjunctival (Meibomian) glands. The author was professor of surgery at the University of Marburg and was best known for his works in the field of plastic surgery.

Hirschberg §543.

Zeller, Christoph David, respondent.

"De setaceo nuchae, auricularum, ipsiusque oculi."

In Dissertationes medicae selectae Tubingenses (112) 2:232-260.

426   Zinn, Johann Gottfried, 1727-1759.

Descriptio anatomica oculi humani iconibus illustrata. Göttingen: Widow of B. A. Vandenhoeck, 1755.

[16], 272 p., 7 plates; 24 cm. (4to)

"Zinn published a fine atlas of the human eye; he was the first adequately to describe the 'zonula of Zinn' and the 'annulus of Zinn' " (G-M 1484). Hirschberg and Duke-Elder concur that this landmark work on the anatomy of the eye was the first complete work in the world's literature on this subject. Zinn correctly described and depicted 'fibrae radiatae' and showed that the number of fiber bundles in the optic nerve is constant and continuous with those of the retina. Zinn, one of Haller's favorite pupils, distinguished himself in both anatomy and botany, becoming professor of medicine and director of the botanical gardens at Göttingen. The illustrations in this work, engraved by Joel Paul Kaltenhofer, mark a new plateau in the graphic representation of the eye, for it becomes, in the modern sense, recognizable both 'in situ' in the orbit and enucleated.

BOA II:117; G-M 1484; Hirschberg §463; Waller 10493.

(424) Zahn, Johann. *Oculus artificialis...*, 1685-86, fund. I, p. 16. Figure 1. (17 x 10.5 cm.)

(424) Zahn, Johann. *Oculus artificialis...*, 1685-86, fund. III, plate 27 (16.5 x 9 cm.)

GRAPHICS

Print 1

Marlé, engr.

Pie. VII. visitant l'Institution des aveugles-nés dirigée par M. Bertrand successeur de M. Haüy, le jeudi 28. fevrier 1805. Paris: Chez l'auteur, [1805].

Aquatint engraving; 261 x 464 mm.

Print 2

Engelbrecht, Martin, 1684-1756, engr.

Faiseur des lunettes. Ein Brillenmacher oder Glass-Schleiffer.

Copperplate engraving; 302 x 193 mm.

Plate no. 153 from Engelbrecht's *Assemblage nouveau des manouvries habilles*, published at Augsburg circa 1730. The print is hand-colored, with legend in both French and German.

Print 3

Engelbrecht, Martin, 1684-1756, engr.

Faiseuse de lunettes. Die Brillenmacherin.

Copperplate engraving; 304 x 194 mm.

Plate no. 154 from Engelbrecht's *Assemblage nouveau des manouvries habilles,* published at Augsburg circa 1730. Hand-colored, with legend in French and German.

Print 4

L'Armessin, Nicholas de, III, 1640-1725, engr.

Habit de marchand miroitier lunettier. Paris: N. de L'Armessin, ca. 1700.

Copperplate engraving; 282 x 195 mm.

Hand-colored engraving from L'Armessin's *Album des métiers.* It was reproduced as the frontispiece to Mme. Heymann's *Lunettes et lorgnettes de jadis* (190).

Print 5

Boudt, Cornelis de, engr.

S. Lucia. Ca. 1700.

Copperplate engraving; hand-colored; 90 x 61 mm.

St. Lucy, the fourth century Sicilian martyr, is the patroness of the eyes. As in this print and the following (6), St. Lucy is frequently portrayed holding two eyes on a plate, and a sword or dagger.

Print 6

Boudt, Cornelis de, engr.

S. Lucia. Ca. 1700.

Copperplate engraving; hand-colored; 86 x 61 mm.

Identical with print 5. Boudt's signature and the plate marks have been cropped off.

Print 7

Man, Jacobus de, b. 1688, engr.

S. Lucia. 18th century.

Copperplate engraving; 109 x 84 mm.

In this hand-colored engraving, Saint Lucy is depicted with several of the traditional symbols of her iconography: the two eyes on a dish, the palm of martyrdom, and the sword.

Print 8

Anonymous.

S. Lucia. 18th century.

Copperplate engraving; 84 x 51 mm.

In this engraving Saint Lucy bears several of the symbols with which she is traditionally depicted: the palm of martyrdom, the pair of eyes, and a book. In this instance however, the eyes, which typically appear on a dish, rest on the cover of the book.

Print 9

Anonymous.

[Saint Lucy]. 20th century.

Woodcut; 193 x 193 mm.

Contemporary woodblock print on Japanese tissue paper. St. Lucy bears the traditional plate with two eyes and the palm of martyrdom. This print appeared as the frontispiece to the first edition of this catalog.

Print 10
Daumier, Honoré Victorin, 1808-1879.

L'oeil du maître. Paris: Le Charivari, 1842.

Lithograph; 359 x 237 mm.

Number 58 in the *Moeurs conjugales* series, published September 16, 1842 in *Le Charivari,* the radical periodical edited by Philipon.

Delteil 681, 3rd state.

Print 11
Daumier, Honoré Victorin, 1808-1879.

Un oculiste breveté. Paris: Aubert, ca. 1837.

Lithograph; 235 x 224 mm.

Hand-colored lithograph. No. 55 of the *Caricaturana* series, lithographed by Daumier with legends by Charles Philipon (1800-1862). This series was also published between 1836 and 1838 in *Le Charivari* (cf. Print 10).

Delteil 410; Mondor 9.

Print 12
Jacque, Charles, 1813-1894.

L'oculiste. Paris: Pannier, [s.a.]

Lithograph; 272 x 177 mm.

No. 18 of *Les malades et les médecins* series.

Print 13
Anonymous.

[Instruments for eye operation]. 18th century.

Copperplate engraving; 237 x 171 mm.

Plate (numbered LXXIV) from an unidentified French surgical text of the eighteenth century.

Print 14
Ostade, Adrian van, 1610-1685, engr.

[The spectacle seller]. Ca. 1650.

Etching; 101 x 86 mm.

Print 15
Bartisch, Georg, 1535-1607?

[Facsimile illustrations from the *Augendienst*].

21 photographs; measurements vary.

Twenty-one framed photographs from the series of ninety-one woodblock prints that illustrate Bartisch's 1583 *Augendienst.* The blocks were probably cut by Hans Hewamaul after Bartisch's own drawings.

Print 16
Rembrandt, Hermanszoon van Rijn, 1607-1669.

The operation of stone cutting. Ca. 1651-52.

Photograph; 101 x 86 mm.

Photographic reproduction of pen and bistre wash drawing (orig. size 243 x 188 mm) sometimes erroneously identified as "The eye operation".

Benesch 1154: figure 1376.

Print 17
Anonymous.

[Indian coucher of the 19th century].

Photograph; 116 x 90 mm.

Color reproduction of a water-color dating from the siege of Delhi.

Print 18
Schedel, Hartmann, 1440-1514.

Liber chronicarum. Nuremberg: Anton Koberger, 1493.

Leaf CCXXXVI; 42 cm.

The woodcut male figure holding a pair of spectacles at the bottom right of the verso of this leaf is one of the earliest representations of a figure with spectacles to appear in a printed book.

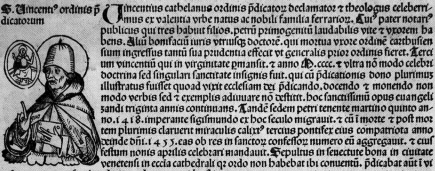

S. Uincenti⁹ ordinis p̄
dicatozum

Uincentius cathelanus ozdinis p̄dicatoz declamatoz z theologus celeberri
mus ex valentia vrbe natus ac nobili familia ferrarioz. Cui⁹ pater notari⁹
publicus qui tres habuit filios. petrũ primogenitũ laudabilis vite z vxozem ha
bens. Alui bonifaciũ iuris vtriusq̃ doctoze. qui moztua vroze ozdine cazthusien
sium ingressus tantũ sua prudentia effecit vt generalis prioz ordinis fieret. Terci
um vincentiũ qui in virginitate pmansit. z anno M̃. cccc. z vltra nõ modo celebri
doctrina sed singulari sanctitate insignis fuit. qui cũ p̄dicationis dono plurimuz
illustratus fuisset quoad vixit ecclesiam dei p̄dicando. docendo z monendo non
modo verbis sed z exemplis adiuuare nõ destitit. hoc sanctissimũ opus euangeli
zandi triginta annis continuans. Tandẽ sedem petri tenente martino quinto an
no. i 4 i 8. imperante sigismundo ex hoc seculo migrauit. z cũ i mozte z post moz
tem plurimis claruerit miraculis calixt⁹ tercius pontifex eius compatriota anno
deinde dñi. i 4 5 5. eas ob res in sanctoz confessoz numero eũ aggregauit. z eius
festum nonis aprilis celebrari mandauit. Sepultus in senectute bona in ciuitate
venetensi in eccia cathedrali q̃z ozdo non habebat ibi conuentũ. p̄dicabat aũt i vi
ta sepenumero de finali iudicio z aduentu antichristi tanto terroze vt omnes in timozes conuerteret. vt pec
catozes futuram dei iram abhozrerent .

Franciscus martini ordinis carmelitaz theologus celeberrimus p hoc ipm tps in precio existens. cuz
multos erudisset discipulos ad agitandum intellectum librũ de conceptiõe virginis Marie opposuit.
Gerhardus groet claret sanctitate vite z scientia. z incepit p̄gregationem in dauadria z plura scripsit
Iohannes rusbzoch clar⁹ habef. vir ad modũ deuot⁹ z illurat⁹. etiã mlta scripta i theutonico reliq̃t
Einricus yota sacre theologie prosessoz. Deinricus quoq̃ de hassia etiam doctoz theologie. hij duo
luminaria ecclesie in vienna pannonie fuerunt.   Haldus iuris doctoz

Baldus perusin⁹ p̄cellentissimus legis peritus bartholi saxoferratensis di
scipulus. z ipe vna cũ angelo z petro germanis hec ipa tempoza clarissi
ma reddidit. qui cũ post magistrũ suũ in iuribus ciuili z pontificio obtineret
principatum infinita p̄pe edidit libroz volumia. Sup toto em iuris ciuilis coz
poze pegregie cõmentatus est. Insup z in scdo decretoliũ ac feudis scripsit. Ad
ditiones ad speculum opposuit. atq̃ clarissima consilia post se reliquit. Tandez
ob doctrine p̄stantiam a philippo mediolanẽsiũ duce publico salario papie vo
catus. anno dñi. i 4 2 3. mense aprili ibidẽ defunctus apd frẽs minozes sepelit

Nicola⁹ florẽtin⁹ medic⁹

Bartholomeus de saliceto iuris consultissimus p hoc tem pus flozuit z in le
gibus nõnullos cõmentarios composuit. Hic cũ apud albertum estensem ferrarie marchione in p̄
cio eẽt cũ ipo egit vt a bonifacio pō. puilegiũ quocãdi studiũ i ferraria obtinerz

Nicolaus eximũ nominis medicus natione flozentinus p hec tpa existens.
in omni medicina grande opus componendo relinquens. qd̃ de omni me
dicina ex veteriozib⁹ z doctis medicis exquisitis accurata lucubzatione extraxit
Obijt deniq̃ flozentie post multas curationes anno dñi. i 4 i 2.

Marsili⁹ de scta sophia patauin⁹ medic⁹. z ipe mltarũ rerũ cognitiõe insigni
tus cum quedaz edidisset in medicina sup hippocratis libros multos scri
ptozes ingenio z subtilitate p̄celluit z suã patriã doctrina z fama exoznauit.

Iohes rauennat⁹ grãmatic⁹ z rhetoz luculẽtissim⁹ his tpib⁹ flozuit. vir certe
maximi ingenij z singularissime doctrine. qui vt leonardus aretinus ei⁹ di
scipulus testaf primus fuit a q̃ eloquẽtie studia tantope longo postliminio in ytaliã sunt redacta. Hic cũ
a francisco petrarcha egregie edoct⁹ fuisset. et ipe viros seq̃ntes excellẽtissimos habuit discipulos.

Emanuel crisolozas bizantinus patria constãtinopolitanus. vir domi nobi
lis. ne dũ litteraz grecaz peritissimus. verũ omni doctrina ac virtutib⁹ no
bilioz atq̃ p̄clarus his tempozibus constantinopoli patria a turchis obsessa. ve
netias mari delatus primo in exudita eius fama inuitatus benigne ac postulat⁹
et litteras grecas ibi docere cepit que iam septingentis annis conticuerant z per
eũ reuiuiscere ceperunt. Hic itaq̃ cũ in italiã venisset primovenetias multos ado
lescentes grecas docuit litteras. indeq̃ a flozentinis publico solario vocat⁹ plu
rimos habuit discipulos. a iohanne rauennato p̄dicto litteris latinis edoctos.
Inter quos fuere leonardus aretinus. paulus strotia. petrus paulus vergerius
iustinopolitanus. omnibonus vicentinus. guarinus veronensis. carolus aretin⁹
pogius flozentin⁹. franciscus barbarus z franciscus philelphus z alij. Indeq̃
curiam romanã cum secutus fuisset z apud constantiã vbi generale conciliũ cele
bzaref accessisset z p̄dicti discipuli dulcedine verborũ suozũ allecti eũ sequi volu
erunt. Hic aũt z si omni sciẽtia edoct⁹ fuerit nihil tñ scripto qd extat reliq̃t. Con
stantie aũt deficiẽs a pogio florẽtino mellisslua ozõne cũ epigrãmate honestat⁹ e.

Crisolozas constantino
politanus

Print 18.

Print 16.

Print 14.

S. LVCIA

Cornelis de Boidt

Print 5.

Print 7.

S. LVCIA .

Print 8.

Print 9.

Faiſeur de lunettes. Ein Brillenmacher oder Glaß-Schleiffer.

1. un verre pour Optique. 1. ein Glaß für Optic. 2. une corbeille avec lunettes et verres. 2. ein Körbel
mit Brillen u. Gläſer. 3. verres ardens. 3. Brenn-Gläſer. 4. miroir de poche. 4. ein Sack-Spiegel. 5. courte perſpective. 5. kurtz Perſpectif. 6. un Microſcopium. 6. ein Microſcopium. 7. marteau. 7. ein Hammer. 8. verre
a moüller. 8. ein ſpruß-Glaß. 9. des tenailles. 9. eine Zange. 10. un Etui. 10. ein Füteral. 11. boette aux lunettes
11. ein Brillen-Kaſten. 12. une perſpective. 12. ein Perſpectif. 13. 14. 15. 16. 17. differens etuis à lunettes. 13. 14. 15.
16. 17. allerley Brillen Füter. 18. 2. tubos. 18. 2. Tubos.

Cum Priv. Maj.   *Mart. Engelbrecht exc. A. V.*

Print 2.

Faiseuse de lunettes   Die Brillenmacherin.

1. verre ardent. 1. Brenn=Glaß. 2. lunettes. 2. Brillen. 3. 4. 5. divers Etuis de lunettes. 3. 4.
5. unterschiedliche Brillen Füter. 6. verre ardent. 6. ein Centrum oder Brenn= Glaß. 7.
perspectives. 7. Perspectif. 8. 2. Microscopia. 8. 2. Microscopia oder vergrößerungs=Gläßer.
9. un Compas. 9. ein Zirckel.

Cum Priv. Maj.   Mart. Engelbrecht exc. A.V.

Print 3.

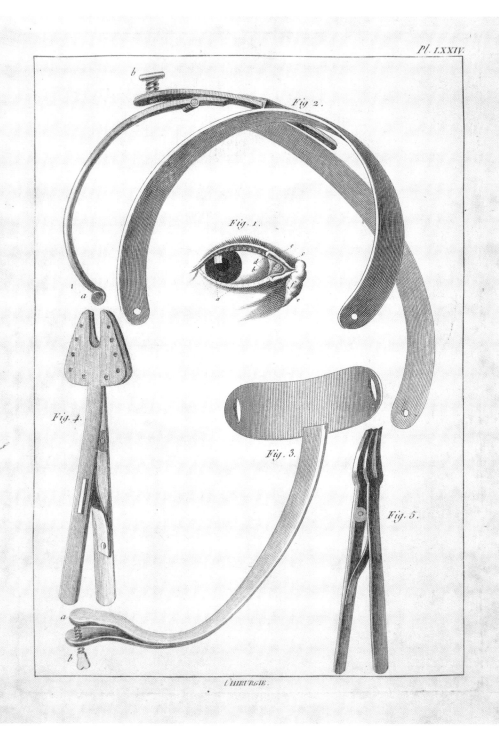

Print 13.

Habit de Marchand Miroitier Lunettier.

Paris, Chez N. de L'Armessin, Rüe S.t Jacques, à la Pôme d'Or.   Auec, Priuil. du Roy,

Print 4.

Chez Aubert gal vero dedat Imp d'Aubert et cie Paris Ch. Ph. vur H.D. Lith.

Un Oculiste breveté.

Ah! ça, Monsieur Macaire depuis six mois vous me bassinez avec votre eau merveilleuse
et je suis toujours aveugle. Cela finit par me couter bien cher, mon argent s'en va, c'est tout
ce que je vois –. .. Hé bien c'est déja quelque chose, continuez, vous finirez par y voir clair
. . . . (à l'art) dans votre bourse.

Print 11.

Print 10.

Chez Pannier Edit.r R. du Croissant, 16.   Chez Aubert, Pl. de la Bourse, 29.   Imp. d' Aubert & C.ie.

L'OCULISTE.

— Voici une eau qui va vous guérir instantanément…en moins de six mois, c'est vingt francs le flacon…

— C'est bien…je vous paierai cela dans quelques temps…

— Non pas, s'il vous plait…aujourd'hui même…je donne mes soins aux yeux, mais jamais à l'œil.

Print 12.

Print 17.

Paper scroll manuscript containing Ethiopic and Amharic prayers for the healing of eye diseases. 19th? century.

Adam, Curt. *Ophthalmoscopic diagnosis based on typical pictures of the fundus of the eye: with special reference to the needs of general practioners and students.* Translated by Matthias Lanckton Foster. New York: Medical Art Agency; Rebman Co., c1913.

Adams, Paul Edward Homer. *Pathology of the eye.* London: H. Frowde; Oxford University Press; . . . et al., 1912.

Agatston, Sigmund Arthur. *General ophthalmology.* New York: Kornicker, 1935.

Alexander, George Forbes. *Ocular dioptrics and lenses.* Baltimore: W. Wood & Co., 1934.

Alvaro, Moacyr Eyck.
See Lexicon ophthalmologicum.

American encyclopedia and dictionary of ophthalmology. Edited by Casey Albert Wood. 18 v. Chicago: Cleveland Press, 1913-21.

American Medical Association. Section on Ophthalmology. *Uveitis: symposium of papers read before the Ophthalmological Section of the American Medical Association, at the annual meeting, Saratoga, N. Y., June, 1902.* Chicago: American Medical Association Press, 1902.

Anderson, Joseph Ringland. *Hydrophthalmia, or congenital glaucoma.* Cambridge, England: British Journal of Ophthalmology, 1939.

Arndt, Wilhelm. *Praktische Lichttechnik.* Berlin: Union Deutsche Verlagsgesellschaft, 1938.

Arrington, George E. *A history of ophthalmology.* New York: MD Publications, 1959.

Atkinson, Donald Taylor. *The ocular fundus in diagnosis and treatment.* Philadelphia: Lea & Febiger, 1937.

Augendienst: the service of the eyes. An English paraphrastic summary of *Ophthalmodouleia* by George Bartish, distrib. at the XIX International Congress of Ophthalmology, New Dehli, December, 1962. Masnow (Barcelona): Laboratorios del Norte de España, 1962.
See also Bartish, George (35).

Bailey, Percival. *A classification of the tumors of the glioma group on a histogenetic basis with a correlated study of prognosis.* Philadelphia: J. B. Lippincott Co., c1926.

Ball, James Moores. *Modern ophthalmology.* Philadelphia: F. A. Davis Co., 1904.

Bedell, Arthur J. *Photographs of the fundus oculi.* Philadelphia: F. A. Davis Co., 1929.

Blaskovics, László & Kreiker, Aladár. *Eingriffe am Auge, eine Anleitung zur operativen Tätigkeit des Augenarztes.* Stuttgart: F. Enke, 1938.

Bothman, Louis & Bennett, Reuel Wellman. *Fundus atlas: stereoscopic photographs of the fundus oculi.* Chicago: The Year Book Publ., c1939.

British Optical Association, London. *Library and museum catalogue.* Compiled and edited by John H. Sutcliffe. 2 v. London: The Council of the British Optical Association, 1932-35.

Brugsch, Theodor & **Schittenhelm, Alfred.** *Lehrbuch: klinischer Untersuchungsmethoden für Studierende und Aertze.* Berlin: Urban & Schwarzenberg, 1911.

Buchanan, Alexander Macgregor. *Manual of anatomy.* 3rd rev. ed. 3 v. St. Louis: C. V. Mosby, Co., 1916.

Butler, Thomas Harrison. *An illustrated guide to the slit lamp.* London: H. Milford; Oxford University Press, 1927.

Byrne, J. Grandson. *Studies on the physiology of the eye.* London: H. K. Lewis, 1933.

Clapp, Clyde Alvin. *Cataract: its etiology and treatment.* Philadelphia: Lea and Febiger, c1934.

Colburn, J. Elliott. *Clinical lectures on diseases of the eye.* 2nd ed. Chicago: The Clinical Review Publ. Co., 1902, c1901.

Contributions to ophthalmic science dedicated to Dr. Edward Jackson in honor of his seventieth birthday, March 30, 1926 by his pupils and colleagues in the United States. Menasha, Wisconsin: G. Banta Publishing Co., 1926.

Copper, A. C. *An introduction to clinical orbitonometry with special reference to intra-orbital involvement in endocrinal disturbances.* Leyden: H. E. Stenfert Kroese's, 1948.

Cross, Sir Francis Richardson. *The Bradshaw lecture on the brain structures concerned in vision and the visual field: delivered before the Royal College of Surgeons of England on December 11th, 1909.* Bristol: J. W. Arrowsmith, 1910?

Darier, Armand. *Ocular therapeutics according to the most recent discoveries.* London: Churchill, 1903.

Davis, Achilles Edward. *Cataract: its preventive and medical treatment.* Philadelphia: F. A. Davis Co., 1937.

Demuth, Fritz. *Praktikum der Züchtung von Warmblütergewebe in vitro.* Munich: R. Müller & Steinicke, 1929.

Doherty, William Brown, ed. *See* Rehabilitation of the war injured: a symposium.

Duke-Elder, William Stewart. *System of ophthalmology.* 2nd ed. 15 v. London: Kimpton; St. Louis: C. V. Mosby Co., 1958-76.

Elliot, Robert Henry. *Sclero-corneal trephining in the operative treatment of glaucoma.* New York: Hoeber, 1913.

Elliot, Robert Henry. *Sclero-corneal trephining in the operative treatment of glaucoma.* 2nd ed. New York: Hoeber, 1914.

Elliot, Robert Henry. *A treatise on glaucoma.* 2nd ed. London: H. Frowde and Hodder & Stoughton, 1922.

Fisher, William Albert. *Senile cataract: methods of operating.* 3rd rev. ed. Chicago: H. G. Adair Printing Co., 1937.

Fox, Lawrence Webster. *A practical treatise on ophthalmology.* New York; London: D. Appleton & Co., 1910.

Fröhlich, Friedrich W. *Die Empfindungszeit: ein Beitrag zur Lehre von der Zeit-, Raum- und Bewegungsempfindung.* Jena: G. Fischer, 1929.

Fuchs, Ernst. *Text-book of ophthalmology.* 3rd ed. Philadelphia; London: J. B. Lippincott, 1908. *See also* Fuchs (144).

Fuchs, Ernst. *Text-book of ophthalmology.* 6th ed. Philadelphia; London: J. B. Lippincott, c1919. *See also* Fuchs (144).

Fuchs, Ernst. *Diseases of the eye.* 10th English ed. Philadelphia: J. B. Lippincott, 1933.

Gibbons, Edward Engler. *The eye: its refraction and diseases.* (Vol. 2 only). New York: The Macmillan Co., 1905.

Glaucoma: a symposium presented at a meeting of the Chicago Ophthalmological Society, November 17, 1913. Chicago: Chicago Medical Book Co., 1914.

Gnudi, Martha Teach & **Webster, Jerome Pierce.** *The life and times of Gaspare Tagliacozzi: surgeon of Bologna, 1545-1599.* New York: H. Reichner, 1950.

Graefe, Alfred Karl, ed.
See Handbuch der gesammten Augenheilkunde.

Grant, Vernon W. *Psychological optics.* Chicago: The Professional Press, c1938.

Greeff, Richard. *Die pathologische Anatomie des Auges.* (Lehrbuch der speciellen pathologischen Anatomie. Ergänzungsband I, 2. Lfg.) Berlin: A. Hirschwald, 1902-06.

Grimsdale, Harold Barr & **Brewerton, Elmore.** *A textbook of ophthalmic operations.* Chicago: W. T. Keener & Co., 1907.

Grimsdale, Harold Barr & **Brewerton, Elmore.** *A textbook of ophthalmic operations.* 3rd ed. London: Balliere, Tindall and Cox, 1937.

Haab, Otto. *Atlas of external diseases of the eye: including a brief treatise on the pathology and treatment.* Edited by George Edmund De Schweinitz. 2nd ed. Philadelphia; London: W. B. Saunders & Co., 1903.

Haab, Otto. *Atlas of external diseases of the eye.* Edited by George Edmund De Schweinitz. 3rd ed. Philadelphia; London: W. B. Saunders Co., 1909.

Haab, Otto. *An atlas of ophthalmoscopy.* Translated and edited by W. B. Barker. London: British Optical Association, 1920?

Hamilton, J. Bruce. *A guide to ophthalmic operations.* London: H. K. Lewis, 1940.

Handbuch der gesammten Augenheilkunde. Hrsg. von Alfred Karl Graefe und Theodor Saemisch. 2 Aufl. 15 v. Various places and publishers, 1903-31. *See also* Handbuch der gesammten Augenheilkunde (176).

Handbuch der gesammten Augenheilkunde. Begründet von Alfred Karl Graefe und Theodor Saemisch. 3 Aufl. 7 v. Various places and publishers, 1911-30. *See also* Handbuch der gesammten Augenheilkunde (176).

Hansell, Howard F. & **Sweet, William M.** *Text-book of diseases of the eye: for students and practitioners of medicine.* Philadelphia: P. Blakiston's Son & Co., 1903.

Hardy, Arthur Cobb & **Perrin, Fred Hiram.** *The principles of optics.* New York: McGraw-Hill, 1932.

Harman, Nathaniel Bishop. *Aids to ophthalmology.* 8th ed. Baltimore: W. Wood and Co., 1935.

Heine, Leopold. *Die Krankheiten des Auges im Zusammenhang mit der inneren Medizin und Kinderheilkunde.* Berlin: J. Springer, 1921.

Helmholtz, Hermann Ludwig Ferdinand von.
See Koenigsberger.

Helmholtz, Hermann Ludwig Ferdinand von.
Helmholtz's treatise on physiological optics. Translated from the 3rd German ed. Edited by James Powell Cocke Southall. 3 v. Rochester, New York: The Optical Society of America, 1924-1925.
See also Helmholtz (185).

Hering, Ewald. *Spatial sense and movements of the eye.* Translated by Carl A. Radde. Baltimore: The American Academy of Optometry, 1942.

Hirschberg, Julius. "Geschichte der Augenheilkunde." In *Handbuch der gesammten Augenheilkunde.* 2. Aufl. Bd. XII-XV. Leipzig: W. Engelmann, 1899-1918.

Howe, Lucien. *The muscles of the eye.* 2 v. New York; London: G. P. Putnam's Sons; The Knickerbocker Press, 1907-08.

Hubbell. Alvin Allace. *The development of ophthalmology in America, 1800 to 1870.* Chicago: W. T. Keener and Co., 1908.

Igersheimer, Josef. *Syphilis und Auge.* Berlin: J. Springer, 1918.

Jackson, Edward.
See Contributions to ophthalmic science.

James, Robert Rutson. *Studies in the history of ophthalmology in England prior to the year 1800.* Cambridge, England: University Press for the British Journal of Ophthalmology, 1933.

Javal, Emile. *On becoming blind: advice for the use of persons losing their sight.* Translated by Carroll E. Edson. New York; London: The Macmillan Co., 1905.

Kleist, Karl. *Gehirn–Pathologie vornehmlich auf Grund der Kriegserfahrungen.* Leipzig: J. A. Barth, 1934.

Kluver, Heinrich, ed.
See Visual mechanisms.

Koby, Frédéric Ed. *Slit-lamp microscopy of the living eye: early diagnosis and symptomatology of affections of the anterior segment of the eye.* Philadelphia: P. Blakiston's Son & Co., 1925.

Koby, Frédéric Ed. *Slit-lamp microscopy of the living eye: early diagnosis and symptomatology of affections of the anterior segment of the eye.* 2nd ed. Philadelphia: P. Blakiston's Son & Co., 1930.

Koenigsberger, Leo. *Hermann von Helmholtz.* 3 v. Braunschweig: F. Vieweg and Son, 1902-03.

Köster, Georg. *Zur Physiologie der Spinalganglien und der tropischen Nerven sowie zur Pathogenese der Tabes dorsalis.* Leipzig: W. Engelmann, 1904.

Kries, Johannes von. *Allgemeine Sinnesphysiologie.* Leipzig: F. C. W. Vogel, 1923.

Kronfeld, Peter Clemens. *Introduction to ophthalmology.* Springfield, Illinois: C. C. Thomas, c1938.

Kronfeld, Peter Clemens. *The human eye in anatomical transparencies.* Rochester, New York: Bausch & Lomb Press, c1943.

Lexicon ophthalmologicum. Multilingual ophthalmological dictionary. Editores: Moacyr Eyck Alvaro, . . . et al. Philadelphia: Lippincott, 1959.

Luckiesh, Matthew. *Seeing and human welfare.* Baltimore: Williams & Wilkins Co., 1934.

Luckiesh, Matthew & **Moss, Frank Kendall.** *The*

science of seeing. New York: Van Nostrand, 1937.

MacCallan, Arthur Ferguson. *Trachoma.* London: Butterworth & Co., 1936.

MacCallum, William George. *A text-book of pathology.* 4th ed. rev. Philadelphia: W. B. Saunders, 1928.

MacNab, Angus. *Ulceration of the cornea.* New York: W. Wood and Co., 1907.

McNally, Harold Joseph. *The readability of certain type sizes and forms in sight-saving classes.* New York: Bureau of Publications, Teachers College, Columbia University, 1943.

Mann, Ida Caroline. *The development of the human eye.* Cambridge, England: The University Press, 1928.

Marshall, James Cole. *Detachment of the retina: operative technique in treatment.* London: Oxford University Press, 1936.

Maurolico, Francesco. *The Photismi de lumine of Maurolycus: a chapter in late medieval optics.* Translated by Henry Crew from the Naples, 1611 edition. New York: The Macmillan Co., 1940.

Maxwell, James Taliaferro. *Outline of ocular refraction.* Omaha, Nebraska: Medical Publishing Co., 1937.

Meesmann, Aloys. *Die Mikroskopie des lebenden Auges an der Gullstrandschen Spaltlampe mit Atlas typischer Befunde.* Berlin; Vienna: Urban & Schwarzenberg, 1927.

Meyer, Julius. *Medizinisches Taschenlexikon in 8 Sprachen (deutsch, englisch, französisch,*

italienisch, japanisch, russisch, spanisch, ungarisch). Berlin: Urban & Schwarzenberg, 1909.

Moore, Robert Foster. *Medical ophthalmology.* London: J. & A. Churchill, 1922.

Nance, Willis Orville, ed.
See Glaucoma.

Newton, Sir Isaac. *Opticks: or, a treatise of the reflections, refractions, inflections and colours of light.* 4th ed., c1730. Reprint. New York: Dover, 1952.
See also Newton (273).

Oatman, Edward Leroy. *Diagnostics of the fundus oculi.* 3 v. Troy, New York: The Southworth Co., 1913.

Obrig, Theodore Ernst. *Modern ophthalmic lenses and optical glass.* New York; Philadelphia: The Chilton Co., 1935.

Ophthalmology in the war years. Edited by Meyer Wiener. 2 v. Chicago: Year Book Publishers, 1946-48.

Ovio, Giuseppe. *L'oculistica di Antonio Scarpa e due secoli di storia.* 2 v. Naples: Casa Editrice Libraria v. Idelson, 1936.

Parsons, Sir John Herbert. *The Arris and Gale lectures on the neurology of vision.* London: Hodder & Stoughton, 1904.

Parsons, Sir John Herbert. *The pathology of the eye.* 4 v. New York: G. P. Putnam's Sons, 1904-08.

Parsons, Sir John Herbert. *Diseases of the eye.* 7th ed. New York: The Macmillan Co., 1934.

Pavia, Justo Lijo. *Temas de oftalmologia.* Buenos Aires: s.n., 1938.

Peck, Wesley Hamilton, ed.
See Glaucoma.

Peter, Luther Crouse. *The extra-ocular muscles: a clinical study of normal and abnormal ocular motility.* Philadelphia: Lea & Febiger, 1927.

Peter, Luther Crouse. *The principles and practice of perimetry.* 4th ed., rev. Philadelphia: Lea & Febiger, 1938.

Rehabilitation of the war injured: a symposium. Edited by William Brown Doherty and Dagobert David Runes. New York: Philosophical Library, 1943.

Romains, Jules. *Eyeless sight: a study of extra-retinal vision and the paroptic sense.* New York: G. P. Putnam's Sons, 1924.

Runes, Dagobert David, ed.
See Rehabilitation of the war injured: a symposium.

Rutherford, Cyrus Wilson. *The eye.* New York; London: D. Appleton and Co., 1928.

Saemisch, Theodor, ed.
See Handbuch der gesammten Augenheilkunde.

Savage, Giles Christopher. *Ophthalmic myology: a systematic treatise on the ocular muscles.* Nashville, Tennessee: Gospel Advocate Publishing Co., 1902.

Schmorl, Georg. *Die pathologisch-histologischen Untersuchungsmethoden.* 7th ed. Leipzig: F. C. W. Vogel, 1914.

Schwarz, Otto. *Die Funktionsprüfung des Auges und ihre Verwertung für die allgemeine Diagnostik für Ärtze und Studierende.* Berlin: S. Karger, 1904.

Seligmann, Siegfried. *Die mikroskopischen Untersuchungsmethoden des Auges.* Berlin: S. Karger, 1911.

Sheard, Charles. *Life-giving light.* Baltimore: Williams and Wilkins Co., c1933.

Sorsby, Arnold. *Genetics in ophthalmology.* St. Louis: C. V. Mosby Co., 1951.

Southall, James Powell Cocke, ed.

See Helmholtz, Hermann Ludwig Ferdinand von.

Sutcliffe, John H., comp. and ed.
See British Optical Association.

Swanzy, Sir Henry Rosborough. *A handbook of the diseases of the eye and their treatment.* 8th ed. Philadelphia: P. Blakiston's Son & Co., 1903.

Szymonowicz, Ladislaus. *A text-book of histology and microscopic anatomy of the human body.* Philadelphia; New York: Lea Bros., 1902.

Thorington, James. *The ophthalmoscope and how to use it: with colored illustrations, descriptions, and treatment of the principal diseases of the fundus.* Philadelphia: P. Blakiston's Son and Co., 1906.

Thorington, James. *Refraction of the human eye and methods of estimating the refraction: including a section on the fitting of spectacles and eye-glasses, etc.* Philadelphia: P. Blakiston's Son and Co., 1916.

Truc, Hermentaire & Pansier, Pierre. *Histoire d'ophthalmologie à l'école de Montpellier du XIIe au XXe siecle.* Paris: A. Malone, 1907.

Uribe y Troncosco, Manuel. *Internal diseases of the eye and atlas of ophthalmology.* Philadelphia: F. A. Davis Co., 1937.

Visual mechanisms. Edited by Heinrich Kluver. (Biological symposia; v. 7) Lancaster, Pennsylvania: The J. Cattell Press, 1942.

Vogt, Alfred. *Lehrbuch und Atlas der Spaltlampenmikroskopie des lebenden Auges.* Berlin: J. Springer, 1931.

Wheeler, John Martin. *The collected papers of John Martin Wheeler, M.D. on ophthalmic subjects.* New York: Columbia University Press, 1939.

Wiener, Meyer, ed.
See Ophthalmology in the war years.

Wilkinson, Oscar. *Strabismus: its etiology and treatment.* St. Louis: C. V. Mosby Co., 1927.

Wood, Casey Albert. *A system of ophthalmic therapeutics: being a complete work on the non-operative treatment, including the prophylaxis, of diseases of the eye.* Chicago: Cleveland Press, 1909.

Wood, Casey Albert. *A system of ophthalmic operations: being a complete treatise on the operative conduct of ocular diseases and some extraocular conditions causing eye symptoms.* 2 v. Chicago: Cleveland Press, 1911.

Wood, Casey Albert, ed.
See American encyclopedia and dictionary of ophthalmology.

Wood, Casey Albert. *The fundus oculi of birds, especially as viewed by the ophthalmoscope.* Chicago: Lakeside Press, 1917.

Worth, Claud Alley. *Squint: its causes, pathology and treatment.* London: J. Bale, Sons & Danielsson, 1903.

SELECTED TITLES
from the Library's Collections Complementing
the Bernard Becker Collection in Ophthalmology

An account of Laura Bridgman, a blind, deaf, and dumb girl: with brief notices of three other blind mutes. 2nd ed. London: J. Wright, 1845.

Adams, Sir William. *A practical inquiry into the causes of the frequent failure of the operations of depression, and of the extraction of the cataract. . . .* London: Baldwin, Cradock, and Joy, 1817.

Aetius, of Amida. *Die Augenheilkunde des Aëtius aus Amida: Griechisch und Deutsch.* Edited by J. Hirschberg. Leipzig: Veit & Co., 1899.

Alt, Adolf. *Compendium der normalen und pathologischen Histologie des Auges.* Wiesbaden: J. F. Bergmann, 1880.

Alt, Adolf. *Lectures on the human eye in its normal and pathological conditions.* New York: G. P. Putnam's Sons, 1880.

Alt, Adolf. *Lectures on the human eye in its normal and pathological conditions.* New York: G. P. Putnam's Sons, 1884. (Signed by the author.)

Alt, Adolf. *A treatise on ophthalmology for the general practitioner.* Chicago; St. Louis; Atlanta: J. H. Chambers & Co., 1884.

Ammon, Friedrich August von. *Histoire du développement de l'oeil humain.* Translated by A. Van Biervliet. Brussels: J. van Buggenhoudt, 1860.

Andreae, August Wilhelm. *Aus den Vorträgen über specielle Augenheilkunde.* Magdeburg: Hænel'sche Hofbuchdruckerei, 1834.

Arlt, Ferdinand, Ritter von. *Retinitis nyctalopica.* Translated by J. F. Weightman. Philadelphia: Lindsay & Blakiston, 1868.

Assalini, Paolo. *Observations on the disease called the plague, on the dysentery, the ophthalmy of Egypt, and on the means of prevention. . . .* Translated from the French by Adam Neale. New York: T. & J. Swords, 1806.

Ball, James Moores. *Modern ophthalmology: a practical treatise on the anatomy, physiology, and diseases of the eye.* Philadelphia: F. A. Davis, 1904.

Becker, Otto Heinrich. *Zur Anatomie der gesunden und kranken Linse.* Wiesbaden: Bergmann, 1883.

Beer, Georg Joseph. *Repertorium aller bis zu Ende des Jahres 1797 erschienenen Schriften über die Augenkrankheiten. Bibliotheca Ophthalmica.* 3 v. Vienna: C. Schaumburg & Co., 1799.

Benedict, Traugott Wilhelm Gustav. *Handbuch der praktischen Augenheilkunde.* 5 v. Leipzig: Dyk, 1822-25.

Bessières, Georges Louis. *Nouvelles considérations sur les affections nerveuses de l'organe de la vue. . . .* Paris: Germer-Baillière, 1838.

Bidloo, Govard. *De oculis et visu variorum animalium observationes physico-anatomicae.* Leyden: S. Luchtmans, 1715.

Boerhaave, Herman. *Des maladies des yeux.* Paris: Huart & Moreau, 1749.

Böhm, Ludwig B. *Das Schielen und der Sehnenschnitt in seinen Wirkungen auf Stellung und Sehkraft der Augen.* Berlin: Duncker und Humblot, 1845.

Böhm, Ludwig B. *Die Therapie des Auges mittels des farbigen Lichtes Lehrbuch.* Berlin: A. Hirschwald, 1862.

Burnett, Swan Moses. *Principles of refraction in the human eye: based on the laws of conjugate foci.* Philadelphia: The Keystone, 1904.

Burow, Carl August. *Ein neues Optometer.* Berlin: H. Peters, 1863.

Calder, Francis William Grant. *Practical hints on the cure of squinting by operation.* London: H. Renshaw, 1841.

Chelius, Maximilian Joseph. *Handbuch der Augenheilkunde.* 2 v. Stuttgart: E. Schweizerbart, 1839-43.

Cornaz, Charles Auguste Edouard. *Des abnormités congéniales [sic] des yeux et de leurs annexes.* Lausanne: G. Bridel, 1848.

Daza de Valdés, Benito. *El Libro del Lic. Benito Daza de Valdés: Uso de los antojos y comentarios a propósito del mismo.* Madrid: Cosano, 1923.

Demarquay, Jean Nicolas. *Des tumeurs de l'orbite.* Paris: M. Crapelet, 1853.

De Schweinitz, George Edmund. *Toxic amblyopias: their classification, history, symptoms, pathology, and treatment.* Philadelphia: Lea Brothers & Co., 1896.

Desmarres, Louis Auguste. *Paralysies des muscles de l'oeil en particulier: aperçu sur le strabisme.* Montpellier: J. Martel, 1864.

Deval, Charles. *Abhandlung über die Amaurose oder den schwarzen Staar. . . .* Quedlinburg; Leipzig: G. Basse, 1853.

Diderot, Denis. *Lettre sur les sourds et muets, à l'usage de ceux qui entendent & qui parlent.* Amsterdam: [s.n.], 1772.

Dix, John Homer. *Treatise on strabismus, or squinting: and the new mode of treatment.* Boston: D. Clapp, Jr.; Office of the Medical and Surgical Journal, 1841.

Dixon, James. *A guide to the practical study of diseases of the eye with an outline of their medical and operative treatment.* 2nd ed. London: John Churchill, 1859.

Elliott, Sir John. *Philosophical observations on the senses of vision and hearing to which are added, a treatise on harmonic sounds, and an essay on combustion and animal heat.* London: Printed for J. Murray, 1780.

Fabricius ab Aquapendente, Hieronymus. *Hieronymi Fabricii ab Aquapendente De visione, voce, auditu.* Venice: F. Bolzetta, 1600.

Fischer, Johann Nepomuk. *Lehrbuch der gesammten Entzündungen und organischen Krankheiten des menschlichen Auges, seiner Schutz- und Hilfsorgane.* Prague: Borrosch & André, 1846.

Förster, Carl Friedrich Richard. *Über Hemeralopie und die Anwendung eines Photometers im Gebiete der Ophthalmologie.* Breslau: L. F. Maske, 1857.

Frick, George. *A treatise on the diseases of the eye.* Baltimore: F. Lucas, 1823.

Galezowski, Xavier. *Étude ophthalmoscopique sur les altérations du nerf optique et sur les maladies cérébrales dont elles dépendent.* Paris: L. Leclerc, 1866.

Galezowski, Xavier. *Diagnostic et traitement des affections oculaires.* Paris: J. B. Baillière, 1883-86.

Gerlach, Joseph von. *Beiträge zur normalen Anatomie des menschlichen Auges.* Leipzig: F. C. W. Vogel, 1880.

Graefe, Albrecht von. *Symptomlehre der Augenmuskellähmungen.* Berlin: Hermann Peters, 1867.

Graefe, Albrecht von. *Albrecht von Graefe's grundlegende Arbeiten über den Heilwert der Iridektomie bei Glaukom.* Leipzig: J. A. Barth, 1911.

Grapheus, Benevenutus. *I Codici Riccardiano Parigino ed Ashburnhamiano dell'opera oftalmojatrica di Benvenuto.* Modena: Società Tipografica, 1897.

Griffin, William Nathaniel. *A treatise on optics.* 2nd ed. Cambridge: Printed for J. & J. J. Deighton, T. Stevenson; London: Whittaker & Co., 1842.

Haguenot, Henri. *Tractatus de morbis capitis externis.* Avignon: J. J. Chabrier, 1751.

Helling, Georg Lebrecht Andreas. *Praktisches Handbuch der Augenkrankheiten. . . .* 2 v. Berlin: F. Dümmler, 1821-22.

Helmholtz, Hermann Ludwig Ferdinand von. Helmholtz's treatise on physiological optics. Translated from the third German edition. Edited by James P. C. Southall. 3 v. Rochester, N. Y.: Optical Society of America, 1824-25.

Helmholtz, Hermann Ludwig Ferdinand von. *Beschreibung eines Augen-Spiegels zur Untersuchung der Netzhaut in lebenden Auge.* Berlin: A. Förstner, 1851.

Helmholtz, Hermann Ludwig Ferdinand von. *Handbuch der physiologischen Optik.* Leipzig: Leopold Voss, 1867.

Hering, Ewald. *Grundzüge der Lehre vom Lichtsinn.* Berlin: J. Springer, 1920.

Hippel, Arthur von. *Über den Einfluss hygienischer Massregeln auf die Schulmyopie.* Giessen: J. Ricker, 1889.

Hirschberg, Julius. *Die Magnet-Operation in der Augenheilkunde.* 2nd ed. Leipzig: Veit & Co., 1899.

Hirschfeld, Ludovic Moritz. *A concise description of the anatomy and physiology of the eye and its appendages.* New York: H. A. Daniels, 1891.

His, Wilhelm. *Beiträge zur normalen und pathologischen Histologie der Cornea.* Basel: Schweighausers, 1856.

Hocken, Edward Octavius. *A treatise on amaurosis and amaurotic affections.* Philadelphia: A. Waldie, 1842.

Huygens, Christiaan. *Abhandlung über das Licht.* Leipzig: W. Engelmann, 1903.

Huygens, Christiaan. *Treatise on light, in which are explained the causes of that which occurs in reflexion & in refraction, and particularly in the strange refraction of Iceland crystal.* Translated by Silvanus P. Thompson. New York: Dover Publications, c1912.

Jacobson, Julius. *Ein neues und gefahrloses Operations-Verfahren zur Heilung des grauen Staares.* Berlin: Hermann Peters, 1863.

Jaeger, Eduard, Ritter von Jaxtthal. *Der Hohlschnitt: eine neue Staar-Extractions-Methode.* Vienna: L. W. Seidel & Sohn, 1873.

Jaeger, Eduard, Ritter von Jaxtthal. *Ophthalmoscopical atlas.* Translated by William A. Martin. Leipzig & Vienna: F. Deuticke; London: Williams & Norgate; New York: B. Westermann & Co., 1890.

Janin de Combe-Blanche, Jean. *Anatomische, physiologische und physikalische Abhandlungen und Beobachtungen über das Auge und dessen Krankheiten.* Berlin: Himburg, 1776.

Kepler, Johannes. *Dioptrik, oder Schilderung der Folgen, die sich der unlängst gemachten Erfindung der Fernröhre für das sehen und die sichtbaren Gegentstände ergeben.* Translated and edited by Ferdinand Plehn. Leipzig: W. Engelmann, 1904.

Kitto, John. *The lost senses: deafness and blindness.* New York: R. Carter & Bros., 1852.

Knapp, Herman. *Die intraocularen Geschwülste: nach eigenen klinischen Beobactungen und anatomischen Untersuchungen.* Carlsruhe: C. F. Müller, 1868.

Kuhnt, Hermann. *Über die Verwertbarkeit der Bindehaut in der praktischen und operativen Augenheilkunde.* Wiesbaden: J. F. Bergmann, 1898.

Labat, Pierre Léon Auguste. *Manière simple et facile de saisir la pierre dans la vessie: avec des instruments lithotriteurs à percussion et à pression.* Paris: Ducessois, 1834.

Liebreich, Richard. *Atlas der Ophthalmoscopie. Darstellung des Augengrundes im gesunden und krankhaften Zustande.* Berlin: A. Hirschwald; Paris: G. Baillière, 1863.

Liebreich, Richard. *Atlas of ophthalmoscopy: representing the normal and pathological conditions of the fundus oculi as seen with the ophthalmoscope.* Translated by H. Rosborough Swanzy. 2nd ed. London: J. A. Churchill, 1870.

Liebreich, Richard. *Eine neue Methode der Cataract-Extraction.* Berlin: A. Hirschwald, 1872.

Lobstein, Johann Friederich Daniel. *A treatise upon the semeiology of the eye: for the use of physicians and of the countenance, for criminal jurisprudence.* New York: C. S. Francis, 1830.

Longmore, Sir Thomas. *Manual of instructions for the guidance of army surgeons: in testing the range and quality of vision of recruits, and in distinguishing the causes of defective vision in soldiers.* London: H.M.S.O., 1864.

Mackenzie, William. *The physiology of vision.* London: Longman, Orme, Brown, Green, & Longmans, 1841.

Maunoir, Théodore David Eugène. *Essai sur quelques points de l'histoire de la cataracte.* Paris: Didot, 1833.

Mercuriale, Girolamo. *Tractatus de compositione medicamentorum. De morbis oculorum, & aurium.* Edited by Michael Colombo. Venice: Giunta, 1590.

Meyer, Édouard. *Traité pratique des maladies des yeux.* 4th ed. Paris: G. Masson, 1895.

Michalorius, Blasius. *Tractatus de coeco, surdo, et muto.* Venice: Guerilios, 1646.

Michel, Julius. *Über Sehnerven-Degeneration und Sehnerven-Kreuzung.* Wiesbaden: J. F. Bergmann, 1887.

Middlemore, Richard. *A treatise on the diseases of the eye and its appendages.* 2 v. London: Longman, Rees, Orme, Brown, Green, & Longman; Birmingham: J. Drake, 1835.

Mooren, Albert. *Die medicinische und operative Behandlung kurzsichtiger Störungen.* Wiesbaden: J. F. Bergmann, 1897.

Müller, Leopold. *Über Ruptur der Corneo-Scleralkapsel durch stumpfe Verletzung.* Leipzig: F. Deuticke, 1895.

Nagel, Albrecht. *Die Behandlung der Amaurosen und Amblyopieen mit Strychnin.* Tübingen: H. Laupp, 1871.

Nagel, Wilibald A. *Die Diagnose der praktisch wichtigen angeborenen Störungen des Farbensinnes.* Wiesbaden: J. F. Bergmann, 1899.

Neill, Hugh. *The practice in the Liverpool Ophthalmic Infirmary, for the year 1834: being the first special report.* London: Longman, Rees, Orme and Co.; Liverpool: W. Grapel, 1935.

Nélaton, Auguste. *Parallèle des divers modes opératoires employés dans le traitement de la cataracte.* Paris: Baillière, 1850.

Nettleship, Edward. *The student's guide to diseases of the eye.* London: J. & A. Churchill, 1879.

Oliver, Charles Augustus. *A description of some of the most important ophthalmic methods employed for the recognition of peripheral and central nerve disease.* Philadelphia: University of Pennsylvania Press, 1895.

Palmerio, Jacopo; Sinzanogio, Marco. *Il Libro delle affezioni oculari . . . ed altri scritti di oculistica.* Edited by Giuseppe Albertotti. Modena: Società Tipographia, 1904.

Pamard, Pierre François Bénézet. *Un contemporain de Daviel: les oeuvres de Pierre François Bénézet Pamard, chirurgien et oculiste, 1728-1793.* Edited by Alfred Pamard and Pierre Pansier. Paris: Masson & Co., 1900.

Pinto, J. R. da Gama. *Untersuchungen über intraoculare Tumoren. Netzhautgliome.* Wiesbaden: J. F. Bergmann, 1886.

Prechtl, Johann Joseph, Ritter von. *Praktische Dioptrik als vollständige und gemeinfassliche Anleitung zur Verfertigung achromatischer Fernröhre.* Vienna: J. G. Heubner, 1828.

Rohr, Moritz von. *Das Auge und die Brille.* Leipzig: B. G. Teubner, 1912.

Rosas, Anton, Edler von. *Handbuch der theoretischen und practischen Augenheilkunde.* Vienna: J. B. Wallishausser, 1830.

Scherffer, Karl. *De emendatione telescopiorum dioptricorum per vitrum objectivum compositum.* Vienna: J. T. Trattner, 1762.

Schmidt-Rimpler, Hermann. *Der Ausdruck im Auge und Blick.* Berlin: H. Peters, 1876.

Schmidt-Rimpler, Hermann. *Die Schulkurzsichtigkeit und ihre Bekämpfung.* Leipzig: W. Engelmann, 1890.

Schoeler, Heinrich Leopold. *Experimentelle Studie über galvanolytische-kataphorische Einwirkungen auf das Auge.* Wiesbaden: J. F. Bergmann, 1894.

Sichel, Jules. *Spectacles: their uses and abuses in long and short sightedness and the pathological conditions resulting from their irrational employment.* Translated by Henry W. Williams. Boston: Phillips, Sampson & Co., 1850.

Sichel, Jules. *Iconographie ophthalmologique: où description, avec figures coloriées, des maladies de l'organe de la vue. . . .* Paris: J. B. Baillière, 1852-59.

Snell, Simeon. *Eyesight and school life.* Bristol: John Wright & Co., 1895.

Snellen, Herman. *Probebuchstaben zur Bestimmung der Sehschärfe.* Utrecht: Van de Weijer, 1862.

Soemmerring, Detmar Wilhelm. *De oculorum hominis animaliumque sectione horizontali commentatio.* Göttingen: Vandenhoek & Ruprecht, 1818.

Stellwag von Carion, Karl. *Die Ophthalmologie vom naturwissenschaftlichen Standpunkte.* 2 v. Freiburg im Breisgau: Herder, 1853-58.

Stewart, Dugald. *Some account of a boy born blind and deaf, collected from authentic sources of information.* Edinburgh: Royal Society of Edinburgh, 1815.

Stilling, Jakob. *Ueber die Heilung der Verengerungen der Thraenenwege mittelst der inneren Incision.* Cassel: J. C. Krieger, 1868.

Stilling, Jakob. *Psychologie der Gesichtsvorstellung nach Kant's Theorie der Erfahrung.* Berlin; Vienna: Urban & Schwarzenberg, 1901.

Thorington, James. *Retinoscopy (or shadow test) in the determination of refraction at one meter distance with the plane mirror.* Philadelphia: P. Blakiston, 1897.

Walton, Henry Haynes. *A treatise on operative ophthalmic surgery.* Edited by Squire Littell. Philadelphia: Lindsay & Blakiston, 1853.

Wardrop, James. *The morbid anatomy of the human eye.* 2nd ed. 2 v. London: J. Churchill, 1834.

Ware, James. *Chirurgical observations relative to the eye: with an appendix, on the introduction of the male catheter and the treatment of the hæmorrhoids.* 2nd ed. 2 v. London: J. Mawman, 1805.

Wecker, Louis de. *Études ophthalmologiques: Traité théorique et pratique des maladies des yeux.* Paris: A. Delahaye, 1863-66.

Wecker, Louis de. *Traité des maladies du fond de l'œil et Atlas d'ophthalmoscopie.* Paris: A. Delahaye, 1870.

Wecker, Louis de. *Ocular therapeutics.* Translated and edited by Litton Forbes. London: Smith, Elder, & Co., 1879.

Weiss, Leopold. *Ueber das Gesichtsfeld der Kurzsichtigen.* Leipzig: F. Deuticke, 1898.

Weiss, Ludwig Samuel. *Die Augenheilkunde und die Lehre der wichtigsten Augenoperationen. . . .* Quedlinburg: Basse, 1837.

Wells, John Soelberg. *A treatise on the diseases of the eye.* Philadelphia: Henry C. Lea, 1869.

Wilbrand, Hermann. *Über Sehstörungen bei functionellen Nervenleiden.* Leipzig: F. C. W. Vogel, 1892.

Zinn, Johann Gottfried. *Descriptio anatomica oculi humani iconibus illustrata.* Göttingen: Widow of B. A. Vandenhoeck, 1780.

SUBJECT INDEX

BOTANY
1677	Fabri (131)

BRAIN
1669	Borri (55)

CATARACT & CATARACT SURGERY
See also EYE DISEASES *and* SURGERY, OCULAR

1559	Stromayr (366)
1675	Harder (178)
1692	La Charriére (225)
1709	Brisseau (63)
1713	Heister (181.1)
1717	Heister (182)
1719	Woolhouse (423)
1722	Saint-Yves (322)
1724	Benevoli (43)
1727	Taylor (370)
1748	Nannoni, A. (270)
1750	Pallucci (282, 283)
1751	Pallucci (284)
1752	Pallucci (285)
1753	Daviel (2)
1753	Hoin (2)
1753	La Faye (2)
1753	Morand (2)
1757	Daviel, J.-H. (93)
1764	Reghellini (311.1)
1765	Colombier (84)
1765	Schaeffer (329)
1769	Guérin (166)
1769	Vespa (388)
1778	Michel (259.1)
1780	Nannoni, L. (271)
1782	Feller (134)
1785	Wathen (405)
1786	Wenzel (415)
1791	Beer, G. J. (37)
1791	Jung-Stilling (215.1)
1791	Richter (313)
1792	Wathen (406)
1794	Cappuri (69)
1795	Ware (402)
1801	Schmidt (334)
1803	Ens (124)
1810	Santerelli (324)
1810	Walther (398)
1811	Gibson (152)
1811	Muter (268)
1812	Adams (4)
1812	Weinhold (410.1)
1813	Stevenson (363)
1814	Benedict (42)
1819	Lusardi (239)
1821	Ammon (12)
1824	Bowen (59)
1826	Gondret (156.1)
1826	Gregoris (162.1)
1827	Parfait-Landrau (289)
1833	Lattier de Laroche (230)
1835	Carron du Villards (70)
1835	Lattier de Laroche (231)
1838	Pauli (291)
1839	Furnari (147)
1842	Maunoir (251)
1843	Alphonse (11)
1844	Jaeger (202)
1854	Jaeger (203)
1866	Graefe (160)
1884	Carter (72)
1886	Stellwag von Carion (357)

CATARACT SURGERY – history
1803	Ens (124)
1890	Delacroix (94)

CHOROIDEA
1764	Heister (184)

CHOROIDITIS
See also EYE DISEASES

1859	Selected monographs (338.1)
1878	Panas (287)
1891	Edridge-Green (122.1)

COCAINE

1885	Knapp (219.1)

COLOR BLINDNESS

1807	Young (423.1)
1855	Wilson (422)
1877	Holmgren (194.1)
1880	Jeffries (211)
1894	Young (423.2)

CONJUNCTIVA

1828	Eble (121)
1862	Furnari (148.1)

CONJUNCTIVITIS
See also EYE DISEASES

1838	Ruete (317)
1850	Landi (227.1)
1894	Morax (262.1)

CORNEA

1863	Canton (68.1)

CORNEAL DISEASES
See also EYE DISEASES

1742	Mauchart (248)
1767	Bose (56)
1862	Furnari (148.1)

DAVIEL, JACQUES, 1693-1762

1890	Delacroix (94)

ECTROPION
See also EYE DISEASES

1733	Keck (216)
1774	Bordenhave (2)
1774	Louis (2)
1812	Adams (4)
1886	Stellwag von Carion (357)

ENTROPION

1886	Stellwag von Carion (357)

ENUCLEATION

1774	Louis (2)
1868	Jeffries (209)

EPILEPSY

1859	Selected monographs (338.1)

EPIPHORA

1792	Wathen (406)
1795	Ware (402)

EYE – anatomy & histology

1814	Baudet-Dulary (35.2)
1818	Soemmerring, D. W. (347)
1842	Pappenheim (288.1)
1868	Metz (257)

EYE – anatomy & physiology

1496	Lacepiera (222)
1574	Carcano Leon (69.1)
1648	Plemp (298)
1651	Michaelius (259)
1671	Coper (87)
1686	Briggs (62)
1688	Boyle (60.2)
1696	Hartmann (179)
1698	Botti (57)
1703	La Charriére (226)

GEOLOGY
    1679   Steno (358)

GLAUCOMA
See also EYE DISEASES
    1709   Brisseau (63)
    1846   Gerold (151.1)
    1859   Selected monographs (338.1)
    1878   Panas (287)
    1879   Smith (344)
    1884   Arlt (23)

GONORRHEAL OPHTHALMIA
See also EYE DISEASES
    1834   Schoen (335)

HEAD – anatomy & physiology
    1703   La Charriére (226)

HEAD – pathology
    1584   Schenck (333)
    1628   Grossius (164)
    1751   Haguenot (174)

HEMORRHAGE
    1877   Mackenzie (240)

HEMOSIDEROSIS
    1877   Mackenzie (240)

HUMORS, OCULAR
See also EYE – anatomy & physiology
    1669   Borri (55)
    1690   Nuck (276)
    1702   Hovius (196)

HYGIENE, OCULAR
    1586   Bailey (30)
    1787   Gleize (155)

    1789   Adams (3)
    1810   Chevallier (78)
    1812   Beer (38)
    1816   Reveillé-Parise (312)
    1824   Kitchiner (218)
    1828   Beer (40)
    1841   Losen de Seltenhoff (238)
    1847   Magne (242)
    1847   Powell (306)
    1864   Chevalier (76)
    1870   Chevalier (77)

HYPOPYON
See also EYE DISEASES
    1704   Bidloo (49)
    1742   Mauchart (248)

INTRAOCULAR PRESSURE
    1868   Stellwag von Carion (353)

IRIDECTOMY
See also PUPIL, ARTIFICIAL *and* SURGERY, OCULAR
    1810   Benedict (41)
    1811   Gibson (152)
    1812   Adams (4)
    1812   Maunoir (250)
    1859   Selected monographs (338.1)

IRIS
    1765   Fontana (140)
    1786   Blumenbach (52.1)
    1819   Neue Bibliothek (272.1)
    1836   Eisenach (122.2)
    1855   Budge (63.2)

IRITIS
See also EYE DISEASES
    1801   Schmidt (334)

1838	Ammon (14)
1859	Selected mongraphs (338.1)
1878	Panas (287)

JURISPRUDENCE, MEDICAL
| 1875 | Arlt (21) |

KERATITIS
| 1830 | Froriep (142.1) |

LACRIMAL APPARATUS
See also EYE – anatomy & physiology
1574	Carcano Leone (69.1)
1680	Steno (359)
1797	Rosenmüller (314)
1803	Fournier (140.1)

LACRIMAL FISTULA
See also EYE DISEASES *and* SURGERY, OCULAR
1692	La Charriére (225)
1713	Anel (16,17)
1713	Signorotti (341)
1714	Anel (18)
1717	Melli (255)
1748	Nannoni, A. (270)
1753	Bordenhave (2)
1753	La Forest (2)
1753	Louis (2)
1758	Pott (305.1)
1762	Pallucci (286)
1772	Pott (305.2)
1792	Wathen (406)
1798	Ware (403)

LARYNGOLOGY
| 1838 | Colombat (83) |

LENS, CRYSTALLINE
See also CATARACT *and* EYE – anatomy & physiology

| 1626 | Platter (297) |

LENSES
See also EYEGLASSES *and* OPTICS, PHYSICAL
1646	Kircher (217)
1685-86	Zahn (424)
1769-71	Euler (126)
1787	Selva (338.2)
1810	Chevallier (78)
1824	Kitchiner (218)
1825	Bate (35.1)

LEUKOMA
See also EYE DISEASES
| 1747 | Benevoli (44) |

MACULA LUTEA
| 1816 | Santi (325) |
| 1830 | Ammon (13) |

MATHEMATICS
1614	Bacon (28)
1632	Cavalieri (73)
1807	Young (423.1)

MEDICINE – collected works
1661	Du Laurens (120)
1740-47	Demours (97)
1764	Gataker (149)
1765	Mead (254)

MEDICINE – general works
1545	Vittori (391)
1565	Houllier (195)
1576	Thurneisser (377)
1590	Heurne (186)
1600	Possevino (304)

MELANEMIA
1877   Mackenzie (240)

MICROSCOPE
1749   Thomin (374.1)
1750   La Caille (221.1)
1787   Selva (338.2)

NEOPLASMS, OCULAR
See also EYE DISEASES *and* SURGERY, OCULAR
1869   Knapp (219)

NERVES, CILIARY
1815   Muck (265.1)

NERVOUS SYSTEM DISEASES – atlases
1895   Jakob (207.1)

NEWTON, SIR ISAAC, 1642-1727
1737   Algarotti (7)
1738   Voltaire (394)
1739   Baniéres (31)
1855   Brewster (61)

NOSE DISEASES
1797   Haase (173)

NURSING, OPHTHALMIC
1894   Stephenson (360)

OPHTHALMIA
See also EYE DISEASES
1745   Sloane (342)
1771   Rowley (315)
1787   Ware (401)
1798   Ware (403)
1804   Griffiths (162.2)
1806   Edmonston (122)
1807   Spindler (351)

1810   Walther (398)
1824   Hewson (189)
1828   Eble (121)
1834   Schoen (335)
1841   Florio (137)
1842   Florio (138)
1844   Boissonneau (53.1)
1849   Cunier (88)
1850   Landi (227.1)
1900   Stephenson (361)

OPHTHALMOLOGY – collected works
1894   Young (423.2)
1903-33   Collectio ophthalmologica (82)

OPHTHALMOLOGY – dictionaries
1808   Wenzel (416)

OPHTHALMOLOGY – essays
1891   Festschrift (134.1)

OPHTHALMOLOGY – general works
9th c.   Ḥunayn ibn Ishāq al-Ibādī (197)
12th c.   Muḥammad ibn Kassūm (266)
1813   Beer, G. J. (38.1)
1880-89   Wecker (408.1)

OPHTHALMOLOGY – history
1818   Wallroth (397)
1841   Andreae (15.1)
1866   Sichel (340.1)

OPHTHALMOLOGY – instruments
1875   Walton (399.1)

OPHTHALMOLOGY – Japan
1815-16   Plenk (300)

OPHTHALMOMETRY
1854   Smee (343)

1869   Reuss (311.2)

1871   Woinow (422.2)

OPHTHALMOSCOPY

1854   Jaeger (203)

1858   Hogg (193)

1860   Jaeger (204.1)

1863   Follin (139)

1863   Hogg (194)

1866   Bouchut (58)

1871   Allbutt (10)

1879   Gowers (158)

1881   Sous (350)

1890   Gowers (159)

OPHTHALMOSCOPY – atlases

1855-70   Jaeger (204)

1869   Jaeger (206)

1870   Jaeger (207)

1885   Liebreich (236)

1896   Frost (143)

1896-99   Oeller (278)

1900-12   Oeller (279)

OPTIC CHIASM

1899   Ramón y Cajal (309.1)

OPTIC GANGLION

1815   Muck (265.1)

OPTIC NERVE

1786   Noethig (273.2)

OPTICS – instruments

1749   Thomin (374.1)

1750   La Caille (221.1)

1760   Bischoff (50.1)

1764   Bischoff (50.2)

1787   Selva (338.2)

1831   Lloyd (237.2)

OPTICS, PHYSICAL

1535   Witelo (422.1)

1572   Alhazen (8)

1573   Euclid (125)

1573   Heliodorus of Larissa (125)

1592   Peckham (291.2)

1604   Kepler (216.1)

1613   Aguilon (6)

1614   Bacon (27)

1619   Porta (301)

1631   Scheiner (332)

1646   Kircher (217)

1648   Plemp (298)

1657   La Chambre (223)

1660   Manzini (245)

1662   La Chambre (224)

1665   Grimaldi (162.3, 163)

1667   Fabri (130)

1675   Traber (378)

1677   Descartes (99,100)

1677-81   Chérubin d'Orléans (75.1)

1682   Ango (19)

1685-86   Zahn (424)

1690   Huygens (198)

1699   Volckhamer (393)

1703   Huygens (199)

1704   Newton (273)

1728   Newton (273.1)

1737   Algarotti (7)

1738   Smith (345)

1738   Voltaire (394)

1739   Baniéres (31)

1740   Martin (247)

1750   La Caille (221.1)

1752   Courtivron (87.1)

1753   Smith (346)

1756   Lehnberg (235.2)

1759   Lambert (227)

1810	Benedict (41)
1811	Gibson (152)
1811	Muter (268)
1812	Adams (4)
1812	Maunoir (250)
1819	Adams (4.1)
1819	Guthrie (171)
1819	Lusardi (239)
1833	Stilling (364)

REFRACTION

1728	Newton (273.1)
1811	Malus (244.1)
1869-70	Verdet (386.1)

REFRACTION, OCULAR
See ACCOMMODATION & REFRACTION

REMEDIES

1690	Russel (321)

RETINA
See also EYE – anatomy & physiology

1836	Langenbeck (229)
1853	Serre (339)
1865	Aubert (26.2)
1877	Mackenzie (240)

RETINOSCOPY

1895	Jackson (200)
1898	Thorington (376)

RHODOPSIN

1877	Kühne (220)
1878	Kühne (221)

SATIRE, MEDICAL

1840	Fabre (129)

SCIENCE – collected works

1807	Young (423.1)

SCIENCE – history

1700	Pasch (290)

SENSATION

1673	Du Hamel (119)
1744	Le Cat (234)
1826	Müller (267)

SIDEROSIS

1894	Hippel (192)

STRABISMUS
See also EYE DISEASES *and* SURGERY, OCULAR

1840	Duffin (118)
1841	Bonnet (54)
1841	Post (305)
1842	Dieffenbach (110)
1842-44	Boyer (60.1)

SURGERY – dictionaries

1787-88	Bernstein (47)

SURGERY – general works

1598	Fabricius von H. (133)
1649	Feyens (135)
1656	Scultetus (337)
1666	Fabricius ab A. (132)
1692	La Charriére (225)
1695	Muys (269)
1704	Bidloo (49)
1708	Dionis (111)
1733	Nuck (277)
1743-74	Académie Royale (2)
1743	Devaux (108)
1750	Heister (183)
1764	Reghellini (311.1)

CHRONOLOGICAL AND GEOGRAPHICAL INDEX

Pre-15th Century

9th Century
    Ḥunayn ibn Ishāq al-Ibādī (197)

10th Century
    ʿAlī ibn ʿĪsā (9)

12th Century
    Muḥammad ibn Kassūm ibn Aslam (266)

15th Century

ITALY
    1474   Grassus (162)
    1496   Lacepiera (222)

16th Century

ENGLAND
    1553   Geminus (151)
    1586   Bailey (30)

FRANCE
    1585   Guillemeau (168)

GERMANY
    1535   Witelo (422.1)
    1538   Fuchs (145)
    1540   Abū Bakr al-Ḥasan (1)
    1545   Vittori (391)
    1559   Stromayr (366)
    1576   Thurneisser (377)
    1583   Bartisch (34, 35)
    1592   Peckham (291.2)

HOLLAND
    1590   Heurne (186)

ITALY
    1534   Aetius (5)

    1550   Porzio (303)
    1573   Euclid (125)
    1573   Heliodorus of Larissa (125)
    1574   Carcano Leone (69.1)
    1597   Tagliacozzi (369)

SWITZERLAND
    1543   Vesalius (387)
    1565   Houllier (195)
    1572   Alhazen (8)
    1578   Rungius (320)
    1584   Schenck (333)
    1598   Fabricius von H. (133)

17th Century

AUSTRIA
    1619   Scheiner (331)
    1675   Traber (378)

BELGIUM
    1613   Aguilon (6)
    1648   Plemp (298)

DENMARK
    1669   Borri (55)

ENGLAND
    1616   Bailey (30.1)
    1616   T., A. (368)
    1622   Banister (32)
    1688   Boyle (60.2)
    1690   Russel (321)

FRANCE
    1615   Fuchs (146)
    1657   La Chambre (223)
    1661   Du Laurens (120)
    1662   La Chambre (224)

1667	Fabri (130)
1673	Du Hamel (119)
1677-81	Chérubin d'Orléans (75.1)
1677	Descartes (99)
1679	Le Clerc (235)
1682	Ango (19)
1692	La Charriére (225)

GERMANY
1604	Kepler (216.1)
1614	Bacon (27)
1614	Bacon (28)
1619	Porta (301)
1649	Feyens (135)
1671	Coper (87)
1677	Fabri (131)
1685-86	Zahn (424)
1699	Volckhamer (393)

HOLLAND
1602	Heurne (187)
1608	Heurne (188)
1651	Bartholin, T. (33)
1651	Michaelius (259)
1656	Scultetus (337)
1677	Descartes (100)
1679	Steno (358)
1680	Steno (359)
1686	Briggs (62)
1690	Huygens (198)
1690	Nuck (276)
1695	Blankaart (52)
1695	Muys (269)

ITALY
1600	Possevino (304)
1601	Mercuriale (256)
1628	Grossius (164)
1631	Scheiner (332)
1632	Cavalieri (73)
1646	Kircher (217)

1660	Manzini (245)
1665	Grimaldi (163)
1666	Fabricius ab A. (132)
1675	Molinetti (261)
1678	Redi (311)
1696	Hartmann (179)
1698	Botti (57)

SWITZERLAND
1626	Platter (297)
1675	Harder (178)

18th Century
AUSTRIA
1762	Pallucci (286)
1777	Plenck (299)
1780-83	Mohrenheim (260)
1781	Trnka von Kržowitz (381)
1783	Trnka von Kržowitz (382)
1791	Beer, G. J. (37)

BELGIUM
1708	Dionis (111)

ENGLAND
1704	Newton (273)
1727	Taylor (370)
1728	Newton (273.1)
1738	Smith (345)
1740	Martin (247)
1745	Sloane (342)
1749	Diderot (109)
1758	Pott (305.1)
1764	Gataker (149)
1768	Mauclerc (249)
1771	Rowley (315)
1772	Pott (305.2)
1772	Priestley (308)
1773	Rowley (316)
1773	Warner (404)
1780	Chandler (74)

1791	Jung-Stilling (215.1)
1796	Arnemann (25)
1797	Haase (173)
1797	Rosenmüller (314)

HOLLAND
1702	Hovius (196)
1703	Huygens (199)
1704	Bidloo (49)
1733	Nuck (277)
1738	Voltaire (394)
1744	Le Cat (234)
1746	Camper (66-68)
1750	Heister (183)
1753	Smith (346)
1759	Lambert (227)
1765	Colombier (84)

IRELAND
| 1709 | Berkeley (45) |
| 1732 | The English impostor (123) |

ITALY
1713	Anel (16, 17)
1713	Signorotti (341)
1714	Anel (18)
1717	Melli (255)
1724	Benevoli (43)
1737	Algarotti (7)
1747	Benevoli (44)
1749	Billi (50)
1755	Taylor (372.1)
1760	Rampinelli (309.2)
1762	Morgagni (263)
1764	Heister (184)
1764	Reghellini (311.1)
1765	Fontana (140)
1769	Vespa (388)
1777	Marescotti (246)
1779	Piazza (295)
1780	Nannoni, L. (271)

1780	Troja (382.1)
1787	Selva (338.2)
1792	Sarti (325.1)
1794	Cappuri (69)

PORTUGAL
| 1793 | Santa Anna Esbarra (323) |

RUSSIA
| 1769-71 | Euler (126) |

SCOTLAND
1759	Porterfield (302)
1765	Mead (254)
1793	Blacklock (51)
1797	Monro (262)

SWEDEN
| 1756 | Lehnberg (235.2) |

SWITZERLAND
1713	Heister (181.1)
1717	Heister (182)
1751	Haguenot (174)

19th Century
Unknown Place
| 1811 | Malus (244.1) |
| 1860? | Jaeger (204.1) |

AUSTRIA
1801	Schmidt (334)
1813	Beer, G. J. (38.1)
1813-17	Beer, G. J. (39)
1828	Eble (121)
1830	Littrow (237.1)
1834	Rosas (313.1)
1844	Jaeger (202)
1854	Jaeger (203)
1855-70	Jaeger (204)
1861	Jaeger (205)
1861	Stellwag von Carion (352)
1868	Stellwag von Carion (353)

1863	Hogg (194)
1864	Donders (115)
1867	Lawson (233.1)
1867	Power (307)
1868	Bader (29)
1869	Scheffler (330)
1871	Allbutt (10)
1875	Walton (399.1)
1877	Carter (71.1)
1877	Mackenzie (240)
1879	Gowers (158)
1879	Smith (344)
1884	Carter (72)
1885	Knapp (219.1)
1891	Edridge-Green (122.1)
1894	Stephenson (360)
1896	Frost (143)

FRANCE

1803	Fournier (140.1)
1803	Lefébure (235.1)
1806	Tenon (373)
1808	Wenzel (416)
1810	Chevallier (78)
1812	Beer (38)
1812	Maunoir (250)
1814	Baudet-Dulary (35.2)
1814	Williams (419)
1815	Delingette (95)
1815	Williams (420)
1816	Reveillé-Parise (312)
1816	Williams (421)
1817	Guillié (169)
1818	Demours (96)
1819	Lusardi (239)
1824	Bowen (59)
1826	Gondret (156.1)
1827	Parfait-Landrau (289)
1827	Tournier (377.1)
1832	Weller (412)

1833	Lattier de Laroche (230)
1835	Carron du Villards (70)
1835	Lattier de Laroche (231)
1837	Sichel (340)
1838	Carron du Villards (71)
1838	Colombat (83)
1839	Furnari (147)
1840	Fabre (129)
1841	Bonnet (54)
1841	Florio (137)
1841	Furnari (148)
1842-44	Boyer (60.1)
1842	Maunoir (251)
1843	Alphonse (11)
1843	Gouillin (157)
1844	Boissonneau (53.1)
1844	Deval (105)
1846	Weylandt d'Hettanges (417)
1847	Desmarres (102)
1847	Magne (242)
1848	Bernard (46)
1850	Dufau (117)
1851	Deval (106)
1853	Serre (339)
1854-58	Desmarres (103)
1855	Denonvilliers (98)
1857	Guépin (165)
1861	Jaeger (205)
1862	Deval (107)
1862	Furnari (148.1)
1863	Follin (139)
1864	Chevalier (76)
1866	Bouchut (58)
1866	Sichel (340.1)
1869-70	Verdet (386.1)
1870	Chevalier (77)
1878	Panas (287)
1878-79	Wecker (408)

1880-89	Wecker (408.1)
1881	Sous (350)
1890	Delacroix (94)
1894	Morax (262.1)

GERMANY

1801	Soemmerring, S. T. (348)
1804	Soemmerring, S. T. (349)
1807	Spindler (351)
1810	Benedict (41)
1810	Walther (398)
1812	Weinhold (410.1)
1815	Muck (265.1)
1818	Wallroth (397)
1819	Neue Bibliothek (272.1)
1821	Ammon (12)
1822	Weller (411)
1824	Ueber Augen (383.1)
1826	Müller (267)
1828	Schoen (334.1)
1828	Treviranus (380)
1830	Ammon (13)
1830	Froriep (142.1)
1832	Arnold (26)
1832	Jüngken (215)
1833	Seiler (338)
1833	Stilling (364)
1834	Schoen (335)
1836	Eisenach (122.2)
1836	Langenbeck (229)
1836	Peters (294)
1838	Ammon (14)
1838-47	Ammon (14.1)
1838	Pauli (291)
1838	Ruete (317)
1841	Andreae (15.1)
1841	Gauss (150)
1841	Kranichfeld (219.2)
1841	Walther (399)
1842	Ammon (15)

1842	Dieffenbach (110)
1843	Himly (191)
1844	Weiss (410.2)
1845	Ruete (318)
1845	Zeis (425)
1846	Gerold (151.1)
1847	Brücke (63.1)
1849	Cunier (88)
1852	Hannover (177)
1853	Beer, A. (36.2)
1854-60	Ruete (319)
1855	Budge (63.2)
1858	Panum (288)
1860-61	Wedl (409)
1863	Classen (79)
1867	Graefe (161)
1867	Helmholtz (185)
1868	Kühne (219.3)
1874-80	Handbuch (176)
1875	Pagenstecher (281.1)
1876	Classen (80)
1877	Kühne (220)
1878	Kühne (221)
1885	Liebreich (236)
1891	Festschrift (134.1)
1893	Fuchs (143.1)
1894	Hippel (192)
1895	Jakob (207.1)
1896-99	Oeller (278)
1899	Ramón y Cajal (309.1)

HOLLAND

| 1803 | Ens (124) |

HUNGARY

| 1823 | Fabini (127) |
| 1831 | Fabini (128) |

ITALY

| 1801 | Scarpa (327) |
| 1810 | Santerelli (324) |

1816	Santi (325)
1826	Gregoris (162.1)
1838	Brenta (60.3)
1842	Florio (138)
1850	Landi (227.1)

JAPAN

1815-16	Plenk (300)

LATVIA

1830	Hueck (196.1)

POLAND

1814	Benedict (42)
1842	Pappenheim (288.1)
1865	Aubert (26.2)

SCOTLAND

1806	Edmonston (122)
1808-18	Wardrop (400)
1818	Wells (414)
1828	Watson (407)
1855	Brewster (61)
1855	Wilson (422)
1886	Landolt (228)
1896	Frost (143)

SWEDEN

1877	Holmgren (194.1)

UNITED STATES

1804	Griffiths (162.2)
1824	Horner (194.2)
1826	Farrar (133.1)
1832	Gibson (153)
1834	Lawrence (232)
1837	Littell (237)
1841	Post (305)
1847	Jones (213)
1847	Lawrence (233)
1847	Powell (306)
1862	Williams (417.1)
1866	Graefe (160)

1868	Jeffries (209)
1868	Metz (257)
1868	Stellwag von Carion (354)
1869	Knapp (219)
1871	Allbutt (10)
1871	Jeffries (210)
1873	Stellwag von Carion (355)
1880	Jeffries (211)
1881	Mauthner (252)
1881	Morton (265)
1881	Noyes (274)
1882	Williams (418)
1883	Nettleship (272)
1883	Wells (413)
1884	Juler (214)
1885	Arlt (24)
1885	Knapp (219.1)
1887	Burnett (64)
1887	Meyer (258)
1889	Berry (48)
1890	Gowers (159)
1890	Noyes (275)
1893	De Schweinitz (100.1)
1895	Jackson (200)
1896	Fuchs (144)
1896	Veasey (386)
1898	Ramsay (310)
1898	Thorington (376)
1899	Donders (116)
1899	Ohlemann (281)

20th Century

ENGLAND

1900	Stephenson (361)
1900	System of diseases (367)

FRANCE

1903-33	Collectio ophthalmologica (82)
1911	Heymann (190)

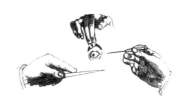